JOSEPH BARCROFT

1872-1947

Sir Joseph Barcroft in February 1943

Frontispiece

JOSEPH BARCROFT

1872–1947

BY

KENNETH J. FRANKLIN

OF THE MEDICAL COLLEGE
OF ST. BARTHOLOMEW'S HOSPITAL

BLACKWELL
SCIENTIFIC PUBLICATIONS
OXFORD

Published simultaneously in the United States of America
by Charles C Thomas, Publisher,
301-327 East Lawrence Avenue, Springfield, Illinois.

First printed, October, 1953.

Printed in Holland by
VERENIGDE DRUKKERIJEN HOITSEMA N.V., GRONINGEN

TO

LADY BARCROFT

WITH

ADMIRATION AND AFFECTION

PREFACE AND ACKNOWLEDGEMENTS

On 11 April 1947 the then Bishop of Lichfield, Dr. Edward Woods, came to Lady Barcroft and, in the course of his talk with her, said that she ought to ask someone to write Sir Joseph's life-story. Both she and her elder son, Professor Henry Barcroft, endorsed the suggestion and John Grant, Managing Director of the firm which had published Sir Joseph's last book, proposed to them, unknown to me, that I should undertake the work. On hearing of the proposal, I could see how Sir Joseph's biography, adequately written, might extend his beneficent and stimulating influence to further generations of physiologists and might also be welcomed by laymen with a general interest in science's advances. I doubted greatly, however, whether on the one hand I was fitted for the task, and whether on the other hand I could spare the time necessary for its accomplishment.

Final judgment on the former point is now a matter for the readers of this book. With regard to the second, my reasonable hesitancy was overridden and, while still enjoying the comparative leisure of an Oxford don, I agreed to write the biography. With my return later in 1947 to the Department of Physiology of St. Bartholomew's Hospital Medical College, I found my leisure time minimal and more than once, in the intervening years, I have wondered if I should not stop work upon so demanding an extra task. In the event, I have fulfilled my undertaking at the inevitable cost of my own researches, and in consequence I hope doubly strongly that the book will be of real service, particularly to the younger generation which has no personal knowledge of Sir Joseph but may perhaps be catalysed, by reading of him and of his way of life, to greater accomplishment. If the biography achieves that purpose, I shall happily write off my own personal research loss. I remember, however, William J. Mayo's words that "it is for the younger people to meet the conditions of their generations in the way that appears to them to be wise and best", and I can merely hope that this book will be of value to them; I cannot guarantee it.

Now let us turn to the specific task which I undertook. Writing someone's life was an entirely novel form of literary pursuit to me, but I recalled Disraeli's dictum that "There is properly no history, only biography", and could therefore visualize, if I accepted his view, the importance of the life-story of a great scientist. Later I heard Henry Sigerist say, in a lecture in London, that "If you write a biography, you recreate a man", and I hoped that this might be the result of my new venture. I recalled, however, that it has been said of good biography that the biographer must be in close spiritual rapport with his subject, and I wondered if on this score I was competent to deal with all of the many facets of Sir Joseph; whether also a more thorough knowledge of Cambridge than I possess was not necessary. Some, however, of my research interests were allied to some of the many that had been his, and I had, in work on the foetal circulation, cooperated with him and with Dr. Donald H. Barron. So, while not being so close to him as some, I began with some measure of understanding of him, and trusted that I would apprehend the rest.

"In a biography", according to Mr. Henry Schuman, "one expects a rounded, three-dimensional portrait of the subject, containing the chief elements: *Background, Personality, Achievement,* unfolded in correct proportions. Some scientists' lives are full of drama and human interest; where this is the case, the problem of holding the reader's interest is relatively easy . . . The subject's background, taking into consideration important social and other historical factors, is highly significant in orienting the lay reader in point of time and circumstances . . . Special emphasis should be given to the impact of a scientist's achievement, immediate or permanent, on society . . ." These were notes sent to me by Mr. Schuman when he was inviting me to write a life of William Harvey, and they are much in line with my own ideas and with what I have attempted to do in relation to Sir Joseph's life-story; they are quoted with Mr. Schuman's kind permission.

Now as to some other points. I did early on wonder if I should produce a short book in which the leading incidents should be made to follow so rapidly one on another that the whole would have something of the non-stop character of Joseph Conrad's *Typhoon.* But I quickly dismissed that as a possible technique, as it would have given the false impression that the difficulties of scientific research are easily surmounted. Certainly Sir Joseph overcame such difficulties with greater skill and speed than most of us, but even he did so far from effortlessly. In the longer and less dramatized story which I have instead written, the physiologist will, I hope, find not only adequate personal details to reconstitute the man, but also sufficiently full analyses of Sir Joseph's more important researches and publications to reconstitute the scientist. At the same time, since this book is meant also for the layman, I trust that the latter will be able to follow the story by disregarding the passages which are for him over-technical and concentrating on the rest.

In my view, except where there is occasionally an advantage to be gained from departure from the rule, historical works should adhere to chronological order; otherwise, the story gets distorted. I have, therefore, kept to the rule in my account. In general, also, I have not passed judgment on particular researches, or looked at investigations of some years past in the light of later discoveries in the same fields. I have merely tried to recreate Joseph Barcroft dealing with problems and giving his contemporary conclusions, leaving it to the scientific reader, if he so wishes, to turn himself, against the background which I have provided, into a contemporary critic. Finally, I have, so frequently as opportunity and considerations of style permitted, let the original words of Sir Joseph and Lady Barcroft and others carry on the story, believing that in that way the narrative would be much more vivid and personal and generally satisfactory. This technique has, I hope, succeeded; I know, at all events, that those closest to Sir Joseph have approved the completed work and have found in its pages that recreation of him which I had hoped to achieve.

By his death we have lost many fine things, but I wish here to mention just one of these, as it is not referred to in the text. The one of which I am thinking is his personal memory of past physiologists and of the history of physiology. One day when he was across at the Nuffield Institute to cooperate with our team in the cineradiography of the foetal circulation, I questioned him during our short luncheon-break about certain persons and events and found him a veritable mine of information. Unfortunately, he never committed such recollections to writing and they have passed for ever with his own passing.

Before now going on to deal with acknowledgements in general, I should like to mention a point of some importance, namely, that the version of the Irish story given in Chapter I is in the main the one which Joseph Barcroft himself is likely to have had presented to him. It is not, on the other hand, an uncontested version and I am indebted to Professor T. W. Moo dy, of Trinity College, Dublin, who pointed this out to me and in other ways gave me the benefit of his critical historical sense.

In preparing my script as a whole, I have used information or material supplied by many, but the greatest single source has been the run of diaries compiled by Lady Barcroft from soon after the first war; she has also contributed in countless other ways, and her two sons likewise. Much help has also been given by the Misses M. and A. H. Barcroft, Miss Muriel Richardson, Dr. A. P. Moore-Anderson, Mrs. George F. Trench, J. S. W. Richardson Esq., A. R. W. Richardson Esq., Mrs. Williams, Mrs. Maynard, Miss Muriel G. E. Harris, Sir William Valentine Ball, and others who will be found mentioned in the early part of the book. Nor must I forget W. J. Barcroft Esq. and the Reverend John P. Barcroft; the latter in particular has provided the greater part of my genealogical information (though some has come from the Richardson brothers and some from J. R. N. Greeves Esq.) and I had hoped to reproduce the Barcroft family tree on which he has done so many years' research – however, that hope has not, for economic reasons, been fulfilled.

Quotations from books and journals are many in my text and I acknowledge gratefully a number of permissions; in the other cases where I have not formally requested such, I crave indulgence on the grounds that the contributions of Joseph Barcroft and others were so widely distributed that a complete list of acknowledgements would be very long and would make for tedious reading. The abbreviated list, which covers the bulk of the quotations, is as follows. Through the courtesy of Butterworth Publications Ltd. and of the individual authors (except Professor Krogh, who died too soon), I have been allowed to use freely the contributions made to the 1949 Cambridge symposium on haemoglobin (see Roughton and Kendrew, 1949) by Professor E. D. Adrian, Sir Henry Dale, Professors A. Krogh, C. G. Douglas, A. V. Hill, and R. A. (now Sir Rudolph) Peters, Dr. G. S. Adair, and Professor F. J. W. Roughton; most of these former colleagues of Joseph Barcroft have also helped me, some of them very considerably, in other ways. The

Cambridge University Press has kindly allowed me to quote from Joseph Barcroft's books, *The Respiratory Function of the Blood* and *Features in the Architecture of Physiological Function;* the Oxford University Press has been equally kind in respect of his book, *The Brain and its Environment*, and of Harvey Cushing's book, *The Life of Sir William Osler*. To Miss A. Ruth Fry and her publishers, Cassell & Co., I am indebted for similar permission in respect of her book, *Quaker Ways;* to J. S. W. Richardson Esq. in respect of *Bessbrook;* and to Edward Arnold & Co. in respect of Sir Francis Younghusband's volume, *The Epic of Mount Everest.*

The journals from which I have most quoted are the *Journal of Physiology* and the publications of the Royal Society (*Philosophical Transactions, Proceedings,* and *Obituary Notices of Fellows of the Royal Society*), and I am much indebted for permissions to the Editorial Board of the Journal and to the Council of the Society respectively. To a lesser extent, my pages contain excerpts from the *British Medical Journal*, the *Lancet, Annals of Science, Nature,* the *Biochemical Journal*, the *Proceedings of the Nutrition Society,* the *British Journal of Radiology*, the *Proceedings of the Royal Society of Medicine*, and *Reports of the British Association for the Advancement of Science*. To the Editors and/or Publishers of these I express my warm gratitude. On the bibliography side, I have been much assisted, though I have not slavishly followed it, by Dr. Donald H. Barron's list of references to Sir Joseph's works. In my last Chapter I quote from some of the many letters of condolence received by Lady Barcroft in 1947 and, except in two cases where assent had to be presumed, Professor Henry Barcroft obtained the agreement of the individual writers for the printing of these extracts from their messages of sympathy. My thanks, therefore, go to these writers.

Others to whom I would express indebtedness include the Assistant Secretary and the Librarian of the Royal Society, Dr. E. J. Baldes, the late Dr. A. E. Barclay, Professor J. P. Baumberger, W. J. Bishop Esq., W. Brown Esq., R. W. B. Burton Esq., Professor E. P. Cathcart, D. J. Cawthron Esq., General J. T. Dreyer, H. C. H. Fairchild Esq., Dr. Morris Fishbein, Professor Henri Fredericq, Dr. C. M. Fletcher, Professors Alexander Forbes, John F. Fulton and L. W. Grensted, Dr. C. F. Hadfield, Dr. L. J. Harris, W. G. Humphrey Esq., Headmaster of the Leys School, Professors

Robert E. Johnson, J. J. Izquierdo and E. B. Krumbhaar, Dr. Alfredo Lanari, Dr. W. B. McDaniel II, Professors Walter J. Meek and Walter R. Miles, A. N. L. Munby Esq., John Nickalls Esq., William H. Palmer Esq., Colonel Robert Parker, D.S.O., Dr. A. T. Phillipson, F. N. L. Poynter Esq., the late W. F. Reddaway Esq., F. J. H. Sanders Esq., Sir John T. Sheppard, Provost of King's College, Cambridge, the late Sir Edmund Spriggs, Professor F. R. Steggerda, the late Reverend Canon R. A. Swanzy, Professor F. Verzár, Dr. M. Wong, Dr. Elizabeth Worth, the Registrar and the Secretary to the Senate of the University of London, and the Registrary and the Registrary's Clerk of the University of Cambridge. The list could be extended almost indefinitely, and I apologize to any whose names I should have included but have inadvertently omitted. I must, however, make certain of acknowledging the very great help which three persons in particular have given me since 1947. These three are my successive Secretaries during that period, namely, Miss Jean Lambourne (now Mrs. Holme), Miss Joyce Monk, and Miss Mary Morse, to each of whom I express my very special thanks.

Of the sixty-two illustrations, the Frontispiece and Plates 2 and 14 are reproduced by permission of Lafayette Ltd., the *Architect and Building News*, and *Country Life* respectively; and Plates 26, 27, 29–32, and 35–37 by permission of the Cambridge University Press, which also very kindly lent the blocks from Joseph Barcroft's *The Respiratory Function of the Blood*, 1914 and 1925.

To W. J. Barcroft Esq. I am indebted for Plate I; to the Misses M. and A. H. Barcroft for Plates 3, 8, and 21; to Professor Henry Barcroft for Plate 7; to Lady Barcroft for Plates 9–13, 24, 28, 34, 39–44, 46–48, 50–52, 55, 56, 58, 60, and 61; to John S. W. Richardson Esq. for Plates 4 and 5; to Alexander R. W. Richardson Esq. for Plates 6 and 20; to Professor Sir Bryan Matthews for Plates 15, 16, and 23; to Dr. J. F. Gaskell for Plate 17; to Mrs. Vandeleur for Plate 19; to Professor Walter R. Miles for Plate 33; to Professor G. L. Brown for Plate 45; to Dr. Anthony Hargreaves for Plate 49; and to Dr. L. J. Harris for Plate 59 – as this last appeared earlier facing p. 211 of *Proc. Nutr. Soc.*, 1947, *5*, my thanks are due also to the Editor and Publishers of that journal.

Plates 18, 22, 25, and 53 similarly appeared earlier in *Ann. Sci.*, 1938, *3*, No. 3, and similar acknowledgement is made to the Editor and Publishers of that journal; the originals were given or lent to me by Sir Charles Sherrington, Professor A. Herlitzka, Professor Achelis, and Professor John F. Fulton respectively. For the rest, the original of Plate 38 was given to me years ago by Professor C. (now Sir Charles) Lovatt Evans; Mrs. J. S. Haldane in or about 1936 kindly allowed me to photograph the drawing of her husband by Tom Van Oss which appears as Plate 54; and Professor Sir Bryan Matthews authorized the inclusion of Plate 57, the original of which was deposited by the subscribers in the Physiology Laboratory, Cambridge – it was photographed at the time by Mr. John Freeman.

Acknowledgements should probably also be made to a number of amateur photographers whose prints, in the possession of Lady Barcroft and others, I have included in the Plates for this book, but at this length of time it is difficult to ascertain who took which, and a general expression of thanks must suffice. I am grateful to Professor Robert E. Johnson for a duplicate, though I did not finally require it, of Plate 56, and for the details given in the legend of that Plate. Professor Walter R. Miles and Professor R. J. Brocklehurst lent me material which had, unfortunately, to be passed over, and Miss Muriel G. E. Harris provided numerous photographs, etc., of the Moyallon Richardsons which I was similarly unable to include, though they helped me much in my writing of Chapter II, etc. To these friends and to some others whom I have not mentioned by name, I remain grateful for help so freely offered. I should like also to express my indebtedness to my publishers, printers, and blockmakers, naming especially in these three connections John Grant, Mijnheer G. Veenma, and Mr. L. Dailley.

Finally, I wish to thank my wife who has read critically through the text as it appeared and whose advice about it has been of the utmost value to me, and to acknowledge the great help given to me by Dr. D. A. McDonald and Miss Mary Morse in the preparation of the Index.

K. J. FRANKLIN

July, 1953

TABLE OF CONTENTS

LIST OF ILLUSTRATIONS

1—THE BARCROFT FAMILY ARMS, CREST, AND MOTTO

2—BARCROFT HALL, IN CLIVIGER, LANCASHIRE. Inset: VIEW FROM THE GARDEN

CHAPTER I

The objects of this introductory Chapter are to give readers some account of Joseph Barcroft's long family history, to relate how his branch of the family went to Ireland in the seventeenth century and there joined the Society of Friends, and to indicate what membership of that body meant in his upbringing. We shall also assess how much of the family story, and of the Friends' version of the Irish story from the seventeenth century onwards, was imparted to him in his home-circle and thereby became, from an early age, part of his mental and spiritual background. Those readers who are uninterested in genealogy can pass direct to the next Chapter, but a greater number should find the details of "J. B" 's centuries-long family history fascinating in themselves, as well as of considerable relevance to his own life-story.

According to Wilkinson and Tattersall (1889, 110), the name Barcroft, originally often spelt Berecroft, Brerecroft, or Bercroft, is derived from the Anglo-Saxon "bear", a crop or rick, and "croft", a meadow. The authors go on to say that "The sheltered pastures where the old [Barcroft] hall is situated, favourable for the growth of hay and other crops, and adjacent to Towneley Park, were probably the origin of the name in Saxon times." According to Bardsley's *English Surnames* (1901), the name means "barley-croft," "croft" itself being, according to Chambers' *Etymological English Dictionary*, a cultivated enclosure, a field, or a small farm.

Burke's *Landed Gentry* states that the lands of Barcroft in Lancashire were held by the family from "the earliest times to which records extend", and the first mention of it takes those times back to before 1216, when lands given to Kirkstall Abbey were regranted. The official Barcroft pedigree registered in the Office of Ulster King of Arms, now called the Genealogical Office, Dublin, begins about two centuries later and the first evidence of the family arms is provided by a seal attached to the marriage settlement of Laurence Whitaker and Agnes Barcroft in the second decade of the sixteenth century. [1] The arms (Plate 1) are argent, a lion rampant,

[1] Shuttleworth (Gawthorpe) deeds at Browsholme. Box A, No. 14. Arms on seal.

sable; [1] the crest a demi-bear rampant, gules, muzzled or; the motto (taken from Horace's *Satires*, Book II, Satire vi, 15) "Utque soles custos adsis." [2]

The descent from Gilbert de Berecroft of King John's time to William Barcroft, of Barcroft, in the late sixteenth century was through Richard, Moccoc (Matthew), Dyk (Richard), and Matthew de Berecroft to William de Bercroft, and then through Thomas and William Bercroft and William and Robert Barcroft to the fourth William in the series. The information available about these men is not very detailed, and in any case the story begins its more interesting development with the sons of the fourth William.

The eldest of these, Robert Barcroft, continued the direct line in England and his son, William Barcroft, rebuilt Barcroft Hall (Plate 2) [3] in Lancashire; William's name, with the date 1614, appears over the door, and his dining table, with his own and his wife's initials and the date 1613 on it, can still be seen in Townley Hall. But two generations later the direct male line seems to have ended, and we must, to continue the story, revert to the fourth William's younger sons, Thomas and Henry.

In 1575 their father settled on them estates in Foulridge, Lancashire. Thomas, described as of Worsthorn and Foulridge in Colne, had earlier married Isabel Carr, and their son Ambrose, who was

[1] College of Arms, Queen Victoria Street, London. Sir William Dugdale's Visitation of Lancashire, 1664.

[2] "And, as is thy wont, be at my side to guard me." The full quotation is "Utque soles, custos mihi maximus adsis," and it is part of a prayer to Mercury to prosper and protect Horace's little Sabine farm.

[3] According to Wilkinson and Tattersall (1889), there are traces of a much earlier edifice in the mainly seventeenth-century building. According to the *Preston Guardian*, Spring, 1906, a copy of which is in the Library of the Friends' House, London, Barcroft Hall is "a sombre-looking mansion which lies just outside the boundaries of Towneley Park [Towneley Hall, near Burnley] at the Cliviger end." A description inserted by the Reverend S. J. Allen in the margin of a page of Dr. Whittaker's *History of Whalley*, and quoted in the *Preston Guardian*, loc. cit., read as follows. "The Hall occupies three sides of a small court, the fourth being formed by a screen, in which, beneath a pediment broken by six gresses, and formerly ornamented with pinnacles, is the gateway – a semi-circular arch, with an indented moulding resembling at first sight a Norman ornament. Above is the date 1636. Over the inner doorway, which enters a projecting porch, is the name of William Barcroft. All the chambers are panelled with oak. The hall has huge transverse beams, and a music gallery, of the same; and a comfortable parlour has been made out of the ancient fireplace. The barns, as usual, are in front." The contributor of the article adds, "The account given by Mr. Allen of Barcroft is mostly correct to-day, for very little alteration has taken place in the hall itself. The old oak panelling has, however, been largely removed, and also a quantity of fine carving. The Hall is said to have contained the finest carved mantelpiece in the neighbourhood, but this has been taken away by the present representative of the Towneley family, who [since 1790] still own the property."

baptized at Burnley in 1574, was connected not only with Foulridge but also with the neighbouring Noyna. He was the first Noyna Barcroft and in consequence the Irish branch of the family, which began with his third son William, is often styled the Noyna branch. This William was born at Noyna in 1611 and in 1652 he married, as his second wife, Margaret, daughter of Daniel Barnard of Alkincoats in Colne. At this point, however, it is necessary to interrupt the Barcroft family story in order to list certain events which took place in England and Ireland during the seventeenth and eighteenth centuries; some reference must also be made to the origin of the Society of Friends in England, and to its spread in Ireland. For such digressions are necessary if we are to appreciate properly the further history of the Irish branch of the Barcroft family into which, in 1872, the subject of this biography was to be born.

We may conveniently begin with the year 1625, in which King Charles I succeeded to the throne which he was to occupy for the next quarter of a century, albeit very insecurely for the last third or so of that time. On 23 October 1641, an Irish insurrection, in which large numbers of Protestants lost their lives, broke out. "When the express that brought the news was read in the House of Commons it produced a general silence, all men being struck with horror; when told without doors it spread like lightning, producing terror over the Kingdom" (George Fox, 1669, quoted by J. M. R[ichardson], 1893). Less than a year later England too was internally divided, and the first and second Civil Wars kept it so from 22 August 1642 to December 1648; they were followed, in January 1649, by the trial and execution of King Charles I, and the establishment of the Commonwealth or Republic. Oliver Cromwell, who was appointed by Parliament in 1653 to be Lord Protector of the Realm, died in 1658, and was succeeded by his son, Richard. In May 1659, however, the latter resigned, and in the following year the Long Parliament and the Commonwealth ended and Charles II returned as King. When he died in 1685, the Earl of Tyrconnell became Lord-Deputy of Ireland under King James II, and almost the first things which he did were to arm the Irish and to disarm most of the English, who were predominantly Protestant, thus setting the stage for further trouble. In 1688 the "glorious Protestant Revolution" took place in England, and on 5 November

William of Orange landed at Torbay and James II fled. Then, in 1689, William and Mary became joint sovereigns and England entered on a somewhat more settled time. But the contest between the new order and the old continued in Ireland, which in this year 1689 once again became a scene of lawlessness, pillage and bloodshed in which the respectable settlers, Quakers and others alike, underwent terrible sufferings. For a third time, in 1798, Ireland experienced similar horrors. For about the middle of May of that year an Irish Rebellion broke out, with armed liberation from the unequal yoke of the British Government as its expressed object. In the consequent civil war there was a repetition of much of the brutality associated with the earlier troubles of 1641 and of 1689, and non-participants such as the Quakers were involved in the general sufferings which, as contemporary accounts very vividly show, were once again most severe.

In marked contrast to this religious and political unrest in seventeenth-century England and in seventeenth and eighteenth century Ireland were the personal peace and inward contentment attained by members of the Society of Friends. [1] The founder of the Society was the Englishman George Fox (1624–1690), and what he did can be regarded as a response to dissatisfaction with the established Church of England and with the various alternative sects which had developed after its establishment. He and his followers did not intend to create any new division or sect, but called themselves simply "Friends of God and Mankind", and met together in little gatherings "to wait upon and worship God in spirit and in truth". Their manner of conduct, plain dress, meetings, tenets, and so forth are perhaps sufficiently well-known for any long account to be superfluous here, but we should at least pay tribute to the faith which enabled so many to live so heroically in the externally troublesome circumstances which were from time to time a feature of the period under consideration.

The Irish development of the Society was in large measure due to William Edmundson, who was born at Musgrove, in Westmorland, in 1627 and who died, at the advanced age of eighty-five, in 1712. He went to live in Ireland about 1652, and "was made the means of

[1] Or, in common parlance, Quakers. The information in this and the next paragraph is derived mainly from J.M.R. (1893) and other publications by Friends; Fitzmaurice (1895) was also consulted.

doing a spiritual work in that country very similar to that of George Fox in England". He "first settled in Antrim, then removed to Lurgan, where his brother joined the family, and a meeting was established at their house in 1654, the first settled meeting of Friends in Ireland . . . In 1696 the first Meeting House was built in Lurgan by his agency" (J. M. R., 1893); it was used by Friends until about 1889, when the time-worn edifice had finally to be replaced. The Irish Friends adhered courageously to their manner of life, including the resolution not to defend themselves and their belongings by force of arms, throughout the difficult times to which we have referred, and their adherents included many of those who went from England to settle in Ireland during the seventeenth century; among such settlers were a number who had served in Cromwell's armies, and thereafter had found in the Quaker faith something for which they were prepared to sacrifice not only their military prospects, but also the territorial awards which could have been theirs in return for past service.

Such an one, apparently, [1] was William Barcroft, the third son of Ambrose and Mary Barcroft, of Noyna and Foulridge (vide supra). He was born at Noyna in 1611, went to Ireland in 1658 in Cromwell's army [2], settled in 1682 at Ballylakin, King's County, and at some unspecified date joined the Society of Friends; he died at Drumcolley, King's County, in 1696. The family tradition is that he held the rank of Major, but he is not mentioned in any known list of Cromwell's officers. In Wilkinson and Tattersall (1889) it is suggested that he refused an estate near Athlone as a reward for his services, and that the estate went, in consequence, to the next in command, one Handcock, ancestor of Lord Castlemaine. If this was so, it seems probable that William Barcroft's refusal was made on conscientious grounds, i.e., that having become a Friend or being about to do so, he would not accept what had been won by the sword. In any case, he seems sooner or later to have done well as a settler, for in 1682 he and two of his sons, namely, Ambrose and John, occupied very considerable and productive holdings in Ballylakin, and could well be regarded as prosperous. Another son, Thomas, had gone to America in 1681 with William Penn (1644–1718), the

[1] See Wilkinson and Tattersall (1889).

[2] Accompanied by his brother Ambrose (1609–1678), the second son of Ambrose and Mary Barcroft, who in 1663 was appointed Archbishop of Kilmore (Personal communication from the Reverend John P. Barcroft).

Quaker founder of Pennsylvania, to assist in the division of the new territory.

From "Major" William eight generations carried the line to the Joseph Barcroft of this biography, and the strong Friends' tradition in which the latter was brought up and by which he was markedly influenced was in no small measure consolidated, soon after its beginning, by John Barcroft (1664–1723), the son of "Major" William. According to the anonymous biography printed in Dublin in 1730 [1], John Barcroft was born at Shralegh, near Rosenallies, Queen's Country, in 1664, about which time his parents "were convinced of the *Blessed Truth*", i.e., presumably, definitely joined the Society of Friends. John himself became affected by religious experience from about the age of five, when he went with his mother to a Quaker meeting held at William Edmundson's house. In 1685 he married, and then about 1696 he began that work as a Friends' preacher which took him constantly to various parts of England and Ireland and which terminated only on his death, in 1723.

A brief extract from the *Life* (pp. 5–7) will show not only the disordered state of Ireland about 1689 but also the strong Quaker convictions held by John Barcroft. "After I was marry'd," it reads, "we dwelt some Time at *Ballymorane*, and had three Children before we removed thence; but the War coming on, the *Irish* grew very wicked, first taking up Horses and Arms from the *Protestants*, so proceeded to Plundering; and we having then a good Stock, they took away not only our Horses (scarce leaving us one to ride on) but also our other Cattle and Sheep, at their Pleasure; so that my Wife often asked, *Had they taken all*? with Desire it were so, that we might be the more quiet: In which troublesom Times the LORD greatly helped us, and I often observed His good Providence, in that I and my Wife were not both cast down at once. Thus one was made very helpful to the other.

"THIS general Calamity of this Nation was often foretold and declar'd of by that antient Servant of the LORD *William Edmundson*, as a Time that would try all our *Foundations*; and we were tried many Ways during the War.

[1] See *Anon.* (1730). The copy to which I have had access belonged to one Thomas Ferrier, was given to Joseph Barcroft, M. A., by his father, Henry Barcroft, at Christmas, 1903, and is now in the possession of Professor Henry Barcroft. – K. J. F.

"AFTER our Stock was mostly gone, the *Ulster-Irish* came in great Numbers, spreading over the Country like a disorderly Camp, filling our Houses with their Officers, without Order of Billets, and many dying of a violent, mortal Fever, that was amongst them, were buried in Ditches; yet in all these perilous Times (except one first Day of the Week) we diligently kept up and attended our Religious Meetings, for the Worship of *Almighty* GOD; and His bowing tendering *Power* was often eminently enjoy'd, to the Comfort of our drooping Spirits; but on the said first Day that we stay'd from Meeting (not thinking it safe to leave our Servants with that Throng of *Irish* Officers in the House, and the Camp near us) I viewed the Guests as they were sitting about my Table, and the Remembrance of my antient, honourable Friends that had sat about it, came fresh to my Mind; and I cried in my Heart to the LORD, *Shall I ever see such Times again?* and received an Answer, *I should*: Then I renewed Covenant with the LORD, *That if he would bring it to pass I would be devoted to serve him all my Days, according to the Ability he would please to give me,* which I have since often remember'd, and endeavour'd thus far to perform, the LORD having greatly helped me in many *Exercises,* to the Praise of His Great Name and Comfort of my Soul."

In association with this religious side, we learn from one of the forewords to John Barcroft's *Life* that he was "a frequent Visiter of the Sick and Afflicted, freely ministring Relief to the Poor and Indigent, (he having some Skill in Physic and Chirurgery) kind and generous in entertaining Friends, and Strangers, charitable towards all, thus bearing the Marks of a true Disciple of the LORD Jesus Christ; and as to his Christian Duty in his own particular Family, I think few (if any) exceeded him in Love and Tenderness as an Husband, in Care and Affection as a Father, or in Gentleness and Equity as a Master". "He was endowed with a good understanding in Natural Things," says another account, "and was very helpful to many by Advice and otherwise, both in Physic and Surgery, which he did freely, without Money".

The above long extracts from John Barcroft's *Life* have been deliberately given because the story which is to be told is henceforward indissolubly linked with the activities and uotlook of Friends, and Joseph Barcroft himself was nominally one up to his death, though his attendance at Meetings ceased to be at all regular soon after the beginning of the first World War. Readers who have no detailed acquaintance with the Friends' way of life could with profit read such a book as that of Ruth Fry (1933). From her account we learn that it was not, in George Fox' time, "a safe religion: to whatever danger or suffering it led, it must be followed unfalteringly; danger, even mistakes, were to be preferred to caution and ease." Through its tenets, it greatly limited the choice of occupation of its members, and the medical profession was almost the only one "open to the strict Quaker with the approval of his Meeting. The Army, the Navy, the Church were all equally impossible," and there were difficulties in connection with the legal profession. Under the circumstances, it is not surprising that many Friends turned to business, to medicine, and to natural science, and – with their qualities – did well in these pursuits. Many non-Quakers realize the success which Quakers have attained in business; they should, however, know, in addition, that the Quaker regards material conditions as of importance mainly in so far as they free the spirit. Medicine is a career which attracted many of the best Friends' minds, "for it offered scope for a scientific bent as well as a humanitarian satisfaction." In 1836 Thomas Hodgkin explained the attraction of science when he wrote: "The temple of Science is erected on a neutral territory, to which no age, and no nation, can lay a peculiar claim. Whilst we see, in its immoveable foundations, those massive stones of memorial which have been laid by the gigantic hands of our great predecessors, Bacon, Harvey, and Newton, we should feel that we are above national jealousy, and be actuated only by a generous emulation; that, while the fabric is happily advancing by the labours of many nations, our proportion of the work may be such, as to prove we are not degenerate." The success of Friends and of Friends' descendants in the scientific field is shown by the fact that, between 1851 and 1900, they had an altogether disproportionate representation (according to their numbers, forty-six times that of other men) among Fellows of the Royal Society. This, wrote Miss Fry, "is not altogether surprising, having regard to their training, which saw in the natural world an expression of the divine, worthy of reverent admiration and intense study. To understand its secrets is one of the highest activities of the human brain, and Quaker parents of many generations have inculcated this idea when they took their children for walks, rather than taught them to find birds' nests or even to play cricket. Relaxations for the Quaker were few, and he could throw his energies, with approval of his Meeting and with happiness to himself, into the fascinating study of natural science . . . It was, too, a part of the curriculum of Quaker schools much before this was the case with others."

With this Friends' background in our minds, we can pass to some items derived from the genealogical trees produced by the Reverend John P. Barcroft on the one hand, and by Mr. J. R. N. Greeves on the other. First, we may note that John Barcroft (1644–1723) was an ancestor of the explorer, Sir Ernest Shackleton. Next we see that his great-nephew, Ambrose Barcroft, and his great-great-nephew, William Barcroft (J. B.'s great-great-grandfather), both became Freemen of the City of Dublin. William's son, John, married Sarah Hogg and thereby introduced a connection with the already important linen trade. Their son, Joseph Inman Barcroft, married Mary Wright of New York, so J. B., as their grandson, was one-quarter American. On the distaff side there was a much stronger connection with the linen trade, as well as one with milling and shipbuilding.

The more recent part of the nearly eight-centuries-long Barcroft family story we shall pick up in the next Chapter; here it only remains for us to see what knowledge J. B. possessed of the whole story, and how it affected his upbringing; we are not in a position to assess critically the influence of his ancestry upon his career, though even the abbreviated account given above suggests that many of the fine qualities and interests which we appreciated in him were legacies bequeathed to him by his forbears.

With regard to his knowledge of the family story, we must state at once that the details which have been made available in this Chapter were not all similarly available to J. B. during his formative years. On the other hand, he did visit Barcroft Hall in Lancashire, and he did doubtless read, in 1903 or 1904, the *Life* of John Barcroft (1664–1723). Further, we know that Friends in general take a keen interest in their ancestry, and that his mother, Anna Richardson Barcroft, was an authority on the family history and endowed with a retentive memory. Though, therefore, J. B. did not read widely on outside subjects during his boyhood and adolescence (see next Chapter), his home life at the Glen, Newry, County Down, must have included talks about his predecessors, and from boyhood onwards he readily absorbed information provided by the reading of others. We can have little doubt, then, that he was acquainted with some aspects of the family history and was influenced by it. He was, one imagines, even more influenced by his Quaker upbringing. For these reasons it has been thought right to precede his biography proper by this account of his ancestry, of the origin of the Society of Friends, and of its development in Ireland. Few scientists can have had a more interesting or better-documented family history, and few can have been born into homes better calculated to provide ideal conditions for the beginnings of their careers. We shall not be disparaging his personal achievement if we regard it as facilitated, in no inconsiderable measure, by the fine inheritance to which he succeeded and by the happiness and opportunities which were his in his home.

CHAPTER II

FAMILY BACKGROUND, BOYHOOD, AND ADOLESCENCE

We may begin this Chapter with a word or two about Joseph Inman Barcroft (1799–1855),[1] J. B.'s paternal grandfather, who is described as "of Lisburn and later of Stangmore Lodge." His Lisburn connection is of interest in view of the subsequent story, and Stangmore Lodge (Plate 3) is the house which he had built, perhaps in preparation for his marriage to Mary, daughter of John Wandesford Wright, of New York. This marriage took place in 1838; as the bride had been born in 1815, she was considerably her husband's junior. The estate in which the house was erected is a small country one, lying southwest of the main Armagh-Dungannon road about half-way between Moy and Dungannon; from a point in the grounds one can see the cathedral towers in distant Armagh. Joseph and Mary's eldest child, Henry, was born in 1839; the second one, Elizabeth, in 1841; and the third one, Sarah, in 1842. Henry, who was to be J. B.'s father, was educated at the Friends' School, Newtown, Waterford, but between what dates is not known; it is, however, of interest, in view of his subsequent career, that Quaker schools made a point of giving instruction in handicrafts. At an early age, too, he may have seen something of the mechanical side of the linen industry, for there is a suggestion that his father owned a small weaving factory at Redford.

The first period of Henry Barcroft's life at Stangmore Lodge ended when he was sixteen or seventeen, for his father's death on 20 November 1855 was followed by that of his mother in January 1856, and the three children went away from the Lodge (now Henry's property) to live with their uncle, William James Barcroft (1801–1878), and his sister, Mary Barcroft (1799–1891), at the

[1] The name Inman suggests, and family tradition subscribes to the idea, that there was a connection between the Barcrofts and the Inmans who founded the shipping line which subsequently merged with the White Star line.

former's home, Redford House, Grange, County Tyrone. On William Barcroft's marriage in 1862, Henry returned to Stangmore Lodge, accompanied by his aunt Mary and by his two sisters. The elder of these, Elizabeth, married in 1863 Samuel Lee Anderson [1]; Henry stayed on until his own marriage in 1867. [2]

We have little knowledge of his activities during his second period of residence at Stangmore Lodge but it is obvious, from his later story, that his particular gifts must have been evolving while he was there; indeed, the fact that he did not, apparently, follow any set vocation in his middle twenties may have helped, rather than hindered, their evolution. At all events, it was not in his character to be idle, and the degree of technical ability which he subsequently exhibited could not have been attained without considerable and long-continued effort. About his recreations we have some information; they included riding, shooting, landscape gardening and others of the usual country pursuits.

About two miles from Stangmore Lodge, but off the main road, is Grange Meeting House (Plate 4), at which Henry and his aunt and sisters must have been regular attendants. Even to-day, a century after those less hurried times, an air of peace surrounds this aged, tree-embosomed place of Friends' worship; and in the older wing, in particular, one is impressed by the simplicity and severity of the main room with its early wooden benches. The newer part, where Meeting now takes place, is larger but not so redolent of antiquity. To the side and back of the Meeting House is the burial ground, with its small, unostentatious, textless gravestones more or less

[1] His dates are 1837–1886, and he was knighted in 1884; his widow died in 1909. Their children were Joseph Barcroft Anderson (1864–1948), or "Bar", who became a doctor; Mary Elizabeth Anderson (1865–1931); and Edith Anderson, who later became Mrs. George F. Trench and who is still living. J. B. was younger than these Anderson cousins, but saw a fair amount of them at a still later period in the history of Stangmore Lodge, for he and they visited it often in their younger years. He and they also kept in touch during later years elsewhere.

[2] The subsequent history of Stangmore Lodge is as follows. From 1867 to her death in 1926 it was occupied by Henry's second sister, Sarah. From 1867 to her death in 1891, their aunt, Mary Barcroft, also resided there. In 1886 Sarah married her first cousin, William Barcroft, and he transferred from Stangmore House, where he had up to then been living, to Stangmore Lodge. He died in 1896. When, finally, Sarah Barcroft died in 1926, the estate came to J. B. and he would have liked to retain it, partly for the long family connection, partly on account of his own attachment to his native land; it is also said that he considered keeping it as a place to retire to at the end of his academic life. Other considerations, however, prevailed over these more sentimental ones and Stangmore Lodge was sold outside the family with which, for a century, it had been associated.

3—Stangmore Lodge, County Tyrone

4—Grange Meeting House

Facing page 12

5—John Grubb Richardson (1813–1890) with his second wife, Jane Marion Richardson (1831–1909), and his ward, Anna Richardson Malcolmson, photographed at the Paris Exhibition in 1861

Facing page 13

uniform in pattern; among them are the Barcroft family ones. [1]

We turn next to J. B.'s maternal great-uncle (Plate 5), John Grubb Richardson (1813–1890), for his story and that of Henry Barcroft's wife-to-be are closely connected. His family had been among the earlier Irish Friends, and had long been connected with the linen business; he himself was born in Lisburn, County Antrim, and from the age of about twenty became very spiritually inclined, with his deep religious convictions dominating all his activities. In 1844 he married a distant cousin, Helena Grubb, and they made their home in Belfast, where the Richardsons had one of their mercantile houses. Soon afterwards, he and his brothers decided that to keep pace with developments they must become flax spinners and manufacturers and, to avoid the unsatisfactory living conditions for workpeople which obtained in Belfast, they purchased the Nicholson family's property in Bessbrook, County Armagh, where the Camlough stream provided water and water-power, and where a linen trade had been carried on since 1760; work began in this pleasant country site, three miles west of Newry, in 1847.

In 1846 a son, James Nicholson, had been born to J. G. R. and his wife, and a daughter, Susan Helena, arrived in 1849. Unfortunately, J. G. R.'s wife died in consequence of this second birth, and he broke up his Belfast home, sent the daughter away to relatives, and retired with his son to Lisnagarvey, near Lisburn, where he had the company of Sarah and of Anna, two of his three sisters. The former of these had in 1838 married David Malcolmson, of Melview, County Tipperary, and their daughter, Anna Richardson Malcolmson, J. B.'s mother-to-be, had been born in 1840. With the unexpected death of David Malcolmson later in the same year, Sarah had returned with her infant to Lisnagarvey, where her sister Anna lived. For about four years, in consequence of all the above, J. G. R. saw much of his niece and ever afterwards was keenly interested in her progress.

As a child, she was a great favourite with him and with her other uncles; she also had within easy reach, in Lisburn and its neighbourhood, a very large circle of first cousins. With the Malcolmson ones, whom she met when she visited her aunts at Clonmel, the

[1] It is probable that J. B.'s ashes will one day be placed there. A number of the Friends who attend Grange Meeting still remember him and his genuine, unaffected, friendliness which remained unchanged with the passage of years.

grand total was seventy-two! As she grew up, she had an Italian master to teach her writing, drawing and painting; attention was also paid to the study of languages, and even the writing of poetry, according to the fashion of the times, was considered a necessary part of her education. Coincident with this, she developed a love of horses; later, she drove her own phaeton and pair of ponies.

In 1853 J. G. R. married, as his second wife, Jane Marion Wakefield (1831–1909), of Moyallon, the wedding taking place in orthodox Friends' costume at Ballitore, County Kildare. The bride had already given evidence of the selflessness and sympathy with others which were so characteristic of her in later life; with these qualities and her intense religious convictions, it is small wonder that she appealed to J. G. R. as an ideal helpmate in his future work. The newly-married couple went to live first at Brookhill, about three or four miles from Lisburn, and their first four children, namely, Marion (1835–1875), Thomas Wakefield (1857–1920), and the twins, Anne Wakefield (1859–1942) and Sarah Edith (1859–), were born to them there. Thereafter came Jean Goff (1861–), Gertrude (1865–1938), Ethel Joanna (1868–1938), and Mary Kathleen (1876–1932), who were born at the new Moyallon House (Plate 6), to which the parents moved in 1860.

As Moyallon, or "the beautiful vale", was often visited by J. B. in his earlier years, we should know something of it. It is a pleasant, flat part of County Down between Portadown and Tanderagee, with the river Bann, the Newry Canal, and the river Cusher bounding it on the west aspect; away to the southeast are the Mourne Mountains. The Meeting House, built in 1736, is architecturally the most pleasing, perhaps, in all Ireland. J. M. Richardson had been offered the use of Moyallon house by her uncle, Charles Frederick Wakefield (1807–1898), and she and J. G. R. had accepted partly because the Moyallon Meeting needed strengthening, partly because Moyallon was less than twenty miles from Bessbrook, the scene of J. G. R.'s large-scale social and temperance experiment. While at Moyallon, he enlarged the house and laid out terraced gardens in order to reduce unemployment resulting from the Irish famine. But he had also, in 1859, purchased the Derrymore House estate in Bessbrook, and in the course of time he enlarged a cottage on the estate and laid out beautiful gardens around it. The cottage became styled The Woodhouse, and it was used by the

6—Moyallon House, County Down

7—The Glen, Newry, County Down, from the south-east

Facing page 14

8—The waterfall of the river Bearnish in the garden of The Glen, Newry

9—Anna and Henry Barcroft

Richardsons for about four months of the year, Moyallon House for the rest. [1]

With that general picture of J. G. R. in our minds, we revert to his niece, Anna Richardson Malcolmson, whose guardian he became on Sarah Malcolmson's death in 1864, and to Henry Barcroft. These two outstanding young members of the Society of Friends, very good-looking according to photographs taken in 1861 and 1859 respectively, met under J. G. R.'s auspices at their mutual houses and also at social gatherings of Friends where many matches were made. J. G. R.'s idea that his ward and Henry Barcroft would be eminently suited to each other was justified, and it proved a most happy union. The wedding took place in the Friends' Meeting House at Lisburn on 29 August, 1867, and in an interesting group photograph, taken after it, the bride looks very self-possessed and charming. After their marriage, she and her husband took up their residence in The Glen, Newry, the house which J. G. R. had selected for them so that they might help the Friends' colony which he had recently established at Bessbrook. He also made Henry Barcroft a Director of Bessbrook in order that he might represent Anna Barcroft's considerable interest.

Of The Glen as it was in 1867 we have no picture, but the building was not greatly different when the present writer visited it a few years ago, and some description of it as it was then is relevant here, since it played so large a part in J. B.'s life. It was a large, tall house (Plate 7), attractively set on rapidly rising ground above and to the west of the main Belfast-Dublin road in the southern part of Newry, the fourth largest city or town of Northern Ireland. Its front faced more or less east, and windows on this side commanded, to the east and southwest, a view of the Mourne Mountains. Parts of the building were eighteenth-century, or earlier, and in large measure weather-slated, but the bow-fronts on the east side were of a later date than the main fabric. Before they were added, this was a brick front; hence the older name of "The Red House" for The Glen. To the north of the building and of its stableyard was a walled garden with greenhouses and two ponds which H. B. had built for him, various special trees (e.g., a weeping *Wellingtonia*)

[1] Since 1934 The Woodhouse has been the property of John S. W. Richardson, J. G. R.'s grandson, who lives there with his aunt, Mrs. George Williams (née Sarah Edith Richardson).

which he had planted, rare ferns collected by him, and so forth. This part was planned on Spanish lines, but with apples in place of oranges. West of it was the fruit garden.

Close to the back of the house was a moderate ravine, to the west of which the ground rose steeply until it was well above the level of the housetop. At its highest part (Plate 8) was a bridge over "The Glen River" or, more correctly, the river Bearnish, which when in spate made a very beautiful fall down the ravine. A few yards from its lower portion, and to the north of it, was a pagan Sunday's well, or pin-well, or wishing-well. It was said that, if one dropped a pin into it and wished, without divulging to anyone the nature of the wish, one's desire was realized within the year. On grassy slopes beside the stream, farther down the ravine, fairies were said to dance on Midsummer's night!

The main rooms on the ground floor of the house were the east-facing drawing and dining-rooms to the left and right, respectively, of the front door; the dining-room contained oil-paintings collected by Henry Barcroft. The library, at the back of the house, commanded a view of the waterfall. In the cross-passage was a model of the steamer *Bessbrook*, which belonged to the Dundalk and Newry Steam Packet Company, of which H. B. was a Director. Down in the basement, in its southwest corner, was the room which he (and, later, also J. B.) used as a workshop; the drilling machine, lathe, and other tools remained much as they were left on his death in 1905; there was also on the shelf the hull of a model boat, and on the bench a file with "J. B." carved into the handle. Such is the description of The Glen as it was in recent times; in 1867 it must have been more open, with the trees not so high, the gardens less finished, and so forth.

To Anna and Henry Barcroft (Plate 9) at The Glen there were born two sons and three daughters, namely, Sarah Richardson (1869–1947), Joseph (1872–1947), David Malcolmson (1875–1938), Mary (1877–), and Anna Henrietta (1883–).[1] At this distance of time it is not easy to form any vivid picture of domestic life there, but Anna appears to have been a good manager and organizer, less suave perhaps than her husband, but of a kindly disposition and ever ready with him to dispense hospitality to

[1] The two last, with their cousin, Miss Muriel Richardson, were the occupants of the house until a short while ago.

10—A photograph taken at Bundoran, County Donegal, on 20 July 1877

Left to right:—*Standing:* Sarah Barcroft, John Barcroft, Anne W. Richardson, Florence Pike, Henry Barcroft, S. Helena Richardson, S. Edith Richardson. *Seated:* Laura R. Pim, E. Lucia Pim, Anna R. Barcroft, Emma Richardson. *On the floor:* Joseph Barcroft (*cf.* Pl. 57) and Sarah Richardson Barcroft.

11—Joseph Barcroft, a month before his third birthday

friends and relations. Both had family connections in many parts of Ireland, and thereby brought their children "into touch with a wide circle of those who thought deeply on a variety of subjects". Both, too, were very well-read and "qualified to instil into their children's minds intelligent interest in such things as natural history, scientific pursuits, and the Friends' tradition." It is said that no question was left unanswered in the Barcroft home if the knowledge could be obtained by either parent, and that, if a point cropped up during a discussion at breakfast, Anna Barcroft would have read all the relevant literature by lunch-time. Henry, as has been suggested in the description of the house, was interested in the mechanical arts, ships and shipping, horticulture, the collecting of oil-paintings, and so forth. He was a good natural historian, very knowledgeable about birds and the like; he was also artistic and could, it is said, have been a fine sculptor. All these cultural interests, combined with a considerable inventive genius, scarcely fitted him for the more purely business side of the Bessbrook firm's activities, and in the course of time, especially after J. G. R.'s death in 1890, the divergence of outlook was to become more pronounced. Here, however, we are not concerned with the turn of the century but with the early family life at The Glen, and we can round off this brief sketch of it by noting that the Barcrofts never discussed persons, either to their praise or to their dispraise, or at least never did so in the presence of others. We can see in this the origin of one of the characteristics which distinguished J. B. in his later life.

Of the family life when on holiday there is one interesting picture, for H. B.'s diary of a summer trip to Bundoran, on the coast of County Donegal, has fortunately been preserved. The party left Edward Street Station, Newry, at 8 a.m. on 2 July 1877, and arrived at Bundoran at 3.35 p.m. It consisted of Anna and Henry, their children Sarah, Joseph, David and Mary, a Miss Bransby, a nurse and a nursery maid, a cook and a housemaid, and the coachman and his wife. Three railway vehicles – a passenger carriage, a horse box, and a carriage truck – were used to convey the personnel, their thirty-eight articles of baggage, the two mares Maggie and Nellie, and a ton of hay, oats and straw. At the other end the luggage was carried up in nine loads! J. B. became five on the 26th, but there is no mention in the diary of any celebration of his birthday. On the other hand, his father's interest in ships, sketching, and picture-collecting is illustrated by a number of entries, while another pays tribute to Anna's planning and foresight. For on the night of the 6th–7th the party slept at Enniskillen, and ". . . on entering the Hotel, Miss Jackson the bar maid read out the names and numbers of the rooms as the party filed past so that each person went straight to the bed room without the least delay. We discovered that Anna had made this arrangement before she left for Bundoran." On the 20th a large party of relatives from Moyallon joined the Barcrofts for a short while, and an interesting group photograph was taken (see Plate 10).

From the above account of the 1877 family holiday we must turn back eight years to describe Henry Barcroft's first major contribution to the mechanical side of the Bessbrook firm. It was a revolutionary one. Before 1869, each of the warp hooks of the power-looms carried just one thread, and the width of cloth which could be produced with an asymmetrical design was very limited. H.B. devised a new machine in which each hook carried three or four threads, and this promptly made possible a greater width of cloth with an asymmetrical design; it also reduced materially the cost of production, and simplified twilling. [1] These advantages of the "Bessbrook" machine, as it became styled, were quickly appreciated throughout the British and foreign linen trade, and they were well demonstrated in a fine linen and silk double-damask tablecloth which was manufactured by the new method for the Philadelphia Exhibition of 1876. The cloth depicted William Penn making his famous treaty with the Indians, "the only league between those nations and the Christians which was never sworn to and never broken" (Voltaire). One need scarcely add that the complex apparatus, required to carry into effect Henry Barcroft's essentially simple idea, was not designed without considerable application and ingenuity, and the numerous Bessbrook machines functioning today offer, many years after his death, a never-ending testimony to his powers. The original patent can still be seen by the interested visitor in the offices at Bessbrook.

Members of the Society of Friends (or, at all events, the Barcroft family) did not believe in their children receiving schooling before the age of six or seven years, and a negligible amount of information

[1] See under the heading "Weaving" in the *Encyclopaedia Britannica* for explanations of this and of other technical terms.

is available about this early period of J.B.'s life, though there are two engaging photographs of him, one of which is reproduced here as Plate 11. From the age of six or seven to that of twelve, he was taught by a Miss Day and a Miss Barritt at The Glen, learning to read when he was seven. Miss Day had a school in Newry, and came out to the house to coach J.B. in arithmetic, Latin, and so forth. Miss Barritt, a Friend from Croydon, was a resident governess, very good at botany, etc.; she instilled a love of science into J.B., and it was she who prepared him for Bootham School (see below). In Lady Barcroft's possession are a number of the seven- and eight-year old J.B.'s answers to test-papers in spelling (at which he was not over-good), arithmetic, and general knowledge. They reveal considerable scientific and mechanical learning in so young a boy, and a tailpiece drawing on one of them depicts a much beflagged lighthouse (presumably the one on Haulbowline Rock was in J.B.'s mind) with a small steamer passing it. An exercise in copperplate writing, dated 9 June 1879, contains the lines:

> "I am so old I can write a letter;
>   My birthday lessons are done;
> The lambs play always, they know no better
>   They are only one times one."

It was during these early years that J. B. began to exhibit that great love of boats which characterized him all his life. It was inherited from, and encouraged by, his father, who would often take his sons the short walk down to the quay at Newry to see the boats there, and who must also have gone frequently with them to Carlingford Lough and Greenore. When J. B. was about ten, David seven, and Mary five, a Company was formed with the three children as Chairman, Secretary, and Directorate respectively, for ships to sail on the more southerly of the two ponds in The Glen garden. The ports were New York at one end and Liverpool at the other, but a projecting stone on the east side, not far from Liverpool, was so reminiscent in shape of Gibraltar that this outpost of empire was included as a port of call on the transatlantic voyages! The boats were made by the two boys in their father's workshop, and were modelled on the White Star vessels of the period. The turning of various parts was done on an old-fashioned foot-treadle lathe under Henry Barcroft's supervision, and in this and other ways he passed on to his sons his own love of craftsmanship in wood. J. B. was constantly in the workshop making fully-rigged boats and other things, and his ingenuity and skill resulted in many useful presents for his family. But the boats were his real love. Subconsciously almost, he knew the names of the ships which were the prototypes of his models; he also knew where the vessels of the different lines (e.g., P. & O., White Star) were stopping at any particular time.

Another pursuit in which he indulged from quite early years was riding; a strong love for it continued right up to the time of his marriage in 1903, and he was very gentle on the horse's mouth. His second cousin, Mrs. J. G. Maynard, daughter of John Grubb Richardson, remembers a summer morning when she, aged nineteen or so, was riding up a steep mountain lane with J. B., then about eight years old, on a pony behind her. Suddenly she heard a clear, defiant voice calling out, "Pity the upper class spend so much of their time horse-racing!" She turned and saw her companion standing up in his stirrups and making this important pronouncement to the rocks and heather!

At this period of private tuition at The Glen, as later, J. B. evinced no inclination towards general literary reading, being in this respect unlike his father and brother and, indeed, most Friends of their social standing. On the other hand, he had a very receptive mind and he absorbed much general education, without the labour of reading for himself, from his father and from his uncle "Willie" Barcroft, of Stangmore House. In respect of his inheritance and of his early years as a whole, it has been stated that he "owed to the mingling in him of the Northern Irish and the Quaker strain, as well as to a singularly free and happy childhood, his own happy blend of enterprise, resilience, and learning without pedantry, of gracious tolerance with staunchness in conviction." We can complete the account by noting that he was already remarkable for the extreme kindness to others which he continued to exhibit through his life. "The lame dog," in particular, "always appealed very much to him."

By 1884, however, the time had come for a change from private tuition at home, and he was sent first to the Friends' School at Bootham, York; he was to remain at it, apart from holidays, until the spring of 1888, when he was nearly sixteen (Plate 12). There is little detailed information about these four important school years, but it was at Bootham that his inclination towards science was first strongly shown, and his bent in that direction was encouraged by one or two masters who were scientifically-minded; this was most fortunate, for in the majority of schools at that time the teaching of science was very little stressed [1]. While at Bootham, also, J. B. developed an inherited love of natural history, and made a considerable collection of ferns and other biological specimens; it was added to during the holidays, when he went to the Mourne Mountains with his father in search of parsley-fern and other rare types. We should also note that, at the time of his first going to school, he was already somewhat of an artist in drawing and painting, and belonged to a club of friends who from time to time would choose a subject which they would each illustrate by a drawing in watercolour [2].

The voyages which J. B. made across the Irish Channel, first on the way between Newry and York, and later between Newry and Cambridge, began or ended at Greenore, at the sea end of Carlingford Lough, and he became a firm friend of all the Captains concerned, who extended to him full bridge privileges. The Lough, both in this way and also, in later days, as a place where he yachted with his sister Mollie, his brother David, Canon Barker, Rector of Rostrevor, and other acquaintances, had a very definite place in J. B.'s boyhood and youthful experiences, and it may assist readers who have not visited it if some brief description is included here. It is reached by rail or by road from Newry. The Dundalk, Newry and Greenore Railway [3] goes via Bridge Street, Newry (which is but

[1] His growing knowledge of the subject was not always put to serious use. For, intrigued by the properties of silver nitrate, he once emptied a solution of it into the Holy Water stoup at the entrance to a Roman Catholic church near Bootham. Thereafter he and a friend remained in a suitable hiding place and were delighted when the worshippers eventually emerged bearing black crosses upon their foreheads!

[2] He kept up his water-colour-painting until about 1910, exhibiting in his choice of subjects a marked preference for seascapes. In his earlier married days, according to Lady Barcroft, he always took his paintbox with him on any holiday during which artistic views (preferably with the sea included in them) were likely to be discovered. One of two of his watercolours which are in her possession is a small, but attractive, seascape which has inscribed on its back the following: – "This was done with a shaving brush on the bridge deck of S.S. New England in Aug. 1900 in ten minutes. The ship was then approaching Boston which she reached about midnight. N. B. I lost the shaving brush. J. Barcroft." We should not forget this creative, artistic side of J. B. in any full evaluation of him and of his achievement.

[3] This railway was leased to the Great Northern Railway of Ireland in 1930 by the London and North Western Railway of England (or, more strictly, by the L. M. S., into which it had by then been incorporated), and its carriages still retain the cream and maroon colours of the latter.

a short distance from The Glen), Omeath (which is in Eire), and Carlingford to Greenore. Another line goes from Newry to Warrenpoint, picturesquely situated at the head of the Lough; this line remains in Ulster throughout its course. By road to Greenore, one goes for some distance alongside the fairly wide ship canal and the broad tidal estuary of the river Clanrye. The double waterway, with the magnificent contour of Carlingford Mountain (1934 feet) showing up to the southeast, reminds one somewhat of scenes on the Rhine. Above Narrow Water Castle (? of King John's time), which is on the left bank of the estuary, the canal unites, via a lock, with the river and thereafter one comes in succession to Omeath and to Carlingford, where a small harbour is dominated by the ruins of a castle above its west end; there are, also, an interesting old street gateway and the ruins of an old abbey to be seen. [1] A short distance farther on is Greenore, where one finds a golf course, a pleasant railway hotel, a low lighthouse with a revolving light, two rows of non-detached two-storied houses transported thither – one could imagine – straight from Crewe, and – by sublime contrast – a magnificent panorama of the Mountains of Mourne on the far side of the Lough to the northwest. Beyond Greenore, on the Ulster side, are Greencastle Point, Green Island, and a small fort. Southwest from this last is Haulbowline Rock with its blockhouse and its lighthouse, and thereafter the open sea. The Isle of Man is at times visible but rain can, on such occasions, be expected. To round off this description, we can add that the Lough is about six and a half miles long from Warrenpoint to Greenore, and in general about two miles wide. Squalls are liable to spring up suddenly through the proximity of the mountains, and a yacht may be capsized without warning; J. B. had one such experience. Climatic conditions favour the Eire side, especially the south-lying Cooley peninsula, and on this side crops grow much better and myrtle flourishes the whole year round. High fuchsia hedges in copious bloom can also surprise a summer visitor from England, but they are hardier growths, and are to be seen on both sides of the Lough.

During the years that J. B. was at school at Bootham, two events of special interest occurred nearer home. These were, first, the opening of The Bessbrook and Newry Tramway to public traffic in October, 1885; and, secondly, the marriage of William Barcroft, of

[1] After his marriage, J. B. spent one or two holidays en famille at Carlingford.

Stangmore House, to Sarah Barcroft, of Stangmore Lodge, in 1886.

The Portrush and Bushmills tramway, serving the Giant's Causeway traffic, was the first electric one in the British Isles and it was opened for use in 1883. The Bessbrook and Newry line was the second one opened in Ireland. It was planned partly to convey workers living in Newry to and from the works at Bessbrook, but mainly to facilitate the movement of coal and flax from the wharves at Newry to the mills at Bessbrook, and of manufactured goods in the reverse direction. The first sod was cut in September, 1883; the Bessbrook and Newry Tramway Company was incorporated in May, 1884, Henry Barcroft being one of its Directors; public traffic began in October, 1885; and the Company took over from the contractor in April, 1886. The length of the three-foot gauge line was just over three miles and there were loops at each of the two termini; there was a total fall of 185 feet from Bessbrook to Newry, and the average speed of the trains was 10 miles per hour. Hydro-electric generators, worked from the Camlough river and developing a maximum of 62 horse-power, supplied ample electric current for all purposes. [1]

The tramway is mentioned here because Henry Barcroft made at least two contributions to its efficacy; he may have made others, but they are not on record. The first was a device by which the trains themselves operated the gates at the level crossing over the public road. "As the car approaches the gates," stated the *Ayrshire Post* in April, 1886, "a projection under the footboard strikes a trigger close to the line, thus opening the valve of a hydraulic cylinder, releasing the water contained therein and allowing the piston to sink. This piston is connected by wires with the gates, and in its sinking pulls on the wires and draws the gates open. When the car has passed, the water flows back into the cylinder, and the gates shut themselves on being released from the weight of the piston." The second contribution was an ingenious arrangement whereby the goods wagons were adapted to run on either rail or road, and trans-shipment of freight was accordingly reduced to a minimum. The front parts of the wagons were supported on fore-carriages which could be pinned for rail-work or run loose for road-work. The

[1] After over three score years of service, the line was closed to traffic on 10 January, 1948, and the rails and so forth are now all removed. No. 2 electric car, the oldest one still surviving in Ireland, for all the early Giant's causeway rolling stock has gone, is probably to be preserved as a museum specimen.

wagon wheels were flangeless and ran on flat rails set outside, and $^{7}/_{8}$ inch lower than, those for the electric cars and trailers, i.e., the rails for these latter acted also as check rails for the wagons. At Newry a ramp was provided for running the wagons on and off the rails; once they were off them, the fore-carriages were unpinned and the wagons were drawn away by horses (or, later, by motor tractors). Thus, Henry Barcroft's inventive powers had once again been of service to the Bessbrook firm, which since 31 January 1878 had been incorporated as the Bessbrook Spinning Company, Limited, with John Grubb Richardson as its first Chairman and with Henry Barcroft as a Director and Managing Director. As already noted, he became also a Director of the subsidiary Tramway Company on its incorporation, and we may add that the various Directorships mentioned were held by him up to his death in 1905 [1]. The account given of the tramway is, therefore, pertinent here not only as providing further examples of H.B.'s inventiveness, but also showing whence the family finances were in part derived. In a minor way the tramway also comes into the general picture, for after it was opened a special Sunday service took the Barcrofts and other Newry Friends to and from the Bessbrook Meeting, thus saving them between four and six miles of walking or driving each First-day; this was, perhaps, not an unimportant consideration whenever weather conditions were adverse.

The marriage of William and Sarah Barcroft in 1886 is also related to our story, because both before and after it Stangmore was an important influence in J. B.'s earlier life. His aunt and uncle were very well-read and had an exceptionally good library, and J. B.'s general education derived much from them. In addition, Stangmore Lodge was the main meeting-place of J. B. with his three Anderson cousins, the children of Henry Barcroft's sister, Elizabeth, and of Samual Lee Anderson (vide supra). All three were older than J. B., but not too much so. They went each summer for about a month to Stangmore Lodge, and were often joined for a day or longer by their cousins from The Glen. After town life, the greater freedom of the country was much appreciated; the children rode on the hay carts and so forth, and by all accounts thoroughly enjoyed them-

[1] Exactly how long he continued to hold his Directorship of the Dundalk and Newry Steam Packet Company it is not possible to discover. But he certainly held it until after 1895.

selves. At the same time, the "atmosphere of unostentatious religion" which existed at Stangmore Lodge helped to mould their characters, and J. B. had inculcated in him there much that distinguished him and was of value to him in his later years, especially his capacity for rapidly establishing friendly relations with people of all classes. For the Stangmore folk not only attended the Friends' First-day Meeting at the nearby Grange Meeting House; they also held afternoon services in the schoolhouse just across the road, with speakers of all denominations taking part, and no discrimination drawn between the rich and the poor. Such width of outlook and practice was paralleled at Moyallon House, but it was certainly not common in most places at the time, and it undoubtedly left its mark on J. B. and the other children. We may also include in this note a mention of Uncle Willie's considerable mechanical ability. "Bar" Anderson and J. B. were devoted to him and were constantly in his workshop, so we should remember William as well as Henry Barcroft when we account for J. B.'s subsequent marked ability in this direction. Finally, Stangmore Lodge is of importance to our story because it was a place where J. B. met his Barcroft cousins, the children of Uncle Willie's brothers.

How much he saw of his Richardson relatives during the Bootham School period of 1884–1888 it is harder to ascertain, for his first signature in the Moyallon House Visitors' Book (which served later for The Woodhouse, Bessbrook) does not occur until 1 September 1894, and almost the only personal recollection available to-day is that J. G. R., when at The Woodhouse, often drove across to The Glen on a Sunday to see the family there, usually taking with him a basket of eggs, including a bantam's one for the young "Netta", or some other present for the children. We may reasonably suppose, in addition to this, that J. B. was across at The Woodhouse from time to time during his winter holidays, and that rather less frequently he got out in the summer ones to the considerably more distant Moyallon House. On the whole, it seems that he visited Moyallon most between 1894 and 1900.

A minor extra item of interest is that in 1888 or 1889 he spent the Easter vacation in Lisieux, Normandy. Twenty-six or twenty-seven years later, when he visited Captain Wolf on a hill outside Boulogne, the smell of the old-style inn in which Captain Wolf had his quarters recalled to J. B. the house in which he had stayed in

Lisieux "when", as he wrote, "I was about sixteen and learned a good deal of this French which I have since very completely forgotten."

When Henry Barcroft was searching for the next school for his elder son, one of the chief things which he bore in mind was the latter's predilection for science. The search was not an easy one for, as has already been stated, schools which encouraged an interest in science were, in the eighteen-eighties, few and far between. Finally, however, Henry discovered the Leys School, Cambridge, which had been founded in 1874, and J. B. entered it, as a member of the Lower Fifth, at the beginning of the summer term of 1888. The Headmaster (and founder) of this school of somewhat under two hundred boys was the Reverend William Fiddian Moulton (1835–1898), a classical scholar of eminence, who appears to have had the faculty of encouraging pupils of widely different interests. "In science, Dr. C. W. Kimmins was a distinguished and attractive master, and contact with the University no doubt helped."

In January, 1889, J. B. matriculated at the University of London, according to its official records, from the Friends' School, York, and the Leys. In the same year, but presumably at the beginning of the Christmas term, he and W. F. Reddaway [1] both became Prefects, and the friendship so begun lasted until J. B.'s death in 1947. On the work side, J. B.'s outstanding ability was early recognized by the Headmaster, who persuaded Henry Barcroft to allow his son to sit for the London University B.Sc. degree while still at school. This degree had been in existence for about thirty years when J. B. was awarded it in 1891 (Plate 13), and the family tradition is that this was the first time it had been gained by a schoolboy.

The rightness of this belief cannot be readily determined from the University records and other sources of information, and the point is not, perhaps, of major importance. What is more relevant is that the effort in some way overtaxed J. B.'s physical strength and that, after leaving the Leys as a member of the Sixth Form at the end of the summer term of 1892, he had to take a year off, falling thereby out of step with his immediate contemporaries. In consequence, Dr. Moulton's wisdom in advocating the course has since been called into question.

Apart from his academic pursuits, J. B.'s school career was not

[1] Later, like J. B., a Fellow of King's College. He died in 1949.

particularly distinguished, his 2nd XI Cricket Colours being his chief achievement in the field of sport, and his Secretaryship of the Missionary and Literary Societies his major attainments in other fields. One of his juniors remembers him as one of the big prefects, who slouched, or rather lurched, as he walked and almost always had a sort of quizzical, detached smile as if he lived a different world from the athletic one in which the majority of boys did. "He was no athlete and seemed to take little interest in such things." According to his contemporary, W. F. Reddaway, on the other hand, J. B. at least showed a Barcroftian originality in the field of cricket, for, "by inventing a batting system of his own, holding his weapon in the middle, he attained a welcome, though modest, eminence as a member of the Second Eleven." Maybe the comparative success of so iconoclastic a technique accounted for the sort of quizzical smile! Little more detail can be added, for few clear-cut reminiscences are now obtainable from those who were at school with him; most of those who survive were somewhat his junior and, as we all know, a year or two's difference in age constitutes, at school, a very definite social barrier. [1]

One of the juniors in question, who writes regretting his inability to add anything of real interest, remembers only "that even as a boy J. B. already had a curious way, after he had spoken, of looking at you with his mouth open." Another writes, "If it had been Clapham or Dale I would have found much to say, but J. B. passed over, round or through me without leaving traces," i.e., J. B.'s personality as a boy was not one that struck other boys. We should, however, miss an important point about his school-time as a whole if we did not add another passage from the pen of the late W. F. Reddaway, who wrote in 1948 as follows. "Looking back over a friendship with Joseph Barcroft which began in our school days and continued through his unbroken residence at Cambridge, I think what most particularly marked him out was the absence of any change. In his happy career . . . he ripened indeed, but never in the slightest broke with his past. As a boy he was distinguished for the same characteristics that marked him until within sight of the end –

[1] Sir Henry Dale, who went to the Leys in 1891, described their relative status in the words: – "I found him there – one of the Olympians, by two or three years my senior, I a cheery youngster looking up at him with the awe which a schoolboy has for his senior."

ambition, unvaried health, rare ingenuity and a cheerfulness that never failed." [1]

To conclude this account of J. B. and his time at the Leys School, we should note some of his fellows and juniors who were destined, like him, to exhibit marked ability and, in a number of instances, to achieve considerable fame in later life. For many of them became, and remained, J. B.'s friends. We may instance H. H. Dale, who was to be President of the Royal Society; J. H. Clapham, who was to be a Fellow of King's College, Professor of Economic History at Cambridge, and President of the British Academy; and H. C. Gutteridge, who was to attain eminence in the field of International Law. There were also W. W. Gibberd, who was to be one of the last Senior Wranglers but died too young for any major accomplishment; F. A. Bainbridge, who was to be the first occupant of the Chair of Physiology at Barts; C. F. Hadfield, whose work in anaesthetics was likewise to add, if in a different way, to the renown of that institution; and A. E. Barclay, who was to be one of the first and foremost in the field of radiology in this country. [2] Few schools of the size of the Leys can ever have had quite such a galaxy at one particular time.

About the middle of J. B.'s time at the Leys School, to be precise, on 28 March 1890, his great-uncle, John Grubb Richardson, died and with his passing the way became open for a gradual change in the atmosphere of the Board Meeting of the Bessbrook firm. For a generation there had been some sort of balance between Henry Barcroft's keenness on experiment without particular respect to cost, and the opposing keenness of certain of the Richardsons to put due financial considerations first; we may imagine that until 1890 J. G. R.'s influence, as Chairman, kept the balance right. After 1890, and particularly (for reasons which need not be detailed here) after 1893, the more business-like element became dominant and Henry Barcroft must have felt himself very much in a minority; nor do we hear of any further products of his inventiveness in connection with

[1] This conclusion of Mr. Reddaway impressed me very much when I was planning this biography, and it gives the reason why I have devoted so much space to the formative influences which, from various quarters, acted upon J. B. during his boyhood years. – K. J. F.

[2] Wilhelm Conrad Röntgen discovered his new kind of rays in Würzburg on 8 November 1895. As the necessary apparatus was available in most Physics Departments, the discovery was rapidly acclaimed, and the use of the X-rays practised, throughout the civilized world.

12—Joseph Barcroft, aged sixteen years

13—Joseph Barcroft, Bachelor of Science of the University of London, at the age of nineteen

the firm. He had, however, many other interests, e.g., his Directorship of the Dundalk and Newry Steam Packet Company, his Deputy-Lieutenantship and his field naturalist pursuits. He was also, during 1890, High Sheriff for Armagh. [1] J. B. shared his father's interest in field biology and in the affairs of the Steam Packet Company, the steamers of which sailed from Newry and Dundalk, and from the former went to Androssan and to Liverpool. They carried a few passengers but were mainly cargo-vessels, and they exerted a great fascination on J. B., who would go and see any one of them that was in dock directly he returned from Cambridge.

Doubtless the accounts given of J. B. at the Leys School overemphasize the academic side and those of him during the holidays overemphasize the opposite one. But he does seem to heve been a vastly different person when he was home from school, and those who knew him at those times have stressed that the Leys picture should be properly balanced by a picture of him on holiday. Miss Muriel Harris, who from 1886, when her brother [2] married Gertrude Richardson, was a frequent visitor at Moyallon House, has provided some details. "As I remember him," she writes, "and he came often to Moyallon, as did his brother and sisters – he was a most enchanting person, slim and good-looking, with the most charming face and an attractiveness of both character and manner which impressed everyone who came into contact with him. He had an inward gaiety which affected us all and we were all devoted to him." Elsewhere she mentions "his extraordinary charm and undoubted brilliance."

We can add to this some details about J. B.'s outdoor pursuits. Though he was not an athlete, as we have seen, in the curiously restricted schoolboy connotation of this word, he rode, played tennis, sailed, skated, and – especially after his B.Sc. year – played golf. His early fondness for riding has already been mentioned and we need only add that he remained keen on it throughout the period with which this Chapter deals and for long afterwards.

[1] This post involved its holder in considerable expense, so few wished to have the honour for longer than a year.

[2] Leverton Harris, later M. P., Director of the Restriction of Enemy Supplies at the Foreign Office, a Privy Councillor, and – much against his personal inclinations – Under Secretary of Blockade. When he finally gave up politics, he developed his hobby of oil-painting, and produced pictures of considerable merit, some of which can be seen at Moyallon House and at The Woodhouse, Bessbrook.

Indeed, in later years he was often to express regret that his professional work prevented him from indulging as often as he could wish in this favourite form of recreation. On one or two occasions during his youth he slipped away with the Newry Harriers but in general he did not follow hounds, despite ample opportunities in Ireland for so doing, for Friends' custom did not encourage this pursuit. Sailing he began about the age of seventeen, first on the Cam, then on the Norfolk Broads, and later on Canlingford Lough; it was to be for years one of his chief delights, and to inspire him in 1913 to write one of his finest passages,[1] which we shall quote later on in this book. He was very sensitive to the external environment, and appreciated the strength or otherwise of the wind on his hands when yachting. Skating he practised, as occasion offered, on a small sheet of ice above the waterfall at The Glen. As he had always to master fully any new technique and to do everything extremely well, he soon passed on to figures of eight and so forth. Golf he had certainly begun by 1891, for on 14 April of that year he partnered his sister Mary (Mollie) in a tournament at Greer's Farm – an illustrated memoir of the occasion is preserved in The Glen Visitors' book. But it was in 1892–3, when he had a year off to recover from his B.Sc. overstrain, that he particularly devoted himself to the game, which thereafter remained for years one of his main recreations (Plate 41). His father had a ninehole course laid down at The Glen and J. B. spent many hours playing on it, with his sister Mary pressed into service as partner; she was similarly expected to act as sailing-companion when J. B. went yachting. Other out-door pursuits in which he indulged were sketching, to which we have already referred, and photography.

A few more notes can be added to round off this account of the twenty-year old J. B. and of his home. With regard to himself, we must first mention that, in contrast to his father and his brother, he had no inclination at all towards a business life, and fixed office hours would have been repugnant to him. Many years were to elapse before he finally decided which calling he would follow, but quite early on it was clear to him that a commercial career was excluded, and to that extent his future choice was made simpler. The second note which we must add concerns something quite

[1] See the Preface to his book, *The Respiratory Function of the Blood*, 1914.

different, namely, his fearlessness. This quality, which was to become widely recognized in him in his later years, was already present during the period we have been discussing; it derived in part from the self-restraint and self-discipline inculcated by his Quaker parents, and it was certainly in no small measure dependent upon his own faith as a member of the Society of Friends. The best was always expected of one and to give one's best, in many circumstances, implied a disregard of fear, as followers of George Fox during the previous two centuries had so abundantly demonstrated. Nor need we confine our remarks to J. B.'s fearlessness, for the basis of his home life as a whole was the family's belief in Quaker faith and practice; all else derived from these and has to be interpreted in their light.

More difficult to assess at all precisely is the influence which his brother and sisters had upon him up to 1893, when he became of age; we can, however, with advantage interpolate here a few notes about them. Sarah, his eldest sister and his senior by about three years, was by all accounts the scholar of the family and, after being at Cheltenham Ladies' College, went to Dresden for some time to continue her education.[1] From her nephew, "Robbie" Barcroft, comes the following story in lighter vein about her. On a certain occasion during his youth, J. B. was driving the family wagonette back from Warrenpoint to Newry when the horse, King by name, got a rein caught under his tail and began kicking the splashboard. In correct coachman style, J. B. caught King a flip with the whip, causing him to swish his tail and to free the rein. Meanwhile, however, Sarah, alarmed at the turn events seemed to be taking, had slipped quietly out of the back of the wagonette on to the road and J. B. drove on for some time before he noticed that she was no longer with him. Returning then to her rescue, he found a pathetic and rather portly figure, panting and blowing after a long trot in pursuit of him and the vanishing wagonette. About David Barcroft, J. B.'s only brother and two and a half years his junior, the only notes pertinent to this Chapter are that he was, like J. B. himself, very good-looking and that he was, at the time of which we are

[1] Later she became an expert on the family history, on horticulture, on archaeology and on many other subjects; her erudition and her powers of memory still remain causes of wonder to the surviving members of the family and to others who knew her. In 1930 she became a "Minister". She died in 1947 not long after J. B. himself.

writing, envisaging a business career. [1] Mollie Barcroft, the second sister, was five years younger than J. B., but she appears to have been a willing and useful member of any concerted effort, especially any outdoor effort, with either or with both of her brothers. [2] The youngest sister, Anna Henrietta (Netta), was in 1892 only nine years old, and scarcely yet figuring at all largely in her elder brother's life.

There are doubtless many other points which could be mentioned in this account of J. B.'s family background, boyhood, and youth, but it is not easy at this distance of time to produce a complete picture, and it is even harder to decide how far he was influenced by the various factors described. In the main, however, we see him born into a well-to-do Quaker home, with every opportunity there and in the houses of nearby relatives for his full development. Later, he derives broadening influences by going away first to Bootham and then to the Leys School; at the former his interest in science receives its first major encouragement, at the latter he precociously achieves the distinction of the Bachelor of Science degree of London University. Finally, owing to overwork for that degree, he has a year off at home, with consequent addition to the long list of outdoor pursuits for which he exhibits much natural aptitude, and with a timely extra opportunity for profiting by all that Ireland can, and does, give in various ways to those of her sons who can appreciate her gifts.

We can say, then, that he was as fortunate in his environment during his earlier formative years as he appears to have been in his ancestry, and that the richness of his opportunities at home, at school, and elsewhere was not wasted so that, as he emerged from his teens, he was already well-equipped in a variety of ways, and adversely affected in no way, for the further and more exacting years which lay ahead. If he was one of those endowed with ten talents rather than the one or two which are all that the majority of us can claim, he had at all events begun to prepare himself, con-

[1] After a few years in business he turned to medicine, took an Edinburgh degree and, with a break for R.A.M.C. service during the 1914–18 war, practised in London until ill-health caused his retirement, when he returned to The Glen. Later, on 29 November 1932, he married Georgiana Eleanor Norman, of Dergmoney House, Omagh, County Tyrone. He died in 1938.

[2] Later she joined David during most of the years that he was in practice in London, and it gave them great pleasure during those years to be visited by J. B. on his way from Porton, or when he attended Royal Society or Royal Institution functions.

sciously or unconsciously, for their full use. And his natural ability, intelligence, and brilliance had their ideal counterparts in a fine sense of humour, gaiety, kindliness, love of outdoor pursuits, and courage. His immediate further career will be considered in our next Chapter; at this point we take our farewell from him as an adolescent.

CHAPTER III

1893–1903

UNDERGRADUATE AND POSTGRADUATE LIFE, AND MARRIAGE

During the year 1892–3, when he was resting from overstrain, J. B. must have been much influenced by a return to full home life in Ireland after spending so large a part of the previous eight years at schools in England; in addition, as we have noted, he increased his range of outdoor activities and his proficiency in those in which he had previously indulged. Doubtless, too, the young graduate in science of London University did some thinking about his future career, but he had as yet no ultimate object and his immediate one was reasonably clear, namely, to get accepted by one of the Cambridge Colleges and to study for the Natural Science Tripos. Clare was his first choice and he entered for a scholarship at that College. But his knowledge of Greek was not up to the Clare requirements, so he applied for entry into King's College, where the standard in Greek was not so high. King's accepted him, whereupon the twenty-one year old J. B. promptly forgot the little amount of Greek which he had acquired in preparation for his entry.

As he was to be ever more closely associated with the College from that time right up to his death fifty-four years later, it is appropriate here to give a brief résumé of its history.[1]

It was founded by the devout King Henry VI (acceded 1422; deposed 1461) in 1440 (O.S.) and on Passion Sunday, 2 April 1441, he laid the first stone of his new College and granted the use of materials from the old Castle at Cambridge in its construction. To begin with it was to be a College of three wings built in a garden purchased from Trinity Hall; a Chapel of modest dimensions was to be outside the quadrangle to the south, and in fact this first Chapel lasted until 1536 or 1537, when it collapsed one evening

[1] Derived from Leigh (1899), Fay (1907), and Hussey (1926).

14—Interior of King's College Chapel, Cambridge, viewed from the west end

Facing page 35

after Vespers. Just before the foundation of King's (to use its final name), William of Wykeham had linked his own foundations of Winchester and New College, Oxford; Henry VI, presumably through this example, in 1443 linked in similar fashion Eton and King's. Through his efforts, also, Pope Eugenius IV issued a Bull in favour of the new foundation, granting it exceptional ecclesiastical privileges, to which in course of time – though the exact date is as unknown as the legality is questionable – was added an extraordinary secular one, that Kingsmen should receive their first University degree without examination. It was not until 1851 that the College voluntarily surrendered the practice in the true interests of education.

"The great [second] Chapel and its services," according to Austen Leigh, "will generally be recognised as the most striking features of King's College; the deepest and widest influences exercised by the College during three and a half centuries are due to them." So this impressive building, "a cathedral built in chapel form and more or less in accordance with a simple design" (Hussey, 1926), requires a few words. In his Will of 1448 Henry VI gave his plan for the church and a southern quadrangle and a western cloister which he intended to build, though of this trio, unfortunately, only the first structure came into being, with consequent lack of correspondence in the proportions of the College buildings to-day. Henry laid the first stone on 25 July 1446 but it was not until 1515 that the fabric was finished, and only in 1536 or 1537, just about the time the first Chapel collapsed, that the new one was ready for constant use. Despite the passage of ninety years during its completion and certain changes caused by John Woolrich succeeding Reginald Ely as master-mason in 1476, [1] the Chapel is a homogeneous work of art, and the supreme example of the Perpendicular style, which in its turn is a peculiar triumph of English architecture. For its immediate College purpose, and certainly in relation to the buildings round it, it can be regarded as too large, but Wordsworth's sonnet is the inspired answer, for all time, to such objections.

Other College buildings, as they exist to-day, are associated with the names of various architects, including James Gibbs (who designed St. Martin-in-the Fields Church) and William Wilkins.

[1] Woolrich was responsible for the exquisite fan-vaulting (Plate 14).

Gibbs' Palladian range [1] was begun in 1724 and was ready for wainscoting in 1730. Wilkins' building, which includes the Hall, was finished in 1828 and its style is Gothic, which was not Wilkins' particular forte; the best part of the new structure is probably the interior of the Hall. Wilkins was also responsible for the screen through which one enters the College from Trumpington Street.

Apart from the above account of King's College we need, for the proper appreciation of much of what is to follow, some details about the Cambridge Physiological Laboratory and its personnel (*Cambridge University Reporter* 7 and 25 October, 1893; Tanner, 1917, 140–1; Rolleston, 1932 [2]; Langdon-Brown, 1946), and some information about wider aspects of the science in question (Sharpey-Schafer, 1927; Franklin, 1938, 1949). With regard to the former, we can say that the modern, dynamic era of Cambridge physiology dates from 1870, when Trinity College created a Praelectorship in the subject for the benefit of the University as a whole and appointed to the post, with which went a Fellowship of the College, Michael Foster (1836–1907) from University College, London. He lectured at first, under some difficulty, in what is now the Philosophical Library, but eventually a separate Department was built; it came into use in January 1879, and in 1887, and again in 1890, it was greatly enlarged. In 1875, while accommodation was still inadequate, John Newport Langley (1852–1925) was appointed Demonstrator; then in 1883 Foster (Plate 15) was promoted to Professor, and Langley, Walter Holbrook Gaskell (1847–1914), and A. Sheridan Lea (1853–1915) were appointed University Lecturers (Plates 16, 17 23). A Senior Demonstratorship and a Junior Demonstratorship were also established in that year, the former going to Sheridan Lea and the latter to D'Arcy Wentworth Thompson; in 1886 and at various times subsequent to that date the posts in question were re-allocated.

In the Lecture-List number of the *Cambridge University Reporter*

[1] In which, in his later days, J. B. had his rooms on the first floor to the north of the main entrance.

[2] The Registrary's Clerk (Mr. William J. Baker), who very kindly supplied me with certain details, told me that to the best of his knowledge and belief the late Professor Sir Humphry Rolleston checked with the records at the University Registry all the facts concerning Cambridge teaching officers which appear in his book, *The Cambridge Medical School A biographical History*. If, however, his usual accuracy is in this publication also conceded to Sir Humphry, there is, for the present purpose, less detail than one could wish. I have, therefore, incorporated some of the facts provided by Tanner, but even so am not completely satisfied. – K. J. F.

for 7 October 1893, the following lectures and practical classes in Physiology were advertised for J. B.'s first undergraduate year:–

(1) For the Michaelmas Term 1893:

Prof. Foster:	Elementary Physiology (with practical work).
Dr. Shore:	Physiology for Medical Students (intermediate).
Mr. Langley:	Physiology and histology (advanced).
Mr. Langley:	Practical work.
Dr. Lea:	Chemical Physiology (advanced).
Mr. Cunningham:	Anatomy and Physiology of the Teeth.

(2) For the Lent Term 1894:

Prof. Foster:	Elementary Physiology (with practical work).
Dr. Shore:	Physiology for Medical Students (intermediate).
Dr. Gaskell:	Advanced Physiology (Vascular system etc.).
Mr. Langley:	Physiology and histology (advanced).
Mr. Langley:	Practical work.
Dr. Lea:	Chemical Physiology (continued).

(3) For the Easter Term 1894:

Prof. Foster:	Elementary Physiology (with practical work).
Dr. Gaskell:	Advanced Physiology (Respiration etc.).
Mr. Langley:	Central Nervous System (elementary).
Mr. Langley:	Central Nervous System (advanced).

In addition to the above, we may note that the *Cambridge University Reporter* list of University Officers etc. for 25 October 1893 included Professor Foster, University Lecturers Dr. Gaskell (Physiology), Dr. Lea (Physiology) and Mr. Langley (Histology), University Demonstrators Dr. Shore and Mr. Hardy, and – as recognized teachers in Physiology with reference to certain regulations for the M. B. degree – Dr. Bradbury, Dr. Lea, Mr. Saunders, Dr. Hill, Dr. Gaskell, and Mr. Langley.

The other information relevant here is that dealing with physiology in its national and international aspects, and it can be briefly summarized as follows. The idea of an association of British physiologists was a direct outcome of the anti-vivisection movement which had developed pari passu with the growth of experimental physiology in this country, and which had led to the appointment of a Royal Commission in 1875. As the opposition was obviously active, experimental physiologists felt obliged to discuss the formation of an association for their own mutual benefit and protection. In consequence, the Physiological Society was founded in 1876 to promote the advancement of the science and to facilitate the intercourse of those actively engaged in it; its membership was at first limited to forty. Two years later the *Journal of Physiology*, the first periodical in the English language to be exclusively devoted to that science, was founded by Foster with the financial help of his friend, A. G. Dew-Smith.

The International Congresses of Physiologists were initiated in 1889 after a preliminary meeting to discuss the project had been held in the previous year. Those primarily responsible appear to have been Gerald F. Yeo (Plate 18), Foster, Frithiof Holmgren (1831–1897), Hugo Kronecker (1839–1914), and Willy Kühne (1837–1900), and again a contributory cause was the anti-vivisectionists' opposition to experimental physiology in Great Britain even if the final, major object of the triennial meetings was to promote co-operation and intercourse between physiologists of all countries. The first Congress took place at Basel in 1889 and was attended by, among others, Foster, Langley, and Gaskell. The second took place in 1892 at Liége, with Charles Scott Sherrington (1857–1952) [1] as the Secretary for the English language. At the end of it, Bern was chosen as the venue for the one to be held in 1895.

With the above necessary incursions into the history of King's College and the development of physiology duly made, we can revert to the freshman J. B., arrived in Cambridge in October 1893 at the beginning of what was to be his very long career there. At King's he not only found his old friend, W. F. Reddaway, but also soon made a new one in the person of William (now Sir William) Valentine Ball, who was – ten years later – to become his brother-in-law. "Bill" was the second son of Sir Robert Stawell Ball (1840–1913) who, after being Royal Astronomer of Ireland from 1874 to 1892, had in the latter year become Lowndean Professor of Astronomy and Geometry, Director of the Cambridge Observatory, and a Professorial Fellow of King's College. A second cousin of his, and her husband, the Reverend H. B. Swanzy, were resident in Newry,

[1] See Liddell (1952); Fulton (1952).

County Down, and were personal friends of the Barcrofts at The Glen, so the intimacy of J. B. with the Ball family is simply explained. [1] In 1947 Sir William recalled that "It was not long before he visited my home at the Observatory, where I was wont to practise vicarious hospitality – inviting my friends to lunch on Sunday. Here it was that Joe met my sister Minnie [Mary Agnetta] with consequences which, some years later, were to prove delightful to us all." Lady Barcroft herself thinks that her first meeting with J. B. occurred – during his first year – at a party given in the Provost's Lodge at King's; she and J. B. played a game of "puff-ball" over the grand piano! It was not, however, until 1901 that the friendship so begun ripened into something more serious.

On the evidence now available, it is not possible to give a detailed chronological account of J. B.'s undergraduate years, and the best that can be done is to collect together in as orderly a fashion as possible the rather scattered data. On the academic side, according to Sir William Ball, J. B. was studious enough but he did not work on conventional lines. So much so that his Tutor – a very prosaic man – was wont to say: "I have never regarded Barcroft as a serious student." Somewhat the same note was struck by W. F. Reddaway, who in 1948 (personal communication) wrote that "To his surprise and regret, J. B. failed to impress the present Sir Sidney Harmer, who reserved his admiration for two (eventually) far less distinguished pupils."

As an undergraduate J. B. retained the mischievous strain which was present in him as a schoolboy, and Sir William Ball in 1947 remarked that "Joe was human like the rest of us in those happy far-off days! I remember his telling me of something which took

[1] The Swanzy-Ball relationship is indicated by the following details, kindly furnished by the late Reverend Canon R. A. Swanzy, Vicar of Newry. Roger Green of Youghal was married twice, in 1753 to Catherine Walker and in 1766 to Mary Ellis. Elizabeth Anne Swanzy, a great-granddaughter by the first marriage, married her second cousin, the Reverend T. B. Swanzy (1836–1884), who in 1876 became Vicar of Newry and remained so until his death. Sir Robert Stawell Ball, on the other hand, was a great-grandson by the second marriage.

It is not out of place to add here certain details about the Swanzy family's further connection with Newry and, therefore, with the residents of The Glen. Elizabeth Ann Swanzy and her husband had three sons; the second of these, Henry Biddall Swanzy (1873–1932), was Vicar of Newry from 1914 to 1932, and Dean of Dromore from 1931 to 1932; he was succeeded as Vicar by his younger brother, Robert Archibald Swanzy, who from 1945 was also Precentor of Dromore, and who died in 1950. Finally, the eldest son, Thomas Erskine Swanzy, who was Prebendary of Lincoln from 1926 to 1947, lived with his surviving brother and his two sisters in Newry during the three years from his retirement to his death in 1950.

place at lecture. 'We were taught organic chemistry,' he said, 'by a German chap, who, in his efforts to speak the King's English, was not much assisted by his class. On one occasion an organ grinder came to play in the street under the window, and we kept time with our feet. I leave you to guess who it was had employed the musician – paying him half-a-crown for his services' ". A very different type of person was the teacher of theoretical chemistry, C. T. Heycock, of King's College, who used no notes for his lectures, "bringing on to the platform nothing but blackboard, chalk, and duster." Like this superb teacher, [1] on whose technique he perhaps patterned his own, J. B. himself in later years never had recourse to notes when lecturing (Plate 49). [2]

The teaching of physiological chemistry in Cambridge was from 1883 to 1896 allotted to the ci-devant classical student, Sheridan Lea; he was also the writer of the relevant section in Foster's *Textbook of Physiology*. Unfortunately, he was off duty through illness during the time that J. B. took the advanced course, such as it then was, in the subject, and his deputy merely attempted to decipher Lea's lecture notes and to demonstrate from his class instructions; in a most depressing way, he handed out printed forms and said, "You had better try to do this, but you will probably find it won't come off." It was not a very inspiring approach and it completely discouraged H. H. Dale, who through J. B.'s year off was now in the same class as the latter. When, however, Dale discussed the matter with J. B., the latter spoke with great assurance and conviction and stated that, when they came to the real thing, they would find that the main line of physiological advance would be via chemistry; it was on that line that J. B. himself proposed to work. Thus, "while still completing his preparation for the final examination of Part II Tripos, J. B. must have begun to choose the general direction of his life's work."

To the above notes about his undergraduate career, we may add the following data. In 1894 he became Prizeman and Exhibitioner of King's College; presumably about the same time, he was appointed

[1] Sir Robert Ball had a similar gift for lecturing. See Ball, W. V. (1915).

[2] "I look things up," he once told W. V. Ball, "some time before the lecture. If the student is expected to remember what he hears for all time, he who tries to teach ought to be able to retain in his own head, for a few hours, that which he intends to say." Asked if he was troubled by students coming in late, he replied – in all modesty – "The question never arises; the room is always packed when I arrive."

Hon. Secretary of the Cambridge Old Leysian Union. On 7 January of the following year, during his Christmas vacation, he gave a lecture on "The properties of the surfaces of liquids" to the Belfast Natural History and Philosophical Society. The lecture, or rather the account of it, is the first of over three hundred publications associated with J. B.'s name, but it was not upon his particular subject. Nor, as Sir Henry Dale said in 1948 (see Dale, 1949), did J. B. know more about it, probably, "than any other eager intelligent student of his time taking the Chemistry course for the first part of his Tripos." The fact, however, that he gave the lecture at all in these circumstances shows the early presence of one of his more marked characteristics, namely, his enterprising interest in branches of science outside his own specialty.

An even more striking example was given by Sir Henry. As already noted in Chapter II, Röntgen discovered X-rays early in November, 1895, and the apparatus necessary for their production was available in most Physics Departments. Almost so soon as the news of the discovery reached Cambridge, J. B. borrowed a Crookes' tube from the Cavendish Laboratory and enabled a meeting of the Natural Science Club, held in his rooms, to make one of the first radiographs produced in Great Britain. [1] "I suppose", said Sir Henry, "he borrowed everything – we all sat round and developed the plate in his bedroom. Physics was never his subject, but he was interested in everything new in science."

In the summer of 1896, a few months later, J. B. took his Bachelor of Arts degree, having been placed in Class I in Parts I and II of the Natural Science Tripos. In three years, therefore, he had gone far in his further scientific training and had distinguished himself in it; he had also envisaged his possible future line of work, and he had met his wife-to-be, though neither he nor she was as yet aware of the coming relationship. With his increasing interest in, and devotion

[1] Sir Henry Dale's suggestion that it may have been the very first one seems unlikely in view of other evidence. C. Thurston Holland (1937) wrote that the first note published in England about the new discovery appeared in the *Standard*, a daily paper, on 7 January, 1896, and that on the evening of that day Campbell Swinton, an electrical engineer living in London, made the first radiograph ever taken in this country. E. Ashworth Underwood (1945) gave the date of the *Standard's* announcement as 6 January, and quoted Pullin (1925) as stating that Swinton produced his first radiograph, of the human hand, on 7 January. Underwood himself wrote that "the first X-ray photograph of the human body taken in this country by Röntgen's method was made by Mr. A. A. Campbell Swinton and Mr. G. Stanton in the second week of January 1896."

to, science he had not lost his gaiety or sense of humour. Nor did he neglect the religious side of his life, for in term-time he was a regular attendant at Cambridge Meeting and there, from the autumn of 1895 onwards, he met a Friend of more than usual interest.

This was Caroline Emelia Stephen (1834–1909), daughter of Sir James Stephen, K. C. B., who had been Permanent Under-Secretary for the Colonies from 1836 to 1847, and then Regius Professor of History at Cambridge from 1849 until his death in 1859. Caroline herself was a semi-invalid from soon after her mother's death in 1875. She had come into contact with Friends before then through her sister-in-law, and before 1890 she joined the Society. In the autumn of 1895, after many years elsewhere, she returned to Cambridge, where one of her nieces was Vice-Principal of Newnham College, and another was living in Newnham Croft and engaged in teaching. Caroline, after a year or two in the Croft, took a house in Merton Street and continued to live there until her death. She seldom missed a Friends' Meeting, and she developed a very beautiful garden at her home. In 1908 she published *Light Arising* and, posthumously, in 1911 appeared her second book, *The Vision of Faith and other Essays.* It is said by his Richardson cousins that J. B. was much influenced by this Quaker mystic; it is also quite certain that he continued in his Friends' faith during the period we are considering and for long afterwards. [1] So this source of inspiration, continuing on from his boyhood years, should be borne in mind as we integrate our picture of him as an undergraduate.

We should also remember his vacations spent at The Glen, Newry, with visits to the nearby Woodhouse at Bessbrook, and to the more distant Stangmore Lodge and Moyallon House. From the respective Visitors' Books we find that he visited Moyallon in September 1894 and September 1896, and that Sir Robert Ball visited The Glen in October, 1894. During his undergraduate days, finally, J. B. kept up his sailing, riding, tennis, golf, and so forth, with sailing and riding, we may imagine, holding first place in his affections. And there we come to the end of the information that

[1] According to W. H. Palmer, Clerk to the Society of Friends, Cambridge Preparative Meeting, J. B. never resigned his membership of the Society though, through differences of opinion arising during the first World War, he ceased to go to Meeting from then onwards. Before the War, he was very helpful with the children's class attached to the Cambridge Meeting.

15—MICHAEL FOSTER (1836–1907), FIRST PROFESSOR OF PHYSIOLOGY AT CAMBRIDGE

16—A. SHERIDAN LEA (1853–1915)

17—W. H. GASKELL (1847–1914) WITH HIS 'LAB-BOY', THOMAS METCALFE, ON HIS LEFT
In the foreground is one of the crocodiles on which Gaskell worked out the separation of the vagus and sympathetic nerve supplies to the heart

Facing page 42

18—Gerald F. Yeo (1845–1909), Professor of Physiology at King's College, London, who first suggested the idea of an International Congress of Physiologists, and who was Hon. Secretary to the first one in 1889

19—The *Arrow*, belonging to the Reverend Canon Barker, of Rostrevor, running towards Carlingford, 1899. Joseph Barcroft often sailed in the *Arrow*

Facing page 43

appears to be obtainable, at this distance of time, about his undergraduate period.

He reached the age of twenty-four soon after qualifying for his Cambridge B. A. degree and we can imagine that the question of what should be his next step must have been much in his mind before he went home for the Long Vacation. Presumably, with the agreement of his father, he obtained permission to return to the Physiological Laboratory in the autumn and to try his hand at original research, or at least to begin making preparations for such activity, but his academic year 1896–7 is poorly documented and we have to make a reasonable conjecture rather than to state known facts. A second problem, which may have worried him little in 1896 but obviously began to do so within the succeeding years, was to choose a career which would give him financial independence. This was not, one presumes, necessary from his parents' point of view, but it was natural enough in a man of his age and later, when his thoughts were turning towards matrimony, he made many efforts to improve his financial status.

His first research, though probably not the method for his attack upon it, was suggested by Langley, was carried out under considerable difficulties, and took until the summer of 1901 for its completion. It dealt with the gaseous metabolism of the submaxillary gland in the dog, and was probably intended by Langley to help decide between the conflicting views of himself and of Rudolf Heidenhain and others, though in point of fact it evolved on quite different lines. [1] Initially, J. B. was confronted by the necessity for improving the standard apparatus – a Toepler mercury pump – used for extracting blood gases so that he could collect and store successive small quantities of blood from a relatively small portion of an animal's body; during its collection and storage, and subsequent passage into the Toepler pump proper, each sample of blood had to be kept from contact with air. In addition, in order to avoid the entry of air through rubber joints, J. B. had to fuse the subsidiary glass receiver system with the Toepler pump for each experiment, and at the end to cut it off for cleaning. As if this was not enough, he

[1] Heidenhain (1834–1897) had attributed the contrasting effects of chorda tympani and sympathetic nerve stimulation to the relative predominance within these nerves of trophic and secretory fibres, while Langley thought that the variations depended upon the very different vasomotor effects of the two nerve-supplies, and other workers again had their own particular interpretations of the experimental findings.

had only a small space, about eight to ten feet square, in which to do his work and this space, protected by a frame-work draped with green baize, was cut off from a corner of a room which also served as a passage through the laboratory. He can certainly be regarded as having won his scientific spurs by the success which he achieved in the face of such difficulties, while still fresh from his undergraduate course, and with only sporadic opportunities of conversation with men senior to himself in the type of work which he had set out to do.

The apparatus was shown and described to members of the 4th International Congress of Physiologists, which took place in Cambridge, on Thursday, 25 August 1898, at the beginning of the afternoon session (see Franklin, 1938). From evidence which will be quoted later, it obviously impressed Angelo Mosso and presumably, therefore, other workers in the blood-respiratory field. For some months, by the time of this demonstration, J. B. had been busy using the apparatus for the special object which he had in mind, namely, the comparison of the gases in the venous blood emerging from the submaxillary gland with those in arterial blood, but it was not until 1900 and 1901 that his triad of papers on the gaseous metabolism appeared in print. In Dale's view (Dale, 1949) the research as a whole is entitled to rank as one of the classics of physiology, for it was a pioneer study, carried on almost single-handed and with cumbrous apparatus, yet with undaunted optimism, to its successful termination. Two of the methods used, namely, that of Haldane for gas analysis, and that of Haldane and Lorrain Smith for the direct colorimetric determination of haemoglobin in a blood sample, did not appear in print until 1898 and 1900 respectively, but J. B. was in touch with Haldane during the work, and may well have received advance information from him.

The findings made by J. B. were, briefly, that water was lost to the saliva and lymph during activity of the gland, so that the oxygen content of the venous blood might equal or exceed that of the arterial blood; that during chorda tympani stimulation the oxygen usage of the gland rose to three or four times its resting value, but that the increase in carbon dioxide production might be even greater, with consequent rise in respiratory quotient; and that atropine, given in high enough dosage to inhibit secretion through chorda stimulation, resulted in a temporary increase in carbonic acid production but no change in oxygen consumption. The results were a great advance on the only previous ones reported (Chauveau and Kaufmann, 1886) and explained some of the anomalies present in those authors' findings. They did not help much in resolving the Heidenhain-Langley controversy, but that does not greatly matter. The main thing is that J. B. had made a resolute beginning of his research career and was beginning to see more clearly the lines along which that career could develop.

Before, however, considering the next steps which he took in research, we need to go back a few years and fit in other parts of his story, and we may begin by noting that in September 1897 he again visited Moyallon House from The Glen, Newry. In the winter, when he was beginning his experimental physiology after the preparatory work of the previous academic year, he was still somewhat uncertain about his future vocation, and he thought that there might be an opening for a man trained both in science and also in the law in regard to patents. The outcome of this idea was that on 24 January 1898 he was admitted to Lincoln's Inn, his sureties being James Alexander Rentoul and Charles Thomas Heycock. [1] A not unimportant happening of the same year was the coming of Frederick Gowland Hopkins (1861–1947) to Foster's Laboratory as University Lecturer in Chemical Physiology, though we have no information as to Hopkins' immediate influence, if any, on J. B. In September the latter again visited Moyallon. Though there is no entry in the Visitors' Book, Miss Muriel Harris recalls that she was out blackberrying when J. B. came from the house to announce the news of the fall of Omdurman, and this gives the date as 2 September 1898.

During the Lent and Summer Terms of 1899 J. B. acted as part-time master at his old school, The Leys; on 18 March he was elected and admitted to a Fellowship, which he was to hold for the next half-century, at King's College. He had submitted as his dissertation "An Investigation of the Gaseous Metabolism of the Salivary Glands." The experts to whom it was passed for report were Langley and Haldane, and a copy of the dissertation is preserved in the College Library. In the same year, again, H. H. W.

[1] The subsequent story is that he kept only six terms, by dining in Hall, towards the requisite number of twelve necessary for Call to the Bar. So he was never called by the Society in question.

Pearson, of Gonville and Caius College, and J. B. were awarded Walsingham Medals by the University. [1] In September he visited Moyallon from The Glen, and he was across again in January, 1900.

Cambridge events of this latter year include the promotion of Langley to the Deputy Professorship of Physiology, and the sharing of the Gedge Prize [2] by J. B. and H. H. Dale, whose efforts were adjudged equal. Dale left Cambridge in this year, J. B. became a member of the Physiological Society, and he and F. H. A. Marshall (1878–1949) met for the first time. During the summer J. B. went to Moyallon House at least twice, on 23 July and 10 October respectively; in August he left home on his first transatlantic crossing, his primary object being to visit the Doukhobors in Canada. He arrived in North America on 10 August, and was back at home on 19 September. On 7 August "Minnie" Ball visited The Glen for the first time.

As his visit on 10 October was J. B.'s last recorded one to Moyallon House, it is appropriate here to make some final mention of the household with which he had for so many years had much to do, and with which many pleasant memories were doubtless associated in his mind. A snapshot (Plate 20) which was taken at this time or before the Canadian trip provides a suitable illustration, and in any case is of interest for its picture of the twenty-eight year old J. B. The permanent residents by this time were reduced to Jane Marion Richardson, J. G. R.'s widow, now aged 69; Susan Helena, her stepdaughter, aged 51 and unmarried; and Mary Kathleen, her youngest child, aged 24, "tall, with a beautiful figure and swift eager movements." [3] In addition, however, to these three, Thomas

[1] In 1891 Lord Walsingham, High Steward of the University, offered an annual gift for three years of a Gold Medal for the best monograph or essay showing evidence of original research in any subject coming under the cognizance of the Special Board for Biology and Geology. The offer was accepted by Grace of Senate in December 1891, and in 1895 Lord Walsingham stated his intention to continue the gifts. Finally, in 1898 he offered to add a bronze replica of the Medal to be awarded as a second Medal in any year in which two essays of nearly equal or of exceptional merit were received. The Medal was awarded for an essay embodying the results of original research in any botanical, geological, or zoological field, zoology being understood to include animal morphology and physiology, and an essay in any field of chemical physiology being valued according to its physiological rather than its chemical importance.

[2] A sum of £1000 was bequeathed to the University by Joseph Gedge, M. B. 1869, of Gonville and Caius College, to found a prize for original observations in physiology or any branch of that subject. The testator had accompanied Sir Samuel Baker's expedition as medical officer, and died at Khartoum on 21 October 1870. Regulations were approved by Grace of the Senate on 25 November 1897. The Prize was awarded biennially.

[3] Muriel Harris (unpublished).

20—A GROUP ON THE TERRACE STEPS AT MOYALLON HOUSE, COUNTY DOWN, IN 1900

Left to right:—Mary Kathleen Richardson, Joseph Barcroft, Anne Wakefield Richardson, then (from above downwards) L. P. Strangman, Sarah Edith Williams (*née* Richardson), and Jean Goff Maynard (*née* Richardson)

CHRISTMAS_1901

Joseph Barcroft

Minnie A. Ball.

Sarah R. Barcroft.

Edith Lee Anderson.

Mollie Barcroft

W. Graham Moore Anderson

Netta Barcroft.

21—PEN AND INK DRAWING, BY W. GRAHAM MOORE ANDERSON, OF MINNIE A. BALL AND JOSEPH BARCROFT AT THE GLEN, NEWRY, CHRISTMAS 1901

Wakefield Richardson and his wife, Hilda, were living nearby at The Grange, Moyallon, and Anne Wakefield Richardson was usually at Moyallon House in vacation. She was certainly there in summer 1900, together with her younger sister, Mrs. Jean Goff Maynard and possibly also her twin, Mrs. Sarah Edith Williams. As throughout its occupation by the Richardsons, Moyallon House was in 1900 a most active centre of Friends' activity, its influence extending for a long distance around, and doubtless it meant much to J. B. from this aspect. But the member of the family with whom he was in closest rapport, not only then but also for many years to come in England, was Anne Wakefield Richardson, who went to Newnham in 1880, but left before finishing the degree course and entered Westfield College in 1883. At this latter she studied classics and obtained first class honours, after which she was taken onto the staff. In London she did much for the Society of Friends, and J. B. probably consulted with her in 1900 before his visit to the Doukhobors and discussed with her, after his return, his experiences during that visit. [1]

The people in question were Russian peasants who, because of their pacifist views, were opposed to the Imperial Russian Government and had been aided in their emigration to Canada by the Society of Friends, with its similar views about non-participation in war. A Friends' Dukhoborti Committee in London collected money and made the necessary arrangements; it also continued to help the colonists after their arrival in Canada, sending out observers from time to time to report. It seems likely that in 1900 J. B. was not an official emissary, but accompanied such through his desire to learn more about the Society's activities in this direction; in other words, while advancing as a scientist, he wanted also to be an active Friend. After his days among the Doukhobors in their settlement, with some sketching and some photographing interspersed among his more serious activities, he travelled to Montreal, whence he paid a short visit to Ottawa. Back at Montreal, he ran into Redpath, who had been a junior when he was at The Leys, and whose grandfather had given a million dollars to McGill University. A messenger was sent to fetch (not ask) the grandfather to see J. B., but arrived too late. J. B. was shown over the various Departments at McGill and then went down to the docks and saw over two ships there. From

[1] The diary kept by J. B. is in Lady Barcroft's possession.

Montreal he went on to New York, [1] where he visited Columbia College but was unsuccessful in finding Professor Frederick S. Lee, who was on holiday.

Then he went on to Boston, where he found that his heavy luggage had gone a-missing and would have to follow in another boat. "At ten I finally got my hand-luggage, took a cab and congratulated myself that the last chance of losing the camera, my return ticket, my money and my precious paper was over." At the boat some friends, "A." and her mother, were waiting to say good-bye and "A". gave him a letter which he read after the boat's departure. This letter he described as "an excellent example of what is the peculiar genius of a type of American girl, namely, the faculty of being indefinitely entertaining." With regard to his place at table on the boat, he "conceived a plan of 'masterly inactivity' which 'A.' was pleased to dignify with the adjective 'foxy'. It seemed that all the pushing people would make a great rush for places. I thought if I waited I would get among the quiet people. My plan succeeded to such an extent that I was given a seat next but one to the Captain . . .".

The diary ends: "I have read several books. The 'Cruise of the Cachalot' which was better than my best expectations. Mr. Lindsay's book and 'In Tune with the Infinite' which is rotten. Now we are sailing along the Irish coast in beautiful sunshine and on a blue sea. It looks indescribably lovely, and there is a softness in the air which I have not felt since leaving Ireland two months ago. In a few minutes the helm will be put a-starboard and the boat headed into Queenstown, so I can say no more now than that those two months have been not only a pleasure to me – they have been a blessing."

The sequelae to the American visit were that J. B. attended the Dukhoborti Committee Meeting of the Society of Friends in London on 4 October, published "The present needs of the Dukhobors" in *The Friend* of 2 November 1900 and "The Doukhobors" in the *Friends' Quarterly Examiner* of 1 January 1901, attended another meeting of the Committee on 3 October, and by 5 December had become a member of it, as had also his cousin, Anne Wakefield Richardson.

[1] The diary reads: "I have left Canada – I wonder whether I shall ever see it again. If I do not, Canada will have no unpleasant association in my mind. If I do I fully expect that my good impression of it will remain unimpaired."

The year 1901 was a red-letter one, for in July J. B. became engaged, at the Observatory, to Mary Agnetta ("Minnie") Ball. The affianced couple, however, were destined to see little of each other for many weeks, for J. B. had to leave soon afterwards for Germany to study the language, and M. A. B., who went off to Switzerland with her parents, fell ill on her return with typhoid fever. The severe nurse in charge labelled M. A. B.'s rises in temperature at the times of J. B.'s visits with the name "Barcroft-itis", and summarily dismissed the cause! So it was not until the patient was convalescent that opportunity came for more prolonged conversations.

In September J. B. recommenced his part-time mastership at the Leys School; it was to continue to December 1905, but he did not do very much teaching during this second period. [1] At Michaelmas his association with King's became even closer than it had been, for he was appointed an Annual Lecturer of the College. [2]

At Christmas M. A. B. and J. B., together with Edith Lee Anderson (later Mrs. George F. Trench) and W. Graham Moore Anderson [3], were at The Glen, Newry, and in the Visitors' Book there is a pen and ink sketch (Plate 21) by W. G. M. A. of a young man and a young woman playing ping-pong; the former must have been J. B. and the latter was presumably M. A. B. After the seasonal festivities were over, J. B. went off to lecture to the Belfast Natural History and Philosophical Society on 6 January 1902 on "Respiration". He began by recalling that, in his earlier address to the Society in 1895, he had spoken of "The properties of liquid surfaces", a subject which, among physical phenomena, had always been of peculiar interest to him. The interest of such a subject as that, however, seemed to fade before the fascination possessed by even the simplest process of living matter. There was a subtlety about the secret of life, an uncertainty as to whether the chemical changes which took place in living matter were governed by the laws which were enunciated in the laboratory, which made the study of the functions of living matter specially alluring.

[1] Even in the first one his duties probably never exceeded half a dozen periods a week of biology with the Sixth Form.

[2] Subsequently, he was reappointed year by year until in 1909 he became a permanent Lecturer on the College Staff.

[3] Edith Lee Anderson was cousin to both J. B. and W.G.M.A. The latter was the third son of Robert Anderson and Agnes Alexander Moore. See A. P. Moore-Anderson (1947) and *Who was Who 1916–1928*.

After this beginning he went on with his subject in typically graphic style, introducing into it demonstrations of blood gas analysis by means – to judge from the context – of the new technique which he and Haldane had been engaged in perfecting. Lorrain Smith, who was Professor of Pathology, proposed the vote of thanks and it was seconded by W. H. Thompson, Dunville Professor of Physiology. The latter said that the lecturer had managed to make clear to everyone the essential features of a very difficult subject, and that in addition he had very successfully maintained his reputation of being a neat and skilful experimenter. The Chairman, Professor Redfern, in putting the motion to the meeting, likewise praised most highly J. B.'s exegesis and demonstrations, and "trusted that in the study of physiology, which is becoming an experimental science for the purpose of investigation of the process of life, Mr. Barcroft would not only have a happy year, but that he would continue a great number of years to teach as he had taught them that evening."

In March 1902 J. B.'s brother-in-law to be, Robert S. Ball, junior, visited The Glen. Then, on 28 May, the *Journal of Physiology* published the paper in which J. B. and J. S. Haldane, M. D., F. R. S., Fellow of New College, Oxford, described their new method for estimating the oxygen and carbonic acid in small quantities of blood. The ferricyanide technique, introduced by Haldane (1900), was employed for determining the oxygen, and the combined carbon dioxide was liberated by the subsequent addition of tartaric acid. In Haldane's original method, the volume of oxygen evolved was measured directly at constant pressure; in the new one now described, the volume was calculated from the alteration in pressure necessary to maintain the gas volume in the apparatus constant. Apart from that, the Barcroft-Haldane technique allowed the oxygen and carbon dioxide in so little as 1 ml. blood to be determined with considerable accuracy.

On a date which has not so far been precisely determined but which was, presumably, in 1902, W. H. Thompson announced his intention of vacating the Dunville Chair of Physiology in Queen's College, Belfast, [1] for that of the Institutes of Medicine attached to the School of Physic, Trinity College, Dublin. J. B. applied, albeit

[1] The change of name to Queen's University was authorized in 1908, and became effective in 1910.

unsuccessfully, for the Belfast post,[1] and his application was supported by the Italian specialist in respiratory physiology, Angelo Mosso (Plate 22), in the following words. "Mr. Barcroft's candidature for the Professorship of Physiology in the University of Belfast gives me an opportunity by which I gladly profit, of expressing my appreciation for his work and methods and my personal esteem for himself. His careful, interesting and valuable work on the analysis of the gases contained in the blood and the constructive talent displayed in the instruments employed testify sufficiently to Mr. Barcroft's scientific ability. As a teacher of physiology Mr. Barcroft has had ample experience in the University of Cambridge and there all acquainted with him are unanimous as to his efficiency in this capacity."

Belfast comes into our story again in September 1902, for in that month is was the venue for the annual meeting of the British Association for the Advancement of Science. Both J. B. and his father became members of the Association for this meeting; in addition, the former was one of the Secretaries for Section I (Physiology, including Experimental Pathology and Experimental Psychology), which had been initiated in 1894, and had continued intermittently in 1896, 1897, 1899, and 1901. The Sectional Presidents before 1902 had been, in order, Schäfer, Gaskell, Foster, Langley, and McKendrick; at Belfast Halliburton presided. It was the beginning of a very long membership for J. B. and, as we shall see in the next Chapter, his researches and the Association's activities were to be closely linked for many years. So a not inconsiderable influence upon his scientific career was rather fortuitously initiated by the choice of Belfast as the site of the 1902 meeting. From the *Report* we learn that on 15 September he read a paper on the estimation of urea in physiological fluids, but no details were printed in the *Report*, and it was not until 16 March 1903 that the account of this new research appeared in the *Journal of Physiology*.

The object which J. B. had had in mind had been to elaborate a technique for the estimation of the substance in small quantities of blood, and at every point of the work, as he acknowledged, he

[1] The Chair went to T. H. Milroy, of the Edinburgh Physiological Laboratory. He occupied it from 1902 until 1935, when he was succeeded by J. B.'s elder son, Henry Barcroft, now Professor at St. Thomas' Hospital Medical School.

had been helped by Hopkins, who in 1902 had been promoted to be the first Reader in Chemical Physiology in Cambridge. We can regard it as a real tribute to the young scientist that men of the calibre of Haldane and Hopkins and Mosso found his work so worthy of encouragement. In the new research, as in the previous one, emphasis was laid on the use of *small* amounts of blood (as little as 1 ml.), such as could readily be obtained from individual organs in the experimental animal or from human patients. The gist of the method was to remove the blood proteins and then to measure the nitrogen set free from the urea (and ammonium salts) by treatment with sodium hypobromite. The apparatus for measuring it was a modification of that devised by J. B. and Haldane for blood gas analysis and already referred to above. So acknowledgement was also duly made to Haldane, "but for whose co-operation on a former occasion the present paper would probably never have been written."

An event of historical importance in 1903 was the resignation of the sixty-seven year old Sir Michael Foster [1] from the Chair of Physiology which he had occupied since 1883; he was succeeded by Langley (Plate 23), who was to occupy it until 1925, when J. B. in his turn was to become Professor. The genius of Langley was very different from that of Foster, but perhaps their respective gifts were peculiarly appropriate to the head of the Cambridge school of physiology during these successive periods of evolution.

Of much more direct importance to our story is the marriage of J. B. to "Minnie" Ball, which took place on 5 August in the church at Coton, Cambridgeshire. [2] The choice of a quiet country church rather than a Cambridge one, as also the absence of bridesmaids and pages in attendance on the bride, and the restriction of the guests to a few near relatives and friends, [3] were dictated by the fact that at

[1] Created K.C.B. in 1899.

[2] The bride remained a member of the Church of England, though she attended Friends' Meeting (to which she was much drawn) for many years with her husband, ceasing to do so, presumably, when he himself did during the 1914–18 war. Thereafter they attended the services in King's College Chapel.

[3] A large number had attended a reception held by Sir Robert and Lady Ball at the Observatory on the previous day. Anne Wakefield Richardson, who had been staying in Newnham to do some vacation work, had attended this reception and, in a letter which she wrote in the evening to her mother in Moyallon, she stated that it had been a lovely afternoon and that the wedding presents, between two and three hundred in number, had been on view. Later she had dined with J. B., his sisters, and his brother in King's College.

22—Angelo Mosso (1846–1910)

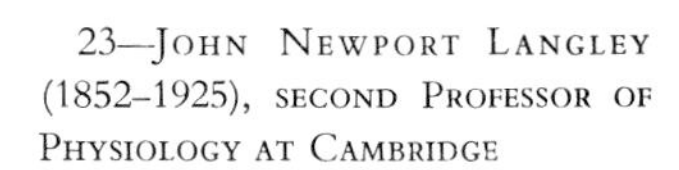

23—John Newport Langley (1852–1925), second Professor of Physiology at Cambridge

Facing page 52

24—MARY AGNETTA BALL AND JOSEPH BARCROFT
ABOUT THE TIME OF THEIR WEDDING IN 1903

From *The Gentlewoman* of 15 August

the time J. B.'s father was seriously ill. [1] The service was conducted by the Reverend S. T. Adams, Vicar of Coton, and the Reverend E. J. Swain, Chaplain of King's College. The best man was J. B.'s brother, David, and the bride, dressed in ivory duchesse satin trimmed with chiffon and Honiton lace, was given away by her father.

Shortly after the ceremony, she and J. B. left for their honeymoon, which was spent at Lamlash in Arran, and Blackwater Foot. At the former J. B. had a boat, but the rain fell so heavily and with so few intermissions that little sailing was possible; instead, the bridal pair donned sea boots and macintoshes and took their fresh air in charming walks. As the time drew near to bid farewell to Lamlash, J. B. took the boat over the water to lay it up, but then found to his dismay that there was no steamer back that day. So he and his bride had the rather unusual experience of spending part of their honeymoon separated, much – Lady Barcroft states – to the amusement of the people in the hotel. From Lamlash they went for a short time to Blackwater Foot, and then over to Howth, near Dublin, to see J. B.'s father and the other members of The Glen household.

From Howth they crossed back to England to attend the annual meeting of the British Association, which took place at Southport from 10 to 16 September. There was no Section I that year and a communication by J. B. on "The origin of water in saliva" was given in title only.

From Southport he and his bride returned to Cambridge and installed themselves in the house which they had rented at 92 (now 106) Chesterton Road. They had prepared this first home in advance, and the sight of the smiling maid at the door as they arrived completed their happiness. "Busy", writes Lady Barcroft, "were the succeeding days and months – J. B. working very hard, frequently dining in Hall and taking men afterwards, and returning home between eleven and twelve o'clock. Friends poured in until my visiting list assumed alarming proportions. Dinner parties when Joe's work permitted were frequent, but all was so gay and happy that the days and months seemed to have wings."

We must not, however, anticipate what is to come, and this beginning of the ideal and happy partnership which Minnie and

[1] The entries in The Glen Visitors' Book cease from March 1903 to the end of January 1906, i.e., from about the time when the family went to Howth on account of Henry Barcroft's failing health until after his death, which took place there on 18 November 1905.

Joe Barcroft were to enjoy for the next forty-four years is an appropriate point at which to end this Chapter, for their marriage marked the close of the second period of J. B.'s life. From now on 'home' meant to him Cambridge and not the Glen, Newry, and the Irishman by birth became (or so we in this country would like to claim) somewhat of an Englishman by attachment, the number and quality of his contributions to science increasing in consequence of his married happiness, and credit accruing more and more to both countries through them, as the subsequent story will reveal.

CHAPTER IV

1904–1910

As Roughton (1949, *b*) remarks, J. B.'s early successes in a difficult field at once attracted the notice of his seniors outside as well as inside Cambridge, leading to co-operation with such men as J. S. Haldane, T. G. Brodie, E. H. Starling, and W. E. Dixon. Another feature of considerable importance is the part which membership of the British Association [1] played in J. B.'s progress. He was a Secretary of Section I in 1902, 1904, 1905, and 1906, and he was a member of certain Committees, namely, those on Metabolism of the Tissues (appointed 1903), on the Effect of Climate upon Health and Disease (appointed 1905), on the Ductless Glands (J. B., however, attended only the 1906 meeting, and that presumably because the pancreas was the subject of discussion), and on the Dissociation of Oxyhaemoglobin at High Altitudes (appointed 1909). The periodic reports of the first and last of these were largely concerned with the work of J. B. and of his colleagues; the Committees' activities thus encouraged his research and gave him useful pre-publication judgments on his findings and views, while the *Reports* afforded opportunities for summarizing progress to date. In the main the Committees brought him into close relationship with other physiologists; through the one on the Effect of Climate he met many whose interests were more clinical. All told, therefore, his progress was greatly assisted through his membership of the Association.

On 11 February 1904 he was appointed Junior Demonstrator of Physiology. The summer holiday that year was spent at home, and between 18 and 24 August he attended the Association meeting, which took place in Cambridge with Sherrington as President of Section I; a report of the Committee on Metabolism of the Tissues dealt with the kidney, pancreas, and submaxillary gland. Thereafter, he attended the 6th International Congress of Physiologists, which

[1] The relevant items are referred to according to the years of the actual meetings rather than of the corresponding published *Reports*.

took place in Bruxelles from 30 August to 2 September, giving with Brodie an account of the gaseous metabolism of the kidney. A month and a half later, on 18 October, his first son, Henry Barcroft, was born to the great joy of both parents. On 2 November and 30 December respectively, the *Journal of Physiology* published accounts of the oxygen exchange of the pancreas (Starling being co-author) and of the gaseous metabolism of the kidney (Brodie being co-author).

These were followed in 1905 by a note on a modification of Bohr's blood-gas receiver (*Proceedings of the Physiological Society*, 2 May), another report of the British Association Committee on the metabolism of the salivary glands, kidneys and pancreas, and a further paper in the *Journal of Physiology*, with Brodie as co-author, on the gaseous metabolism of the kidney (8 September).

In late July, i.e., before these two last, J. B. set off to take part in the meeting of the British Association in South Africa; M. A. B., with the infant Henry to look after, had perforce to take a simpler holiday and went with relations-by-marriage to Hunstanton, where her doctor brother, C. R. H. Ball, and his wife were in residence at Minna Lodge. The main scientific sessions of the Association meeting were to take place at Cape Town and Johannesburg, but in addition Durban, Pietermaritzburg, Bloemfontein, and Buluwayo were to be visited, and a variety of optional excursions had been arranged. Colonel David Bruce, [1] C. B., F. R. S., of sleeping sickness fame, was President of Section I, and J. B. one of its Secretaries. Fortunately, letters written by him to M. A. B. from 30 July to 6 October have been preserved, and on various counts they are so interesting that a disproportionate allocation of space to extracts from them is well justified.

J. B. sailed with the official party on 29 July in the third ship, the Union Castle liner R. M. S. *Saxon*, 12,385 tons register, sharing a first class cabin with Professor G. S. Woodhead [2], who was also of Quaker stock. Amongst other fellow-passengers were the physiologists, Professor Christian Bohr of Copenhagen and Dr. A. D. Waller of London. The former's interests were very akin to J. B.'s own, and the latter had thought of bringing his copy of Bohr's recently published book to read on the voyage. As usual, however,

[1] 1855–1931.
[2] 1855–1921. Elected Professor of Pathology at Cambridge in 1899.

he preferred to acquire knowledge by personal discussion rather than by reading, and he mentions several talks with Bohr, whom he found "rather interesting to talk to as he has thought a great deal". Other characteristics which we have already learned to associate with J. B. are in evidence in the letters. He wrote on both sides of the paper "to save money in the postage", and other sentences show that the need for economy was constantly in the mind of the young married don. His Irish turn of thought is instanced in the note, "This is my Monday letter it is written on Tuesday morning but never mind that", his spelling difficulties in the passage, "It is a long time before you get a bath, quite a long 'Q' (I dont know how to spell it)". His keenness on sketching and painting, and on ships and shipping, is equally in evidence; so are his companionableness, his eagerness on physiology and his desire to advance it, his personal but at the same time disinterested ambitiousness, and so forth. An interesting sentence, in view of the diverse ways in which researches suggest themselves to the receptive mind, is the one, "Finally I went to bed and thought a little about my work and got some rather good ideas."

In the letter of 2 August a fine piece of descriptive prose begins, "This has been a great day – to come into Funchal in the early morning is something to live for. I put my head out of the porthole about five and there was Madeira rising up out of the sea a dream of purple and chocolate, just tipped with light at the top where the sun lit up the summit of the peak." Of the later ascent in the funicular railway he wrote, "We were not long going up. I was rather disappointed with the flowers on the way, but the foliage was superb. Sugar canes, sago palms, tobacco, but chiefly vines with their grapes which filled the air with the peculiar perfume of an English hot-house. When we got to the top however the flowers appeared in their glory, chiefly stramonium with its immense white bells many times as large as the flowers of a lily and hanging in large festoons from the trees. Every piece of wall was gay with creeping geraniums while there was bank upon bank of blue hydrangeas and here and there hanging over the top of a wall there was a profusion of white roses and of beautiful hibiscus."

The letter of the following day records, ". . . I was up before sunrise to see what is regarded as one of the sights of the world, namely the Peak of Teneriffe being tipped by the first rays of dawn.

There it was 50 or 60 miles away pointing its cone up into the air. It was abreast of us on the port side, about half the mountain jutting above a low bank of cloud which lay along the horizon . . ." Later it goes on, "This evening . . . Professor Bohr and I sat in front of the deck house chatting and looking at the stars. You have never seen anything like them. I was wishing we could have had two chairs together out in the night and gazed at the sky. The milky way is a glowing mass of phosphorescent light and the stars shine out like diamonds."

On the late evening of 5 August he writes, "For the first time we really know we are at sea . . . there is the hiss of the waves as they break and the huge ship throws them off her side and the wind plays on my cheeks."

Two days later there is a reference to Stangmore Lodge. Discussing all sorts of things, especially the simple life, with Mrs. Balfour after breakfast, J. B. found that her views corresponded with those of M. A. B. "She says she thinks I wont be able to manage Stangmore Lodge in the winter when I am old!" On the following morning "Col. Bruce gave a lecture in the saloon on Sleeping Sickness which was much enjoyed."

On 15 August the ship reached Cape Town, and there were receptions and sectional meetings, constituting the first part of the scientific programme. On the 18th the *Saxon* left for Port Elizabeth and, with business over, J. B. found it was comparable to a yachting trip on a large scale. At 7.30 a.m. on the 21st he was wakened by the entry of his cousin, Barcroft Anderson, into his cabin; the ship had reached East London and "Bar", in his capacity as Medical Officer, had come on board to examine the passengers who were landing. J. B. spend the next few hours ashore with him, and presumably indulged in some talk of past times at Stangmore Lodge, though his letter is concerned with the local scenery and flora of the most go-ahead place he had so far visited in South Africa.

The rest of the tour must be briefly dealt with, a few passages only being extracted where a great part of the text is worthy of publication. On the morning of 25 August a party of about five hundred saw a Kaffir war dance and marriage at Henley; J. B. described it as one of the most remarkable days of the trip. In the evening, by contrast, there was a lecture by H. D. Ferrar on the antarctic regions. The Town Hall of Pietermaritzburg was packed, the slides really magnificent. On 27 August J. B. heard that his family were again rather uneasy about the condition of his father, Henry Barcroft. On the 30th, from Johannesburg, he visited a gold mine, and the next day he went to the Premier Diamond mine, and was shown round by the man who had found the large Cullinan diamond some months earlier. In the letter of 1 September is the note, "My Section ended this morning, and has throughout been very successful I think." Between 2 and 4 September he and a Mr. W. H. Macaulay and a driver went from Bloemfontein to Kimberley in a Cape cart drawn by four horses; on the evening of the 3rd they outspanned in the trenches about a mile up river from Cronje's Laager at Paardeberg. At 8.30 J. B. rolled up and went to sleep in his cholera belt, his clothes, his two coats and a blanket. "It was a lovely night, bright star light, no breath of wind, but cold . . . I slept as well as the unaccustomed nature of the circumstances would admit. Wakened sometimes by the horses and enjoyed a peep now and again at the brilliant stars and of course we could not help contrasting the scene of perfect peace, broken only by the croak of the bull frogs or the shriek of an occasional water bird, with the scenes which had taken place in these same trenches but five years ago, whose monument remains in the skeletons of endless horses whitening on the sand, and here and there a little graveyard, with a cross to one, a slab to another and a pile of stones.

In the evening of the 5th there was a very fine lecture on "Diamonds" at Kimberley by Sir William Crookes. Six days later J. B. set off by special train from Buluwayo for Victoria Falls, passing early on through a cloud of locusts. "If you can imagine the thickest snow you have ever seen with flakes as big as oak leaves you will have some conception of what a flight of locusts is like and we went through miles of that." Breakfast at Victoria Falls on the morning of the 12th was rather a scramble with four hundred scientists let loose in equatorial Africa. "The actual opening of the bridge you will probably have read about in the newspaper. It only occupied a few minutes. The bridge itself is very inconspicuous and not at all an eyesore. After the opening we went on across the bridge and soon got into boats which took us to Livingstone Island. This is about half way across the top edge of the falls and the fall is so steep that you lie down on your stomach and look over the edge 380 feet down. Words quite fail to describe the beauty and charm of the place. The water is almost entirely broken up into spray before it reaches the bottom, and it comes up again in festoons of smoke which look like immense quantities of steam being blown gently upwards hundreds of feet, and opposite you so near that a golf ball could be (and was) driven across . . . there is a sheer face of rock down to the bottom . . . After lunch I ran across Dr. Harmer and we walked all along the edge of the rock opposite the falls. It is more than a mile and is really magnificent – all the colour and forms of the water falling over the rock face, perhaps 100 yards in front of us. It was all lit up with the sun and the light formed itself into rainbows where ever we looked. The ground through which we trod was called the rain forest because it is continually wet with the falling spray. Underground one is treading upon a carpet of maidenhair the whole way."

On the 17th J. B. embarked on the *Durham Castle,* 8217 tons register, at Beira, and on the way home (via the Suez Canal) he and Professor Bohr had a day in Cairo, and visited the pyramids and museums and so forth. With his description of that the correspondence ceases, but the extracts given, together with the scientific details contained in the relevant *Report*, should allow the reader to envisage how much was added to J. B.'s experience, and thereby enable him the better to appreciate the rest of this story. For J. B., as has already been said, drew always upon all his past and to understand him fully we have to remember his whole background.

Because of a considerable shipping delay on the way home (a dynamite boat had sunk and blocked the Suez Canal), he must have got back to Cambridge well after term had begun. When it was only about half over, on 18 November, his father died at Howth, and we can imagine what this must have meant to J. B. when we remember earlier passages in this book and the home life at The Glen, Newry, which is described in them.

About any pertinent events in the first half of the following year, 1906, there is no information available, but on 2 August, according to the Visitors' Book, M. A. B. and J. B. and Henry (aged 21 months) arrived at The Glen for their summer holiday. J. B. must, however, have returned to England almost at once for the York meeting of the British Association, which took place from 2 to 8

August. Francis Gotch, Waynflete Professor of Physiology at Oxford, was President of Section I and J. B. – for the last time – one of its Secretaries.

The first report of the Committee, appointed in August 1905 to make further research and inquiries into the effect of climate upon health and disease, was presented. The Committee, with a very long list of attached consultants, had confined its work to the collection of data (especially from Lieut. Colonel Simpson, R. A. M. C., of the War Office); to arranging for appropriate research to be done, as required, in various countries; and to questions of procedure. In so far as our story is concerned, we may note that J. B. came into relation with a large number of clinicians and with the War Office, and must have corresponded with many foreign physiologists; also that "internal respiration" was the potential research field allotted to him.

Of more immediate interest was the report of the Committee on the Metabolic Balance Sheet of the Individual Tissues. Three organs had been investigated during the previous twelvemonth, namely, striated muscle, the heart, and the kidney. J. B. and others had made preliminary measurements of the oxygen usage of mammalian skeletal muscle, and W. M. Fletcher and Hopkins had studied the effects of anaerobic and aerobic conditions respectively on the survival life of frog's muscle, i.e., had initiated their now classic researches. [1] The Committee's report also mentions elsewhere that apparatus had been devised for estimating the quantity of oxygen dissolved in salt solutions. This is a reference to the work of J. B. and P. Hamill, which was more fully described in a paper published in the *Journal of Physiology* two days after the Association meeting had ended.

Apart from these more scientific matters, 1906 was of interest because it saw the removal of J. B. and his family to their permanent home at 13 Grange Road, Cambridge. The landlord of 92 (now 106) Chesterton Road had wished to sell it and the Barcrofts had not been anxious to own it, so he had offered to build a new house and to rent it to them. To their great joy it was to be in Grange Road where there were some old allotments that had always

[1] It is, however, worth remembering that in 1877 Claude Bernard had stated that lactic acid was not the cause of rigor, only its *usual* accompaniment. Had his observation been remembered and appreciated, the determination of the more essential processes of muscle metabolism during the twentieth century would have been accelerated.

attracted them. In this way No. 13 came into being and from 16 October M. A. B. and J. B. "much enjoyed settling in to a more roomy home. The land was in a bad way needing much labour to get it into order, and the making of the garden became an absorbing interest. J. B. spent every moment he could spare helping to make the rockery and general laying out of it all." [1]

On 28 January 1907, Sir Michael Foster died suddenly, in his seventy-first year, in London; the funeral took place at Huntingdon. For the past three or four years he had been in retirement and even before that, from 1900 to 1903, he had largely handed over the running of the Physiological Laboratory in Cambridge to his deputy, Langley, because of increasing outside calls upon his time. Nevertheless, his death ended an epoch (Langdon-Brown, 1946) and, as he had indirectly contributed to the beginning of J. B.'s earlier career, this note about his passing is in place here.

On 23 March, at a meeting of the Physiological Society held at University College, London, with Starling in the chair, it was decided to send out notices regarding the forthcoming International Congress of Physiologists. [2] At the same meeting J. B. gave a preliminary communication on the velocity and nature of the blood emerging from the submaxillary gland of the cat during stimulation of the cervical sympathetic nerve. Apart from its main findings, it is interesting for the suggestion that the vascular dilation observed at a certain point was due to a direct action of metabolites from the gland. Two days later Part I of "The gaseous metabolism of the heart", by J. B. and W. E. Dixon (1871–1931), appeared in the *Journal of Physiology* [3]. The excised hearts of small animals had been perfused from the circulations of previously hirudinized larger animals of the same species; the only previous observations on cardiac gaseous metabolism had been relatively minor ones by Yeo (1885) and Fletcher (1900).

On 28 March J. B. was promoted to be Senior Demonstrator in

[1] As the garden (Plate 61) figures happily in the memories of many physiologists and other friends of the Barcrofts, there is excuse for quoting now the rest of Lady Barcroft's account, though it really belongs passim to subsequent pages of this book. "Ever since that time", the letter goes on, "the interest of the garden remained one of the chief delights of his home, and he enjoyed looking out for a rare iris or other rock plant and tenderly watching its development, and bringing in the news that at last the gentian *had* flowered after all!"

[2] The shortness of this notice is in marked contrast to that which has been necessary in respect of recent Congresses, with their much greater numbers.

[3] No Part II ever followed.

25—Some of the members of the International Committee of the Congresses of Physiologists, Heidelberg, 1907

Front row, left to right:—Kronecker, Kossel, Exner, Grützner, Prévost, Sherrington. Back row, left to right:—Heger, Nicolaides, Bohr, Wedensky, Langley, Einthoven, Johannson, Mislawsky, Richet, Cybulski, Porter

Facing page 63

Physiology at Cambridge and, as such, became largely responsible for the organization of the practical classes and demonstrations; he was also enabled to reduce the amount of outside coaching which he undertook.

From 31 July to 7 August the British Association met at Leicester, and there were reports by the Committees on the 'Metabolic Balance Sheet' of the Individual Tissues (of which Committee J. B. was Secretary) and on the Effect of Climate on Health and Disease. The former included studies on the frog's kidney, dog's intestine, mammalian heart, and submaxillary gland; it was also stated that hirudin had no specific effect upon the blood and its gases.

From Leicester, J. B. presumably went with his family to The Glen, Newry, or else joined them there for a few days; at all events, the family holiday was at The Glen that year. J. B. cannot, however, have got much rest, for he was present at the 8th International Congress of Physiologists, which took place in Heidelberg (Plate 25) from 12 to 16 August under the Presidency of Albrecht Kossel (1853–1927), the authority on protein chemistry. The number of members was 325 and the sessions were run in quadruplicate [1]. J. B. described methods for studying the metabolism of the mammalian heart, the amphibian kidney, and the cat's salivary gland. More important, however, he met for the first time Shack August Steenberg Krogh (1874–1949), the Danish physiologist, who since 1899 had been assistant to Professor Christian Bohr in Copenhagen; Krogh's lines of research had had, and were to continue to have, much in common with J. B.'s own. [2] In a letter to Lady Barcroft after J. B.'s death in 1947, Krogh wrote as follows. "I met Barcroft in 1907 in Heidelberg and a few days later again in Zuntz' laboratory in Berlin, and the sympathy between us rapidly became very deep. [3] I have a most vivid memory of those happy, far off days and of the delight of old Zuntz in your husband's micro-method for O_2 in blood: 'Das ist ja für die Kliniker geradezu gefundenes Fressen'." Nathan Zuntz (1847–1920) as early as 1867 had made the pregnant suggestion that the carbon dioxide is carried in the blood plasma in virtue of some substance present in the red corpuscles, and in the following four decades he had been prominent in metabolism and

[1] They had been run in duplicate at the 1901 Congress, and in triplicate at the 1904 one (Franklin, 1938).
[2] See bibliographies in Hagedorn (1949) and Spärck (1949).
[3] For a statement by J. B. about Krogh, see Liljestrand (1950, 111).

respiration studies. Indeed, he had come straight to the 5th International Congress, held at Torino in 1901, from such studies, carried out in the recently erected Capanna Regina Margherita (Plate 31) on Monte Rosa (4,560 m.). In view of J. B.'s own later work on the effects of altitude, this 1907 visit by him to Zuntz' laboratory is of definite interest, but no details are available.

In December the *Journal of Physiology* published a paper by him and by G. R. Mines [1] (1885–1914) on the effect of hirudin upon the gases in arterial blood. It is interesting for various reasons. In the first place it was an early use of purified leech extract, the properties of which had become known through the work of Jacobj (1902) and others. It was also a successful one, in as much as the hirudin prevented the proneness of the blood to clot in the cannulae and apparatus used for the study of the gaseous exchange of organs, but did not have any other, adverse effects provided certain precautions were taken. Apart from these technical points, the paper was the first produced by J. B. in collaboration with someone younger than himself. It thus inaugurated a long series describing researches through which he gave a helping hand to his juniors at the earlier stages of their careers; few physiologists can have encouraged in this way quite so many workers from so many countries, even if the palm goes to Carl Ludwig (1816–1895) of Leipzig, who is credited with over two hundred scientific pupils (Kronecker. See Stirling, 1895).

The next year, 1908, was also of considerable importance to our story. On 25 January, at King's College, London, J. B. made three contributions (one of them with P. Morawitz, of Heidelberg) to the *Proceedings of the Physiological Society*; the first was on a differential method of blood gas analysis and introduced a technique now permanently associated with J. B.'s name and, in its more delicate micrometric form, with that of Warburg. A longer account appeared in the *Journal of Physiology* of 6 May; it included a calculation by J. B.'s father-in-law, Sir Robert Ball. The object of the method was to reduce the chance of error in comparative determinations of the gas contents of arterial and venous blood samples from particular organs; at the same time, it enormously simplified the technical

[1] At the time a recently-graduated B. A. He became a member of the Physiological Society in 1910 and later, until his untimely death, was Professor of Physiology at McGill University, Montreal.

operations involved in such determinations; the principle of the method, practised either with the use of J. B.'s apparatus or with Warburg's special development of it, is now the basis for measurements of the respiratory metabolism of living organs and of surviving isolated tissues in biological laboratories throughout most of the world; J. B. himself was to employ the technique in expeditions to great altitudes, and in direct services to his country in the two great wars of our time.[1]

In May J. B. and Morawitz published a paper on the ferricyanide method of blood gas determination for clinical purposes, and in July J. B. had a note on a simplification of Bohr's method of raising mercury in the Töpler pump. Then, from 3 to 8 September, there was the meeting of the British Association in Dublin, at which the Final Report of the Committee on the 'Metabolic Balance Sheet' of the Individual Tissues was presented, and also the Third Report of the Committee on the Effect of Climate upon Health and Disease. The former gave an interesting review of technique and of the results obtained in individual organs – heart, kidneys, salivary glands, pancreas, intestines, and to some extent skeletal muscle and liver; it also listed the publications resulting from the work. Both reports contained references to body temperature and exercise.

J. B.'s outstanding publication of the year was, however, his ninety-five pages long contribution, entitled, "Zur Lehre vom Blutgaswechsel in den verschiedenen Organen," which appeared in *Ergebnisse der Physiologie*. It summarized current knowledge, derived from his own and others' researches, about this wide field. Part I dealt with the individual organs (skeletal muscle, lungs, heart, salivary glands, pancreas, intestinal canal, kidneys, adrenal glands and central nervous system), Part II with the partition of oxygen among the organs, and Part III with the methods of blood gas analysis particularly suited to research on specific organs. The review (Roughton, 1949, *b*) marked the end of the first phase of J. B.'s original work, and established him "as a first-hand and first-rate authority on gaseous metabolism of isolated organs." It

[1] It is too well known to require description here; we ought, however, to note that the Oxford school has always been somewhat guarded about it, or at least about its use by any but expert practitioners. Douglas and Priestley (1937, 139) stated that the apparatus is calibrated with considerable difficulty because it works at neither constant volume nor constant pressure. The theoretical basis, they added, is not at all simple and anyone using the apparatus should read with care the original papers so as to be fully au fait with the principles involved and with the methods of calibration.

was also an indication of his original-mindedness, determination, technical inventiveness, and capacity for persistent hard work in the pursuit of his objectives.

According to Lady Barcroft, the family holiday in 1908 was taken at Harrow. It cannot, however, have given J. B. much of a rest, for the late Sir Edmund Spriggs (1871–1949) wrote (personal communication) in 1948 as follows. "I knew Barcroft most of his life, from early years in the Physiological Society. [1] In August 1908 when Dean of St. George's Hospital Medical School I had the pleasure of entering him there as a medical student. He thought, and I believe rightly, it would be an advantage to him in his physiological work to get qualified. He discussed thoroughly the difficulties of doing that while working at Cambridge. In effect these proved too great and after working as a surgical dresser through August and September of that year he found that he could not continue the clinical course in London." As his friends know, J. B. in subsequent years was proud of his status of perpetual medical student!

Two other items conclude this account of 1908. In the first place, A. V. Hill during the academic year 1908–9 attended J. B.'s classes and was helped and encouraged by him. In the second place, J. B. heard towards the end of December from his cousin, Anne Wakefield Richardson, that her mother, Jane Marion Richardson of Moyallon, was failing – she had been paralysed for some years. She died on 4 January 1909, thus severing one of J. B.'s links with the past. In a letter which he sent on 8 January to his cousin, he wrote that he knew something of what it meant to lose a central figure in the family life. "I have", he said, "missed the sympathy and thought of my father more than I could have believed. He always made an effort to follow what I was working at, and being gifted in that sort of direction, he generally had sufficient knowledge of my work, as well as my aims, and life generally, to give just that sympathy and counsel which a parent can give." Further on he wrote that "Sorrow is a very precious thing . . . *Sorrow* and *work* are the makers of character."

Joy, however, alternates with sorrow in most of our lives, and joy certainly came to 13 Grange Road on 4 May, 1909, with the birth of a second son, Robert Ball Barcroft, to M. A. B. and J. B.

About this time, one of the two Honorary Secretaryships of the

[1] E. I. Spriggs, like J. B., was elected a member in 1900.

Physiological Society fell vacant through the appointment of J. B. Leathes to a chair at Toronto. On 26 June J. B. was elected in his place; he was destined to continue in office until 1920, and during the whole of that long period he had as his fellow Secretary W. M. Bayliss (Plate 38).

From 25 August to 1 September the British Association held its annual meeting, the rendezvous this time being Winnipeg. The Committee (of which J. B. was a Secretary) on the Effect of Climate upon Health and Disease presented its fourth report, but J. B. himself was not present – instead he went en famille to Felixstowe for his summer holiday. In the Report it was stated that he was now engaged on a study of certain conditions of the blood which influence respiration at high altitudes. These researches would be ready for publication, in part at all events, in the course of the ensuing year.

As Roughton (1949, *b*, 319) wrote, "The latter part of each phase of J. B.'s scientific work was wont to contain some problem or line of thought which naturally led him on to the next phase. It had seemed to him that a very important factor in determining the oxygen uptake of the isolated organs which he had been studying must be the average tension of dissolved oxygen in the blood vessels supplying the organ. The latter quantity in turn is conditioned by the reversible equilibrium between oxygen and haemoglobin in the blood, i.e. the oxyhaemoglobin dissociation curve. In the next phase of his work, 1907–1914, he gave much attention to the properties of haemoglobin and its dissociation curve under various conditions, though to a lesser extent he continued with various collaborators his work on isolated organs. He also led two high altitude expeditions, the first to Teneriffe in 1910, and the second to Monte Rosa in 1911."

In correspondence with this résumé, we find that on 26 August 1909 J. B. published two papers, with M. Camis on the dissociation curve of blood, and with Ff. Roberts on that of haemoglobin. [1] Then, on 11 December, in the Proceedings of the Physiological Society, (though it never appeared in the *Journal of Physiology*), he and A. V. Hill gave a communication on the heat of combination of oxygen with haemoglobin and its relation to the molecular weight of the latter. Finally, on 23 December, there was published the

[1] For very pertinent comment on this second paper see Roughton, 1949, *b*, 319–320.

paper by J. B. and W. O. R. King on the effect of temperature on the dissociation curve of blood. Before 1909 the subject had been in considerable confusion. J. B., with his differential blood gas analysis apparatus and with his tonometer for saturating blood or haemoglobin with oxygen, eliminated the cumbrous apparatus of earlier workers and so speeded up the oxygen determinations that he was able to complete a curve in the course of a day. This, in view of the changeability of haemoglobin during prolonged procedures, was a very major factor in the success which attended his efforts. One other item concludes the story of this year, namely, that during it he became a permanent Lecturer on the staff of Kings' College.

The next year, 1910, which is more publicly memorable for the death of King Edward VII and the accession of King George V, was an eventful one for J. B., though it began on a simple domestic note with a visit by M. A. B. and himself, from 8 to 17 January, to The Glen, Newry. Then, on 22 January, he attended the Annual General Meeting of the Physiological Society at King's College, London, with A. V. Hill as his guest – this appears to have been Hill's introduction to the Society with which, in the coming years, he was to have so much to do. Four years later J. B. acknowledged his particular indebtedness to him when he wrote: "There are occasions on which every sailor of the deep sea has to ship a pilot. Mr. A. V. Hill has brought me into those harbours which are best approached through the, to me, unknown channels of mathematics." At the January 1910 meeting Hill spoke of the possible effects of the aggregation of the molecules of haemoglobin on its dissociation curves, and showed that the divergent results found in the literature could be explained if salts present in the solutions caused such aggregation. Acting on this assumption, he had produced his equation

$$y - 100 \frac{Kx^n}{1 - Kx^n}$$

to see if an equation *of that type* could satisfy all the experimental observations rather than to base any direct physical meaning on n and K. In fact, the varied findings of Barcroft and Camis (1909) had been satisfied, and that was a gain as instead of a curve one now had two constants n and K, and the effect of any given treatment on the dissociation curve could be estimated as a numerical effect on those constants. The advantage of such method of analysing the results was that much labour could be saved: *two* observations could give the *two* constants for any curve, and then the rest of the curve be calculated.

Though this was a great step forward, that fact was not immediately appreciated for want (see Barcroft, 1913, *Biochem J.*, 7) of a fuller presentation. It was not, in other words, evident from a casual study of the data tabulated by Hill "that all the curves they represented for which the value of *n* was more than unity were in essence *S*-shaped. It therefore seemed that there was an essential difference between these curves and those which were known to exist for blood, the latter being *S*-shaped curves." [1]

A month or two later, on 8 March 1910, two more papers by J. B. appeared in the *Journal of Physiology*. The first, with A. V. Hill, was on the nature of oxyhaemoglobin, with a note on its molecular weight; as pointed out by Fegler and Banister (1946), this paper contained the first estimations of the velocity of release of oxygen from a solution of haemoglobin; the molecular weight of haemoglobin in dialysed solution was the least possible value, namely, 16,669. The second paper, with Ff. Roberts, described improvements in the technique of blood gas analysis.

About a week later, J. B. left England for Teneriffe on the first of his expeditions to great altitudes, his object being to investigate the effect of such altitudes upon the oxygen dissociation curve of the individual, and so to add to knowledge of the ways in which, during the course of evolution, the respiratory process has adapted itself to various unusual conditions (Barcroft, 1911, *J. Physiol.*, *42*, 44). The full story of the genesis of the expedition need not be detailed here; it suffices to state that the immediate organization was carried out by Professor Pannwitz, of Berlin, who was Secretary-General of the International Anti-Tuberculosis Commission and President of the Special Commission for the Study of the Biochemical Effects of High Altitudes and Solar Radiation. The scientists who took part

[1] For the continuation of the story, reference should be made to Douglas, Haldane, and Haldane (1912), Hill (1913), and Barcroft (1931 *Biochem. J.*, 7). Here it is relevant to stress J. B.'s insistence on the proper and adequate presentation of findings, for that was a part of his character as a scientist, and among his own capacities was a marked ability for gauging his audience and for choosing aright the way in which to get what he wished across to them. On the other hand, even when present as in this instance, he would not, except on occasion, take the opportunity to amplify or clarify. Presumably, he preferred not to criticize in public a colleague's, especially a younger colleague's, technique of presentation but to mention the point to him later in a more private fashion.

were Professors Zuntz (who had invited J. B. to join) and Neuberg of Berlin, Professors Durig and von Schroetter of Vienna, J. B., and Dr. C. G. Douglas, Fellow of St. John's College, Oxford. Their objectives were not identical, and included – according to a contemporary lay account – the study of the influence of climatic conditions upon gas exchanges in the lungs, the blood circulation, the action of sunlight upon the skin, and so forth. Spatially associated with these biological investigations in Teneriffe were two Frenchmen, who were concerned with observing Halley's comet [1] in the clear atmosphere obtaining on the island.

Lady Barcroft has, fortunately, preserved J. B.'s letters about the trip, and their interest justifies a fairly lengthy extract from their contents as a complement to the more formal account given by J. B., in 1914, in Chapter XVII of his book, *The Respiratory Function of the Blood.* He went out in the *König Friedrich August,* and on 18 March wrote as follows. "Long day at sea . . . Nothing much done – a little sketching – some examination questions set for the tripos. I am afraid I am still a sea bird, for apart from *the one consideration* I should like to be settling down now for weeks of sea and air and sunshine . . . Last night we spent a good while in the wireless telegraphy [2] room which is one of the most fascinating places in the ship, we were somewhere a little north of Gibraltar and I heard with my ears messages from Holland, from Madeira and from Marseilles within a few minutes of one another. They were none of them meant for this ship, but fancy the whole air alive all day with messages going to and from one part of the world to another." The next day he landed at Santa Cruz, on the south side of the island of Teneriffe, and went by tram and motor to the German Grand Hotel Humboldt-Kurhaus at Orotava, on the north side, arriving in bright moonlight. He began work at this level, 300 feet above the sea, on the 21st, checking dissociation curves against those determined at Cambridge. To begin with they differed, but an explanation was found – the gas brought by Professor Zuntz contained a trace of impurity. On the 25th is the note, "The party

[1] Halley saw it in 1682, and predicted its return about 1758 – it was, in fact, sighted on Christmas Day in that year.

[2] In 1896 Signor Marconi (1874–1937) brought over to England a system of wireless telegraphy which could be worked over short distances. In 1902 land messages were received by the system on the Italian cruiser, *Carlo Alberto,* during her voyage from England to Russia.

for Monte Rosa [1] seems to be growing. First yourself then myself and Dr. Camis. Then I think Prof Durig and to day Prof Zuntz asked to come. This is all rather gratifying as they would not want to come unless we were getting on pretty well."

On the 28th, after the Orotava base-lines had been completed, eight mules (five pack animals, the other three carrying Professors Zuntz and Durig and J. B.) left in single file for the seven to eight hours journey to the Cañadas, the vast plateau about 7000 feet up, with mountains of about 1000–2000 feet all round it and the Peak of Teneriffe rising about 6000 more feet from the middle (Plate 26). From Orotava J. B. had seen the Peak "all red in the sunrise and later glistening white." About two thirds of the way to the Cañadas, as the party suddenly emerged from the clouds, it beggared even J. B.'s powers of description. A short distance farther on, the procession stopped ascending and dropped a little through a pass into the Cañadas, came round to the south of the Peak, and stopped off at the iron and asbestos hut which was to be their headquarters for the second period of the research. Behind it was another building to be used as a laboratory; in the background was the Peak, and nearby Espigone and Guajara, summits in the encircling mountain range.

On the next day the apparatus arrived safely and J. B. completed one curve from 3 p.m. onwards. Five persons (Douglas, von Schrötter, the two Frenchmen, and J. B.) shared a bed-sitting room about fifteen feet square, but against that inconvenience they could set an excellent cuisine, despite the fact that everything had to be brought up on mules from Orotava. In the evenings it got very cold outside, but a stove inside kept the temperature at 65–70° F. "It is of course commonplace to dilate on the clearness of the air and the beauty of the heavens at night, but as well as being commonplace it would be useless for nothing can give any idea of it especially Jupiter which we see in front looking intensely bright."

After completing his work at the Cañadas station (7000 feet), J. B. went up to the more Spartan establishment (Plate 27) at Alta Vista (11,000 feet). There is no account of this in his letters, but there are interesting passages about his trip to Guajara on the day before leaving. They are reproduced verbatim as they show here and there to a slight degree the combined affect of altitude plus exercise,

[1] See 1911.

i.e., of oxygen lack, upon cerebration. "It has been one of the days of my life as we walked to Guajara that is the peak on which the astronomers have there abode, we walked up and up the inside of the old crater in which we live and suddenly got to the top and a magnificent sight met our view. We looked down a majestic gorge which end in clouds while in the sunshine beyond the clouds there was a blue haze which was the sea. Then in the misty horizon we divined the top of Grand Canary also peeping up above the clouds which surrounded the lower altitudes. The still upwards we reached the site of the observatory of Piazzi Smith. [1] The little wooden house in which the Frenchmen live is inside the stout old stone wall, the telescope close at hand, for the photographing of Halley's comet looks very curious with its polar axis at what seems an unfamiliar angle . . .

"More. A little a more about Guajara. As the crow flies it is not very far as the great rock towers almost over our heads, i e the base is about a mile a way. When you get up ~~there~~ ~~there~~ you see a wonderful sight. I can only repeat what is obvious namely that it resembles as closely as any thing earthy can, a lunar landscape. Of vegetation you see nothing, except when you pick of stray plants of brown. E Every where there stick up peaks of varying sizes ~~sp~~ castling there long shaddows on the bare rock in the afternoon sun. Opposite you is the bare peak and you can just see the two jets of steam coming out of the top. ~~We stayed ther.~~ The cliff is precipitous if you throw a stone over $5\frac{1}{2}$ seconds expire before you hear the sound of its touching anything. I must stop again"

Similar anoxic effects were present at the Alta Vista hut (Barcroft, 1920, *Rep. Brit. Ass.*, *88*, 158), for a page written in his note-book there commenced with a scrawl which was crossed out, then came "6 Sept.", which was changed successively to "6 March" and to the correct date, "6 April", and after that followed more crossings out and corrections.

On 8 April he was back at the Cañadas working at the blood brought down from Alta Vista and very excited to see if all the extra bits of evidence dovetailed in as hoped. Dinner that day was even better than usual because of the presence of three visitors, reputed to be the King of Italy's brother and his aide-de-camp travelling incognito, and an important inhabitant of Teneriffe. "In this exalted

[1] Author of *Teneriffe. An Astronomer's Experiment.*

society the conversation at dinner turned largely upon fleas about which many stories were recounted but of which I may say we have seen none."

On Sunday, 10 April, he wrote that he had hoped for a day of rest, but some special samples of blood from Professor Zuntz which had come down from Alta Vista had made him work harder than ever – twelve determinations had had to be made on three dissociation curves. "But at the end it is done and now at dinner time the things are all used for the last time on the island; fortunately the results all came out quite cleanly . . . After dinner the packing began. Now I am full of joy; to start with I am well; to go on with my work is done and in this I might well consider myself somewhat fortunate. One might so well have taken the whole three weeks without really having begun. Yet events have turned out so fortunately for me that there is really little more that I could do if I were to stay longer, short of course of investigating a new point of some sort, so that I can well pack feeling that I may pack intellectually as well as actually. Then I am going home . . ."

The next day's diary states that the mule has gone off with the luggage to Orotava, and "I am left here with no effects but my night things and my paint box. I can have a luxury that has hardly come my way, that of helping my friends, so I have spent the day doing odd jobs and reading Conan Doyle's history of the Boer War and doing a little sketching." Early on 12 April he set off by mule and went round the south side of the Peak to the new volcano which had come into existence only a few months earlier. Then he went on to Icod on the north coast, reaching it about 8.30 p.m. after passing through extremely beautiful vegetation. He stayed overnight in the Spanish inn there, was called at 5.15 a.m. and went on by "automobile" to Orotava, arriving there about 7.30 a.m. after a very beautiful drive. "The serious business which confronted one was to try and resume a civilised appearance. This task was begun before breakfast for which I was very ready and subsequently it was resumed with greater vigour. But some fresh clothes, a visit to the hair dresser and extensive bath made one at home in the atmosphere of the Humboldt-Kurhaus."

On 14 April he had an early breakfast, at which Professors Zuntz and Durig and a Mr. Sharper kept him company, and was given a lift by car to Tacarontá. He left there by train about 12.30 p.m., reached Santa Cruz an hour or so later, and after 5 p.m. went on board R. P. D. *Prinzregent*, of the German East Africa Line, which was due at Southampton on Tuesday, 19 April.

It has seemed worth while to give this long account, partly because it is a valuable addition to the information contained in the 1914 book, but also because it helps to build up our picture of J. B. in all his aspects. We can conclude by indicating what J. B. had learned as a result of the expedition. He had found that an individual's oxygen dissociation curve (his and that of Douglas were the ones most studied) remained virtually unaltered whether that person was at sea-level, at 7000 feet, or at 11,000 feet, provided the determinations were made at the carbon dioxide pressure obtaining in the individual's blood at that particular level. In other words, as he wrote in 1914, "the affinity of the blood for oxygen remains as a first approximation unaltered in spite of the lowered CO_2 tension." According to Bohr's prediction there should have been increased affinity, and this discrepancy between forecast and fact set J. B. wondering if, during the rise to greater altitude, the carbon dioxide was displaced in the blood by something else which produced an equal effect upon the affinity of the haemoglobin for oxygen.

Shortly after his return home, namely, on 5 May 1910, his long series of original contributions to physiology were appropriately recognized by his election to the Fellowship of the Royal Society. He thus joined the proportionately very high number of members of the Society of Friends who since 1663, the year after the Royal Society's foundation, had become Fellows; among the earlier ones had been William Penn (1681), John Coakley Lettsom (1773), Thomas Young (1794), and Joseph Lister (1832), the father of Lord Lister. So J. B. had distinguished predecessors.

In July he went, apparently, to Berlin to cooperate for a while with Professor Franz Müller (Barcroft, 1911, *J. Physiol.*, *42*, 46, 62). This was in connection with the work at Teneriffe.

For their summer holiday M. A. B. and he and the family appear to have gone to The Glen, Newry, and then from 31 August to 7 September he presumably attended the meeting of the British Association at Sheffield. The proceedings included the Report of the Committee, set up in 1909 (with J. B. as Secretary) on The Dissociation of Oxyhaemoglobin at High Altitudes, together with the fourth Report of the Committee (of which J. B. was co-Secretary)

26—Teneriffe, 1910. The station in the Canadas (7,000 feet). The Peak in the background. (Douglas)

27—Teneriffe, 1910. The Alta Vista hut (11,000 feet). Standing near the door, dressed in black, is Geheimrat Prof. Dr. Zuntz. (Douglas)

Facing page 74

28—Cambridge, 1910. Joseph Barcroft, Proctor, with his two 'bulldogs'

Facing page 75

on the Effect of Climate upon Health and Disease; both reports were entirely concerned with the altitude researches in which J. B. had been, and was to be, involved. The first stated that the work planned for Monte Rosa had to be postponed to 1911, and asked that the grant for it should be increased so as to cover the expenses of Mr. Ff. Roberts, as colleague to J. B. The second gave a résumé of the results obtained at Teneriffe and was an expansion of what has already been written above. It stated that the dissociation curves of four members of the party had been studied, those of two of them completely. The ones thus fully studied, namely, the ones of Douglas and J. B., showed interesting individual differences, accounted for by the facts that Douglas had taken exercise and become compensated for it at altitude, whereas J. B. had deliberately restricted his exercise and was uncompensated. Hence J. B. had suffered from mountain sickness when he attempted to take exercise at 11,000 feet [and, presumably, during the climb from the Cañadas to Guajara], whereas Douglas had not. From one of J. B.'s letters written in Teneriffe, it seems that the Royal Society had helped with his personal expenses (see also Barcroft, 1911, *J. Physiol.*, *42*, 60). So the expedition had been subsidized by both bodies.

At the end of September the eighth International Congress of Physiologists took place in Vienna; J. B. was not present but a communication was made by Hermann Straub, of Stuttgart, on their joint behalf, the subject being the work of the kidney in the rabbit. From the accounts of the Congress (see Franklin, 1938) it is obvious that, though goodwill and co-operation obtained between the physiologists of all the countries represented, the international political situation had already begun to deteriorate. At the first plenary session, for instance, Charles Richet ended his address with a plea that money should be spent in supporting productive research rather than in the purchase of armaments. "Tout ce qu'il y a d'énergie dans les peuples, énergie en hommes et énergie en argent, est consacré à nourrir des haines absurdes et des rivalités fratricides. *La guerre, la guerre qui ruine et désole les hommes, la guerre prend tout, et la science, la science bienfaisante et féconde, la science n'a que des restes.*"

In November J. B. became Assistant Tutor in Natural Sciences at Kings College; he was destined to hold the office until Michaelmas 1926. Some time in 1910, also, he assumed the duties of Proctor

(Plate 28); unfortunately, no interesting accounts of his doings in this capacity appear to have been preserved for the benefit of posterity!

To close the year's story we must refer to two papers, published on 9 November and 31 December respectively in the *Journal of Physiology*. The first, with H. Straub, was on the secretion of urine or, more precisely, on the metabolic exchange of the kidney of the cat and rabbit as affected by various diuretics. The second paper, with L. Orbeli, was on the influence of lactic acid upon the dissociation curve of blood. The experiments were planned to test the suggestion, arising out of the Teneriffe findings, that lactic acid, the production of which is increased in asphyxia, affects the oxygen dissociation curve of blood in similar fashion to carbon dioxide. The results were positive in so far as they went. That is to say, asphyxia shifted the curve to the right and so did addition of lactic acid to defibrinated blood.

CHAPTER V

1911–1918

On 27 January 1911 J. B. published an account of the Teneriffe expedition in the *Journal of Physiology* under the title, "The effects of altitude on the dissociation curve of blood"; on 15 July, in the same journal, there was a paper by him and Higgins on "The determination of the constants of the differential blood-gas apparatus". Then in the first three weeks of August he was associated with Camis, Mathison, Ff. Roberts, and Ryffel (of Guy's Hospital) in further work, this time in Italy, on the effects of altitude on the blood dissociation curve. The immediate object was to test for an acidosis occurring in the blood at great altitude, but the main object was to extend the studies in another direction, namely, to discover the effect of exercise (climbing) upon the reactions of the human subject – in Teneriffe the conditions had been those of rest. There were other incidental differences, e.g., the highest point in Italy considerably exceeded the corresponding one in Teneriffe, and the difference in temperature between ground and mountain levels was far greater in Italy. The expenses of the expedition were defrayed by grants from the Royal Society and the British Association. It is of interest that almost simultaneously Haldane, Douglas, Yandell Henderson, and Schneider were studying altitude effects on Pike's Peak, Colorado (14,000 feet).

The ground level studies in Italy would have been more conveniently made at Turin [1], but – presumably through Dr. Camis' association with the expedition – they were in fact made in the laboratories of the ancient University of Pisa, where Professor Aducco placed every facility at the disposal of the investigators. The high level studies were thereafter made, through the courtesy of Professor Aggazzotti, on Monte Rosa at Col d'Olen (*c.* 10,000 feet)

[1] As being nearer to Monte Rosa. Angelo Mosso, who had occupied the chair in Turin and who had not only been greatly interested in altitude effects but also well-disposed towards J. B., had died in 1910.

and Capanna Regina Margherita (*c.* 15,000 feet) respectively.[1]

A detailed diary appears not to be available, but from various sources we learn that J. B. walked the 5600 feet from Alagna up to Col d'Olen (Plate 29) on 5 August, made a 1000 feet climb from that level on 14 August, and the 5300 feet ascent to the Capanna Regina Margherita on 17 August. This last took seven or eight hours, including a rest of an hour at the Capanna Gnifetti, and the only serious climbing was the final 1500 feet up steps cut in the ice (Plate 30). From the Capanna Regina Margherita (Plate 31) there was a wonderful vista of mountains, including the Matterhorn (Plate 32).

The full account of the findings of the expedition, together with extra information acquired by J. B. at Carlingford in August 1912, by Mathison on the Sugar Loaf, Abergavenny, in September 1912, and by J. B., R. A. Peters, Roberts and Ryffel at Carlingford in January 1913, was not published until 10 November 1914 (Barcroft, Camis, *et al.*, 1914), but a preliminary report was made to the British Association for the Advancement of Science at its meeting in Portsmouth from 31 August to 7 September. It was the second report to the Committee, set up in 1909, upon the dissociation of oxy-haemoglobin at high altitudes, and it included the following. "The addition of acid to the blood decreases the affinity of the haemoglobin for oxygen . . . A scale was made out at Pisa for the blood of each member of the party, and successive given quantities of lactic acid were added to the blood, and the degree of saturation with oxygen was noted in each case. When the scale had once been made it became possible to estimate the abnormal acid present in the blood at higher altitudes, by observing the percentage saturation under standard conditions. All members of the party at Col d'Olen showed an addition of acid which in most cases was equivalent to about 0.025 per cent. lactic acid, and about twice that amount at Capanna Margherita. After exercise, however, the amount of acid present was much greater. Thus, immediately on arrival at Col d'Olen, after walking from Alagna Sesia, . . . Mr. Roberts' blood contained excess of acid equivalent to 0.08 per cent. lactic acid, and on arrival at Capanna Margherita, after a nine days' stay at Col d'Olen, 0.7 per cent. An interesting point about the addition of

[1] This first international physiological laboratory had been in existence for a decade (Franklin, 1938, 263).

29—MONTE ROSA, 1911. THE HUT AT COL D'OLEN (*c.* 10,000 feet). (Aggazotti)

30—MONTE ROSA, 1911. PUNTA GNIFETTI, WITH THE CAPANNA REGINA MARGHERITA ON THE SUMMIT. (Durig)

31—MONTE ROSA, 1911. CAPANNA REGINA MARGHERITA. (Aggazotti)

32—MONTE ROSA, 1911. View of MATTERHORN FROM CAPANNA REGINA MARGHERITA AT SUNSET. (Durig)

Facing page 79

acid is that it is not immediately excreted on descent from a high altitude. This fact leads to a lower CO_2 tension in the alveolar air at Col d'Olen after descent from the Capanna Margherita than before the ascent; and in order that the respiratory quotient might be maintained, there was a correspondingly higher oxygen tension – a striking demonstration of the advantage, at a given altitude, of making an ascent and returning."

To conclude this account of 1911, we can mention the appearance of a preliminary note by J. B. and F. Müller, in *Proceedings of the Physiological Society* of 21 October, on "The formation and estimation of methaemoglobin", and we can report the beginning of the association between J. B. and R. A. Peters, who wrote in 1929 as follows." In 1911 in my first research Professor Barcroft directed my attention to a problem in adsorption. In those days there was a considerable belief that the combination of oxygen with haemoglobin was chemical, but this was not settled, because others held that haemoglobin was a colloid, and by its surface merely adsorbed oxygen. Working with Barcroft's new methods of oxygen determination, and with the new titanium methods for iron analysis, I was able to show that the specific oxygen capacity, the ratio O_2: Fe never exceeded the definite value of 401. This settled the matter so far as adsorption was concerned, but I was never quite satisfied in my own mind that this was all. Somehow I felt that there was some deeper significance in regard to life to be extracted from this fact. It was only slowly that I took in the full significance of it." It is of interest that Peters, when he published his results in 1912, did so as a Scholar of Gonville and Caius College, i.e., we have here another instance of J. B.'s capacity for encouraging the young in original investigation; he did in fact carry out several of the oxygen determinations himself.

In 1912 there appears to have been nothing noteworthy until 12 June, when J. B., in collaboration with Franz Müller of Berlin, published in the *Journal of Physiology* a paper on "The relation of blood flow to metabolism in the salivary gland." The object of the research was to discover if increasing the blood flow to a gland would per se increase its oxygen uptake, and the answer was in the negative. A month later, in another paper in the same journal, J. B. and H. Piper of Berlin described the effect of adrenaline upon the gaseous metabolism of the cat's submaxillary gland; there was increased usage of oxygen during, and for some minutes after, the short–lasting secretion produced by the hormone. In between the two dates J. B. spent three days at The Glen, Newry, perhaps to arrange the summer holiday at nearby Carlingford. At all events, he and his wife and family were there for parts of August and September, and on 17 August J. B. investigated the effect of a 1000 feet climb, up Carlingford Mountain from sea-level, upon the haemacidosis of his blood. The reason for this appears in the third Report of the Committee upon the dissociation of oxyhaemoglobin at high altitudes, which was made to the British Association at its meeting in Dundee from 4 to 11 September. "The work of this Committee," the report reads, "was practically completed, as it seemed, when they returned from Monte Rosa a year ago . . . During the past year certain control experiments have been carried out which show that the value of the work carried out in the Alps can only be duly appraised when similar experiments have been carried out during ascents from the sea-level to 1,000 feet. Carlingford Mountain offers an ascent of 1,000 feet which is very similar to that overlooked by Col d'Olen. A grant of 15 *l.* is asked for for the purpose of carrying out experiments at Carlingford similar to these at Col d'Olen, on the same persons as far as possible."

The same British Association meeting received the sixth and final Report of the Committee on the effect of climate on health and disease. This stated that the Committee had been in treaty with the Royal Society of Medicine, which had altered its rules so that the Committee could be co-opted with the Society's Section of Balneology and Climatology – in consequence the Committee did not seek re-appointment.

On 27 September Mathison, of the Monte Rosa expedition, made a 1000 feet ascent, parallelling that of J. B. at Carlingford, on the Sugar Loaf at Abergavenny.

Finally, on 22 October, J. B. and L. E. Shore published in the *Journal of Physiology* their paper on "The gaseous metabolism of the liver. Part I. In fasting and late digestion." The results indicated that the oxygen usage was increased threefold to fivefold by feeding and that the hepatic arterial blood was the main source of the liver's oxygen supply, especially in the cases of the fed animals.

In January 1913 J. B., Peters, Roberts and Ryffel, three of whom had been at Monte Rosa in 1911, went to Carlingford and determined the effect of exercise, uncomplicated by altitude, during the ascent of Carlingford Mountain (i.e., Slieve Foy). "The apparatus used was that which had been taken to Monte Rosa, with the exception of the bath for rotating the tonometer, this was of a different design. The laboratory used proved to be exceedingly efficient, it was the bathroom of a lodging-house [Falcon House], containing a bath provided with hot and cold water, a wash-hand basin with the same equipment, and a water-closet, with the addition of a pail for the things which we wished to throw away. This equipment left little to be desired, and the luxury of hot water was felt to be very great in view of the difficulty which we had encountered in heating it at high altitudes" (Barcroft, Camis, *et al.*, 1914).

On 18 January the Physiological Society met in King's College, London[1], and J. B. and various colleagues (Camis, G. Graham, Higgins, Mathison, Peters, Roberts, and Ryffel) presented preliminary communications on the effects of exercise, altitude, carbohydrate-free diet, and moist heat on the dissociation curve of blood. In the communications the blood was termed "mesectic" when the balance of ions in it was such that the dissociation curve of the individual was in the normal position, "pleonectic" and "meionectic" respectively when the curve was shifted (to the left or right) so that at a given pressure of oxygen haemoglobin took up more or less oxygen than normal. If exercise was severe around sea-level, the curve became meionectic, even though the carbonic acid tension was reduced. At altitudes up to 15,000 feet the curve remained mesectic in the resting subject, despite a lowering of the carbonic acid pressure; on the other hand, a given degree of meionexy resulted from a lesser degree of activity, and a greater degree of meionexy resulted from a given degree of activity, than at altitude. In two out of five subjects a carbohydrate-free diet produced pleonexy and the subjects became "knocked up"; the other three remained mesectic as regards their curves, and well subjectively. Rise in the wet bulb thermometer reading, with the properties of the blood remaining unchanged, resulted in pleonexy. The generalization formulated from the four researches together was "that under circumstances in which the blood is mesectic the subject

[1] This meeting was of some special interest in that J. S. Haldane proposed, and Cathcart seconded, that "it is desirable that women should be regarded as eligible for membership of the Society." It was not, however, until 23 January 1915 that the proposal was carried.

feels in normal health, even though the blood may be abnormal, while when the blood is either pleonectic or meionectic the subject feels out of his usual normal condition and betrays symptoms of the change which has taken place."

On 6 February J. B. and J. H. Burn published a paper on the "Determination of the constant of the differential blood gas apparatus. With a note on the specific oxygen capacity of blood." Previous determination of the constant (Barcroft and Higgins, 1911) had been by a method depending for its accuracy upon the extent to which the gas laws hold good in practice. The new method of calibration was by liberation of a known quantity of oxygen from a standard solution of hydrogen peroxide by potassium permanganate, and it gave a constant 2–2.5 per cent. higher. If this constant was applied to Peters' (1912) results for the specific oxygen capacity of haemoglobin, the figure became 401.8, the theoretical one being 400.8 ml. of oxygen per g. of iron. On 15 February J. B. and E. P. Poulton stated, in the Proceedings of the Physiological Society, that the effect upon the dissociation curve of blood of variations in the carbon dioxide pressure was to alter the value of K in Hill's equation, the value of n remaining unchanged. On 17 May, J. B. told the Society that, in subjects at rest at altitude, the reduced CO_2 pressure of the blood was so nearly balanced by an acidosis that the dissociation curve was only slightly meionectic, the mean value of K at 15,000 feet being 0.93 x the mesectic K. "Judged by the data published by Barcroft and Poulton, such a change in K would correspond to an elevation of CO_2 pressure in the blood of the order of 2 mm. and would provide the necessary stimulus for the increased ventilation observed at high altitudes."

At the meeting on 28 June (which owing to the death of Professor Francis Gotch took place in University College, London, instead of in Oxford), Lewis, Ryffel, Wolf, Cotton, Evans and Barcroft described a type of case of "cardiac" or "renal asthma" in which the urea, non-protein nitrogen, and lactic acid (at least in the milder stages) remained normal but there was a fall in the alveolar CO_2, meionexy, and acidosis, the fundamental factor being an increase in the proportion of acids (exclusive of CO_2) to bases in the blood. A longer account was published by five of the six authors in October, and in it they stated that the acidosis was not due to formation of an abnormal amount of any organic acid, but appeared "to be another instance of the same phenomenon of retention of acids in excess of bases which is shown during residence at high altitudes." In between these two clinical publications the Committee on the dissociation of oxy-haemoglobin at high altitudes made its fourth and final Report to the British Association, meeting from 10–17 September in Birmingham; the Report contained nothing that had not already been communicated to the Physiological Society, so it needs no further mention here.

We should, however, refer at some length to two papers, by A. V. Hill and J. B. respectively, which appeared in the October number of the *Biochemical Journal* and dealt with the mathematics of the dissociation curves, especially the CO and O_2 ones, and the objections raised to Hill's theory by Douglas, Haldane, and Haldane (1912). In his text Hill wrote that his equation $y = 100 \frac{Kx^n}{1 + Kx^n}$ where K was the equilibrium constant and n was a whole number greater than 1, seemed "to suit all known dissociation curves of oxyhaemoglobin with a very high degree of accuracy, as numerous published and unpublished experiments of Barcroft (1913) and others (see, e.g., Douglas, Haldane, J. S., and Haldane, J. B. S. (1912)) will show. In point of fact n does not turn out to be a whole number, but this is due simply to the fact that aggregation is not into one particular type of molecule, but rather into a whole series of different molecules." In his summary and conclusions Hill stated that his theory was capable of including all the known facts in relation to CO- and O_2-dissociation curves, provided one were allowed to make two simple assumptions as to the order of magnitude of the equilibrium constants in the several reactions involved.

In the text of his paper, J. B. wrote that Hill's 1910 formula, with the introduction of certain assumptions, could now be applied (1) to the affinity of blood for oxygen in the absence of carbonic acid, (2) to the affinity of blood for carbon monoxide in the absence of oxygen, (3) to the partition of haemoglobin between oxygen and carbon monoxide in the presence of the two gases and either with or without acids such as CO_2 in the system. "The validity of the theory," he went on, "depends not only upon the soundness of the reasoning on which it rests, but upon the accuracy with which it fits the vast number of experimental data by which it may be tested. It may here be pointed out that the formula contains but two constants n and K:

the experimental test therefore is a much more crucial one than in the case of the more adaptable formula of Douglas, Haldane and Haldane (1912), which contains three constants. Since the formula was first published by Hill, I have devoted a great deal of attention to the accuracy with which it fits the facts. The correspondence is so striking that I propose to record it in the present paper."

J. B.'s conclusions were as follows:–

1. The available data for the dissociation curves of blood agree very closely with the theoretical curves deduced from the following physical conceptions.

(a) That the reaction between haemoglobin and oxygen is a reversible chemical change $Hb_n + nO_2 \rightleftarrows Hb_nO_{2n}$.

(b) That n is the average number of molecules aggregated together, the value of n depending upon the nature and concentration of the electrolytes in the solution.

(c) That the effect of acids is to change the equilibrium constant of the reaction without sensibly altering the degree of aggregation of the molecules.

(d) That the above reaction does not involve the breakdown or reformation of the aggregates.

(e) That unsaturated oxides are unstable and break up into haemoglobin and saturated oxides.

2. The available data with regard to the reaction of CO and oxygen support an entirely similar conception of carboxyhaemoglobin.

3. So far as the curves deduced from Hill's formula can be distinguished from those yielded by Douglas, Haldane and Haldane's formula, the experimental evidence leans towards the former.

Two communications to the Physiological Society (Barcroft and Means, 1913; Cooke and Barcroft, 1913) on 13 December completed J. B.'s publications for the year. In the former, "The effect of CO_2 on the dissociation curve of haemoglobin," it was noted that the degree of aggregation of the molecules was very sensitive to CO_2 at low concentrations of the gas, but relatively insensitive when n in Hill's equation attained the figure 2.5, that which obtained for blood. The second communication was entitled, "Direct determination of the percentage saturation of arterial blood with oxygen in a normal person", and was the first reported instance of such, preceding by some time Stadie's inauguration of the technique of arterial puncture. Advantage had been taken of a clinical blood transfusion to obtain arterial blood, uncontaminated by either air or anaesthetics, for an analysis, which was carried out by means of the differential blood gas apparatus. "The blood proved to be 94 % saturated with oxygen, after due correction had been made for the exchange of gases in a state of physical solution under the conditions of temperature and pressure which obtained in the body and in the apparatus."

Two further notes are needed about 1913. First, J. B. did not attend the ninth International Congress of Physiologists, which took place from 2–5 September in Groningen. This is somewhat surprising in view of the nearness of the locale, and one must presume that he was over–busy with his own work, in particular with the preparation of the account of the Monte Rosa expedition and with that of his forthcoming book, *The Respiratory Function of the Blood*; the Preface to the latter was dated December 1913, suggesting that the compilation of the text must have been going on during most of the year. The second note is to the effect that J. B.'s father-in-law, Sir Robert Stawell Ball, died in November at the age of seventy-three.

The year 1914 began with a visit by J. B. and M. A. B. on 2–3 January to The Glen, Newry. On 7 January the report of the Monte Rosa expedition of 1911 was received by the Royal Society, and on 5 February it was read by J. B. to the Society, though it did not appear in print (Barcroft, Camis, *et al.*, 1914) until 10 November. It integrated the various earlier communications which have already been mentioned, and classified the information and discussions under the headings:- "Factors which affect the blood of resting individuals," "The effect of exercise on the reaction of the blood," "The effect of altitude on that of exercise," "The after-effects of altitude," and "On the possible aggregation of haemoglobin molecules. "It is easy to pick out individual clarifications and items of interest, e.g., the effect of acid on the dissociation of haemoglobin is to increase the velocity of the reaction $Hb + O_2 \rightarrow HbO_2$ relative to $Hb + O_2 \leftarrow HbO_2$ (p. 50); if the blood is more acid than normal, K will be less than usual and a meionectic curve will result; if the blood is less acid, K will have an abnormally large value (p. 62). Of interest, too, is the comment on the meionexy of exercise with, ceteris paribus, a less easy uptake of oxygen in exercise than at rest.

This, the comment went on, was odd but *pulmonary* respiration is not the final process; "the object and end of respiration is the supply of oxygen to the tissues, and in exercise haemoglobin parts with its oxygen more readily at the time when the tissue wants to take up the oxygen more rapidly;" there are also compensatory processes even within the lungs (p. 78). Of interest, too, are the pH values (p. 79) for J. B.'s blood, both per se and also as an early example of the use of Sørensen's notation.

The authors' summary of the paper read as follows:-

"1. Although there is a marked fall in the CO_2 pressure at high altitudes the blood does not become pleonectic. This fact is due to an acidosis, the specific nature of which has not been discovered at altitudes below 10,000 feet, though it is in part a lactic acidosis, but above 10,000 feet is largely a lactic acidosis. It is probable that the acidosis which takes place below 10,000 feet is less due to any acid abnormal in kind than to a fresh adjustment of the usual acid and basic radicals. This readjustment is probably set up by the kidney.

2. The question of whether the blood becomes meionectic at high altitudes is more difficult to answer. The mean of over 20 observations on different persons at rest, taken at and above 10,000 feet, indicates a trifling degree of meionexy which corresponds to a diminution of 7 per cent. in the equilibrium constant of the reaction $Hb_n + {}_nO_2 \rightleftarrows n\,HbO_2$: or, when applied to Barcroft's blood, of 0.03 in the exponent of the hydrogen-ion concentration. This very trifling departure from the mesectic condition would, according to Haldane and his colleagues, suffice to explain the increased pulmonary ventilation.

3. Sustained exercise causes meionexy, in spite of a fall in the alveolar carbonic acid pressure. The exercise consisted in climbing 1,000 feet. The degree of meionexy and the degree of acidosis depended upon the rate of the climb. Estimations of the lactic acid in the blood showed that the acidosis was entirely a *lactic* acidosis. Relatively little lactic acid was secreted in the urine, the acid therefore accumulated in the blood, displacing the carbonic acid. The degree of meionexy corresponded to a change in P_H from 7.29 to 7.09 when the climb was made in 30 minutes, and to 7.22 when the climb was made in 45 minutes.

4. At high altitudes the effects of exercise are the same as at low ones, namely, meionexy and acidosis. The acidosis is, moreover,

entirely a *lactic* acidosis; but, on account of the altitude, a relatively small amount of exercise produces a given degree of meionexy; the lactic acidosis is very evident, even as the result of a quite slow ascent, and, being cumulative, a long slow ascent at high altitudes produces marked symptoms.

5. An acidosis, so marked, may produce an appreciable aggregation of the molecules of haemoglobin, and doubtless, therefore, of other protein molecules in the body. It is by no means improbable that many of the functional abnormalities of the mind and of the body are referable to this result of acid intoxication.

6. The acidosis produced by residence at high altitudes to some extent outlasts the residence.

7. The meionexy which takes place during exercise forms a physiological adaptation by which the blood can be more easily reduced in the capillary tissues and the oxygen can diffuse more rapidly from them. This adaptation is heightened by the degree of aggregation of the molecules of haemoglobin which we observed."

These findings of the Monte Rosa expedition were included, with much other material, in the first of J. B.'s books, *The Respiratory Function of the Blood*, which was published at the University Press, Cambridge, in February 1914 [1]. It opened with a Preface of such quality that the first three paragraphs should be recalled here.

"At one time, which seems too long ago," J. B. wrote, "most of my leisure was spent in boats. In them I learned what little I know of research, not of technique or of physiology, but of the qualities essential to those who would venture beyond the visible horizon.

"The story of my physiological 'ventures' will be found in the following pages. Sometimes I have sailed single handed, sometimes I have been one of a crew, sometimes I have sent the ship's boat on some expedition without me. Any merit which attaches to my narrative lies in the fact that it is in some sense at first hand. I have refrained from discussing subjects which I have not actually touched, but which might fittingly have been included in a modern account of the blood as a vehicle for oxygen. Such are the relation of narcosis to oxygen-want and the properties of intracellular oxidative enzymes. The omission of these and other important subjects has made the

[1] In the copy of the book which J. B. gave to M.A.B. is inscribed the following:– I want to present this little volume to my wife as a trifling memento of the work she has been doing whilst I have been occupied with the investigations which it contains. J. Barcroft."

choice of a title somewhat difficult. I should like to have called the book, what it frankly is – a log; did not such a title involve an air of flippancy quite out of place in the description of the serious work of a man's life. I have therefore chosen a less exact, though more comprehensive title.

"After all, the pleasantest memories of a cruise are those of the men with whom one has sailed. The debt which I owe to my colleagues, whether older or younger than myself, will be evident enough to any reader of the book. It leaves me well-nigh bankrupt – a condition well-known to most sailors. But I owe another debt of gratitude to those who, as teachers, first showed me the fascination of physiology, to Dr. Kimmins, [1] and especially to Dr. Anderson. [2] At a later stage I learned much from Dr. Gaskell, Professor Langley and Dr. Haldane."

To give a brief account of the book is not easy, but the attempt must be made. To begin with, we may note that the references at the ends of Chapters totalled only about a hundred even though a number of them appeared more than once, and that publications with which J. B. himself had been concerned made up over a quarter of the total. So in the bibliography there was straightway an indication of the relative newness of the subject, while the text revealed that the bulk of the more recent work was by J. B. and his collaborators. The attractive and graphic style of the writing was such as could have been expected from the extracts from J. B.'s personal letters already quoted in this biography, but it had had little chance of appearing in papers in scientfic journals. His subsequent books were all to be noteworthy for this picturesqueness of style, and many tributes have been paid to it. It was on a par with his mastery of the spoken word, as demonstrated in lectures and in communications to societies, and it was an essential part of his make-up, so attention is rightly called to it in this initial instance.

The book consisted of three Parts, subdivided into nineteen Chapters, and four Appendices. Part I dealt with the chemistry of haemoglobin, at first without regard to chronological order, and its five Chapters were on the specific oxygen capacity of blood, the dissociation curve of haemoglobin, the effects of temperature and of

[1] "Formerly science master at the Leys School now Chief Inspector of the Educational Department of the London County Council."

[2] "Formerly supervisor in physiology to King's College, now Master of Gonville and Caius College."

electrolytes respectively on the affinity of haemoglobin for oxygen, and the effect of acid on the dissociation curve of blood. It was wider in treatment, and in details about persons who had been concerned in the researches, than had been possible in individual papers; it was also a synthesis of the whole of the relevant literature. In these respects the other Parts were similar.

Part II dealt with the passage of oxygen to and from the blood, and was subdivided into Chapters on the call for oxygen by the tissues, the call for oxygen considered as a physiological test, the metabolism of the blood itself, the regulation of the supply of oxygen to the tissues, the unloading of oxygen from the blood, the rate of exchange of oxygen between the blood and the tissues, and the acquisition of oxygen by the blood in the lung. The Part opened with a passage which deserves quoting as showing J. B.'s advanced, but obviously correct, outlook upon respiration as a whole. "The classical work of Pflüger," he wrote, "on the combustion of living material settled for all time, it seems to me, the logical order in which the constituent processes of respiration should be treated. The issue before Pflüger may be stated in a few words. Is the quantity of oxygen taken up by the cell conditioned primarily by the needs of the cell, or by the supply of oxygen? The answer was clear, the cell takes what it needs and leaves the rest. Respiration therefore should be considered in the following sequence. Firstly the call for oxygen, secondly the mechanism by which the call elicits a response, the immediate response consisting in the carriage of oxygen to the tissues by the blood and its transference from the blood to the cell. Thirdly in the background you have the mechanism by which the blood acquires its oxygen. It is not the habit of writers on respiration to adopt this order, quite the contrary, but their reason for placing pulmonary respiration in the foreground of the picture is a purely practical one – pulmonary respiration is more evident, both to the eye and to the understanding. I imagine they will not quarrel with me if I make the attempt to treat the matter in what appears to me to be its logical sequence and make some estimate of the call which the blood has to meet, before entering into a discussion of how the call is to be met."

Part III dealt with the dissociation curve considered as an "indicator" of the "reaction" of the blood, and its Chapters were on the dissociation curve in man, the effects of diet, exercise, and altitude respectively on the dissociation curve of blood, the effect of altitude on that of exercise, and some clinical aspects.

The book as a whole was, therefore, a proper and timely review of that field of physiology to which J. B. had devoted himself for nearly two decades. It was enlivened by illustrations, among them reproductions of photographs relating to the Teneriffe and Monte Rosa expeditions and to the less strenuous activities at Carlingford. It was, finally, a welcome addition to the literature upon the blood and respiration at a time when the total number of physiologists was far smaller than now, when review journals were very few, and when the output of monographs was infinitely less than it is to-day. Because of its own intrinsic worth, and because of these contemporary circumstances, the publication of *The Respiratory Function of the Blood* was an event of considerable importance in the more recent history of animal physiology, and the reception accorded to it corresponded.

The next happening which we have to chronicle was in a different, if related, category; it was the opening, on 9 June, of the new physiological laboratory, built with funds provided by the Drapers' Company of London. The ceremony was performed by H. R. H. Prince Arthur of Connaught and a unique feature was that the guests found the new rooms equipped and in full use. For demonstrations had been prepared by Professor Langley, J. B. and his Teneriffe colleague C. G. Douglas of Oxford, Walter Fletcher, W.B. Hardy, Keith Lucas, G. R. Mines, A. V. Hill, R. A. Peters, W. H. R. Rivers, Miss Dale, and others. One of them wrote later, when war had dispersed most of them to other duties, "How little we thought that day of what was coming! We thought the big new building would become a busy hive at once. All of us had plans for work in the Long Vacation, and several good Germans and Austrians were coming; but from August and for five years it stood almost empty, with poor Langley working away in a couple of rooms." No such anticipations, however, marred 9 June, and following the official opening there was a colourful ceremony in the Senate House, where the following degrees were conferred – LL. D. upon H. R. H. Prince Arthur of Connaught, Lord Esher, Lord Moulton, and Colonel S. M. Benson, Master of the Drapers' Company; Sc.D.

upon Sir William Osler [1], Sir David Ferrier, Professor E. A. Schäfer, and E. H. Starling, four men who had made contributions of importance to the advancement of physiology.

J. B.'s holiday this summer was spent at Carlingford; on 25 June he was in Cork, and the next day was sailing on the *Osprey*, passing the *Copeland* of the Clyde Shipping Company fifteen miles east of Carlingford bar. A little over a month later the international situation had completely changed and on 4 August Great Britain, in accordance with her treaty obligations to Belgium, declared war on Germany. It is no part of this book's object to go into the political story except in so far as it affects J. B.'s story, but for the ordinary person the outbreak of war in 1914 occurred with an abruptness that remains in the memory – in 1939 one's thoughts had been prepared by knowledge of the events from 1914, and particularly from Munich 1938, onwards so that the only suddenness lay in the precise point of termination of a long period of semi-expectancy.

There is no documentary information about the impact which the decision of 4 August 1914 made upon J. B., then aged 42, a practising member of the Society of Friends, and one who had strong personal and scientific ties with a number of foreign colleagues now officially designated as enemies. We can merely conjecture what he must have thought as science in general became applied to the special problems of war, as Cambridge became denuded through undergraduates and others responding to Lord Kitchener's appeal for volunteers, and as thereafter the casualty lists began to appear. His personal solution of the problem was such as might perhaps have been anticipated, for he went against the out-and-out pacifism of most of the Quakers (thereby involving himself in disaccord with the local Cambridge Meeting of the Society [2]), and based his action upon a New Testament passage which appealed to him as indicating the right course. "I thought of the parable of the good Samaritan", he is stated to have said, "and obviously I did not want to pass by on the other side." Accordingly, he wrote to the War Office and offered to help in any way that the

[1] Sir William had to deny himself attendance at the celebration, in Oxford, of the septencentenary of Roger Bacon's birth, as that celebration clashed with the Cambridge ceremony (see Cushing, 1940).

[2] Though he never, apparently, resigned his membership, from about this time he and M.A.B. changed rather to attendance at the services in King's College Chapel.

authorities liked. He was told to stay where he was but, as will be detailed later, his help was called for at short notice in 1915, and thereafter he became occupied with war-work for which he was particularly fitted but which did not, at first at least, go against the principles of more liberally-minded members of the Society of Friends.

There are some miscellaneous items that need to be included before we leave the 1914 part of this story. On 7 September occurred the death of Walter Holbrook Gaskell (born 1 November 1847), who had helped so greatly to establish the prestige of the Cambridge Medical School in its early stages; on 9 November came that of the promising young physiologist, G. R. Mines, who had published with J. B. in 1907 and had later been appointed Professor in McGill University. For the purposes of the subsequent story, we have also to note here that the first War Committee of the Royal Society was appointed on 5 November, and held its first meeting on 12 November. The object of the Committee was "to organize assistance to the Government in conducting or suggesting scientific investigations in relation to the War, the Committee to have power to add to their number and to appoint sub-committees not necessarily restricted to Fellows of the Society." At the meeting on 12 November the Secretaries of the Society were requested to inform the Admiralty, the War Office, and the Board of Trade of the Committee's appointment and of its readiness to fulfil the object just stated. On 16 December F. G. Hopkins was appointed first occupant of the newly-created Chair (the first regular one in Great Britain) of Biochemistry at Cambridge; the Department took over the old Physiology Laboratory as its quarters. On 22 December the paper by Wolf and J. B., entitled, "The metabolism of the salivary gland. I. The nitrogen metabolism of the resting gland", appeared in the *Journal of Physiology*.

A note, written by Dr. M. Wong in 1948, appears very probably to relate to the winter of 1914–15, and may therefore be inserted here. "During the first world war," it reads, "when Cambridge was shorn of students, about four or five of us undergraduates attended an advanced course of lectures on the autonomic nervous system, given by the late Professor Langley in the small theatre on cold, dark winter evenings. Joseph Barcroft, then a Lecturer and F. R. S., used to steal in quietly and sit on the back bench. On the rare occasions that he did not come, he used to ask us for our notes. This serves to illumine the man's humility and love for learning."

In January 1915 Lewis and J. B. published their account of a few more cases in which non-cyanotic dyspnoea was accompanied by acidosis of the blood, i.e., by excessive acid, exclusive of carbon dioxide, relative to the bases present. As before, such acidosis was deduced from fall in percentage saturation of the blood with oxygen at a standard pressure of the gas and at body temperature. On 23 January, at the Physiological Society Meeting at University College, London, J. B. reported on the secretion of urine in decerebrate animals (work done with H. Piper) and on the effect of sodium sulphate in the submaxillary gland. The former research disposed of some objections raised against the work of Barcroft and Straub, 1910, while the latter invalidated the suggestion of Dixon that sodium sulphate, in the dosage found by Barcroft and Straub to produce a diuresis, was a general stimulus to increased metabolism. Perhaps through thoughts of these two German colleagues, Straub and Piper, with whom he had worked in peace-time, J. B. was reminded of a much senior German physiologist, Nathan Zuntz (1947–1920), and on 1 February, in a letter to August Krogh (1874–1949) of Copenhagen, he asked the latter to forward a message to Zuntz (for the sequel see below).

On 25 February J. B. and Toyojiro Kato, Professor of Medicine in Sendai University, communicated to the Royal Society a paper on the effect of functional activity upon the metabolism, blood flow, and exudation in skeletal muscle and the submaxillary gland, and on 26 March J. B. read a communication to the Section of Anatomy and Physiology of the Royal Academy of Medicine in Ireland on the after-effects of the activity of organs, confining his remarks to the particular case of skeletal muscle. The same subject was treated of in publications by J. B. and Kato in *Proc. roy. Soc., B, 88,* of 3 May and in *Phil. Trans., B, 207,* of 20 December (paper read to the Royal Society on 11 November), so a general account will be given later, and here we will merely note that twenty years or so later J. B. stated his view (personal communication to the present writer) that the work on muscle by Kato and himself had never attracted the attention which he thought it had deserved.

On 3 April Krogh penned a reply to J. B.'s letter of 1 February. After referring to technical points about which J. B. had written to him, he added:- "I enclose two notes which I would like to have read at a meeting of the Physiological Society and printed in the Proceedings. Will you show me the kindness to attend to this matter. For several reasons – excluding mines and German submarines, which count for very little – I am unable to come over and read them in person . . . It was a great pleasure for me to write to Zuntz as you desired me to do, and I had a most kind answer from him. As you may like to have his own words I shall quote it verbatim.

'25.2.15

Lieber, verehrter College Krogh!

Ich habe lange keine so grosse und reine Freude gehabt, wie sie mir Ihr Brief vom 19 d.s. bereitet hat. Ihre Wörte drücken kurz und treffend aus, was uns gegenüber dem Ausbrücken feindlicher Leidenschaft, die wir auch von hochstehenden Gelehrten aller Länder, Deutschland nicht ausgenommen, hören mussten, am meisten Not tut. Barcroft weiss auch ohne dass ich es ihm sage, dass die Gefühle der Hochachtung für den Forscher und der warmen Sympathie für den Menschen, die ich ihm gegenüber trage, durch keinen Krieg vermindert werden können und in diesem Sinne bitte ich Sie ihm meine wärmsten, herzlichsten Grüsse zu übermitteln. Noch zwei Männer gibt es unter den englischen Gelehrten für die ich ähnliche Empfindungen trage: das ist John Haldane und Gordon Douglas in Oxford. Barcroft wird ihnen gewiss gern meine Grüsse übermitteln; ich bitte ihn darum.

'Ich bin noch nicht dazu gekommen, Barcroft über sein wundervolles Buch, in dem er die Arbeiten so vieler Jahre zu schönen Kranz zusammenfasst, ausführlich zu schreiben. Wenn wir wieder Frieden haben wird das noch zu mancher Correspondenz führen. Bitte grüssen Sie auch Ihre verehrte Gattin von mir.

Ihr
N. Zuntz'

"It would certainly be delightful", Krogh resumed, "to go to Pike's Peak in your company but I am afraid my pulmonary epithelium, which is the most impervious so far known, will not allow me enough oxygen at that height. At all events I should begin by going into the air chamber here and see how I could stand it. It is difficult to describe my feelings on the news that A. V. Hill is in the Army. I quite understand that he must wish to do anything in his power for his country and his brains are sure to be of great value also in war, but in my opinion he is one of the very few whom our science cannot afford to lose.

With kindest regards from my wife,

Yours very truly,
August Krogh' "

On 13 and 15 April J. B. gave the Oliver-Sharpey Lectures at the Royal College of Physicians of London, his subject being, "The comparisons between some physiological and pathological conditions"[1]. In them he dealt with the pyrexia of exercise, with inflammation and functional activity in the submaxillary gland and striated muscle, and with renal oxygen want at high altitudes and in the wards. With regard to the first two, he pointed out that the scientific value of the comparisons between normal and abnormal depended upon the identity or otherwise of the causes giving rise to the conditions, and that these underlying causes were still obscure. With regard to the third, his view was that in the "adaptations" to special sets of circumstances there lay the germ of certain "chemical lesions", and the pathological was sometimes the exaggeration of the physiological rather than its antithesis.

On the day between the two lectures the second battle of Ypres began (it was to last on into June) and eight days later a new feature, namely, the use of poison gas, was introduced into warfare. For at 5.30 p.m. on 22 April (Cruttwell, 1934, 152–5) the Germans launched the first cloud gas attack, by the Kaiser's wish, so it is stated (see Roughton, 1949, *b*, 322), and against the judgment of the German High Command. More or less immediately this led to J. B.'s initial contribution to the national war-time activity; in the long run it determined his main contributions in both world wars and his consultant work in the two decades between them. For, about a fortnight after the first gassings had occurred, he was sent to Boulogne to study the patients in the base hospitals there, and he was occupied with those studies from 9 to 17 May, and from 26 May to 26 June, while later in the war he became head of the physiology section of the Government's Chemical Warfare station at Porton.

[1] Changed, for publication in abstract form in *Brit. med. J.* of 24 April and 1 May, to "A comparison . . ."

The gas problem, raised in such terrible manner for the troops exposed to the chlorine clouds on 22 April and subsequently, was, of course, completely unexpected. It was, therefore, fortunate but coincidental that J. B.'s previous altitude work had prepared him and others to recognize oxygen lack and, therefore, to feel able to tackle this new problem, with its apparently similar symptoms and signs. From his contemporary notes and other sources we learn that in Boulogne on Sunday, 9 May, he was staying at Grand Hotel du Louvre et Terminus, that he collected blood samples in the morning, had lunch in company with Sir John Bradford (Secretary of the Royal Society 1908–15) and others at the hotel, and in the afternoon, after an hour and a half's discussion of the whole subject with Sir Almoth Wright, who had dropped in unexpectedly, got on with the analyses. One of the cases seen by J. B. on this day was referred to by him in a lecture given at the Royal Army Medical College in 1919. It was that of a Private G., who had been gassed on 5 May, presumably by chlorine. "On effort or even the suggestion of effort," said J. B., "his face at once took on a blue colour. You cannot say exactly that his face flushed because the colour was wrong; but if my reading of the case is correct you can say that his lung flushed: and in flushing it passed increased quantities of blood without adequately oxygenating the haemoglobin. At all events his face presented just the appearance which one might expect on the assumption of vascular dilatation in the unaerated areas."

On the evening of the next day J. B. watched new troops coming in. "They line up at half past ten. Of course everything is dark, then the quay suddenly lights up and out of the dusk come innumerable figures in khaki, company by company they come and form up in the large area in front of the hotel. They are the first of Kitchener's army . . . and they are said to be the Black Watch . . . a fine looking set of men; then off they go to a rest camp before going up to the front." On 11 May he spent the whole of the day trying methods for the measurement of the carbonic acid pressure in venous blood, and thought at the end that as a first approximation he was getting something out of them. On the next day he noted that the change in the wind meant no more gassing cases and that it looked as if he would very soon be among the unemployed. On 15 May he finished his report and expected to leave the next day, but did not in fact sail until the day after. From Folkestone he went to

London, where he reported to Sir Alfred Keogh and later had a discussion with Haldane, who had come up from Oxford for the purpose.

Presumably on 26 May he returned to Boulogne and on the next day he noted that the strong wind from the north meant no fresh gas cases, but that about 3000 old ones were about. The severe cases were not so ill, on the whole, as those of three weeks earlier. "Whether this," the note reads, "is due to the respirators or whether the Germans are using a different gas I don't know. The morning was spent in the wards, the afternoon in the laboratory, as also the evening until about half past ten, so I have had a long day." The next day he noted that he was getting results that were most satisfactory, some of them quite illuminating, to an experimental physiologist, and he added, "It is surprising how little is known about the circulation through the lungs in various chest disorders." On Sunday, 30 May, he wrote:- "This, I imagine, is one of the days which I shall always remember. A European war is a rare enough event; the problem in this war of gas poisoning is unique; for a civilian to be at the official discussion of such a question is I suppose absolutely unknown. So I echo the words of the Catholic bandsman in Newry who played 'God save the King' the night the Home Rule Bill became law – 'This is a memorable occasion'!" Consultants from the base hospitals and from the front attended the meeting, and among those who spoke were Sir John Bradford, Sir Wilmot Herringham, and Sir John Atkins. J. B., to his embarrassment, "had to get on his pins and talk 'gases' " after these very first-rate clinicians had made their orations. "However," he wrote, "I cut it pretty short! Finally the whole thing was wound up by Sir Almoth Wright."

Thereafter for a while there was a lull in gassings and on 2 June J. B.'s work had temporarily stopped and he was finishing the Index of T. H. Huxley's *Lessons in elementary physiology.* [1]

[1] The fifth edition of this work had appeared in 1900, and had merely been reprinted in 1902, 1905, 1908, and 1911. Barcroft's sixth edition must have proved popular, for it was reprinted in September 1915. The Preface opened as follows. "In approaching the revision of 'Huxley's Physiology', my feelings have been similar to those of an architect to whom is entrusted the restoration of a historic building designed by a master hand. Written by Huxley, the book was revised, and in fact almost rewritten, by Foster. The former was as great a writer as any scientist of his time, the latter may almost be said to have created English Physiology. To 'restore' the work of these men from the dilapidations made by two decades of scientific progress is the task now entrusted to me. The sense of responsibility with which I approach it is, if possible, heightened by the affection which I have for the memory of Foster, who was my master."

There was then no note of importance until 16 June, when J. B., having no gas case, decided to do some control experiments and Sir John Bradford offered himself for the purpose of being bled. "In the afternoon", J. B. wrote, "I met a person in whom I was much interested and of whom I had often heard – McNee. In peace time he is a pathologist in Glasgow. Now he has a travelling laboratory attached to the Second Army and goes about doing all sorts of excellent work in a thing somewhat smaller than a furniture van." The note of 19 June included the following:- "... I may perhaps give an account of one or two interesting cases which I have been asked to look at because they are physiological rather than clinical. One man was shot through the spine just at the junction of the neck and the back. Of course all the lower part of his body was quite paralysed. In addition to this he had vaso-motor paralysis, that is to say the blood vessels all over the body were dilated. The result of this was that his blood lay about in his skin and his temperature fell so that shortly before I saw him it was only 86 instead of 98! Unlike ordinary people, however, you can make his temperature what you like by the simple expedient of heating him up. One man they tried this with but they heated him too rapidly and he died. Of course this case cannot live very long.

"Another man was shot through the chest. The curious part of his case is the amount of fluid, blood and other things that accumulate there. Every few days they have got to be drawn off to the extent of perhaps two bottles of Guiness porter and with much the same appearance. The man in fact said to-day 'I hope I am not going to be a hogshead for life.' "

The note on 21 June read:- "The longer I stay out here the more impressed I become with the effect of this gassing upon morale. That is to say that men fall back from it in a way that is wholly avoidable. At present I am starting a feeble campaign to set this right if possible. I dare say it is all being done at home but of that I have no knowledge." Four days later he wrote that his report had gone in and that he expected before long to be returning home. In point of fact this report, dated 23 June 1915, was not finally published until April 1918, when it appeared as pp. 4–6 of *Chemical Warfare Medical Committee Report* No. 6, I. From that account, from the one by Barcroft and Wolf (*ibid.*, II), and from that by Momose, it appears that J. B. and Captain C. G. L. Wolf, R.A.M.C.

did experiments on dogs in Boulogne in June 1915, and at some time on J. B. himself, in order to see what could be done, by oral administration of alkalies, to control the fixed alkalinity of the blood. Momose, a surgeon in the Imperial Japanese Navy, continued that work in Cambridge in July and August, but one cannot say that the outcome was encouraging (Momose, 1915); the work was being extended to the injection of alkalies by the end of 1915.

J. B.'s report of 23 June on the condition of the blood in 16 cases of gas poisoning, examined by him at the base hospitals, read as follows:-

"(1) In no case have I found evidence of any retention in the blood of inspired gases of an acid character.

(2) In practically all cases there is an accumulation of carbonic acid in the blood, due to the impairment of the lungs and their consequent failure to evacuate carbonic acid with their usual facility.

In the more severe cases – those in which the face is blue and in which there is, perhaps, considerable secondary bronchitis or pneumonia – other acid substances also collect in the blood, and these acids are due to want of oxygen.

The breathlessness of the patients is due to excessive carbonic acid in the blood, and is accentuated by accumulation of other acid bodies, when this takes place.

(3) As the patients recover from their breathlessness, the blood assumes its normal healthy character. In all these cases, the blood has been normal before their departure from Boulogne.

(4) There seems little to be gained by any form of treatment specially designed to correct the accumulation of carbonic and other acids in the blood."

We must now mention certain other happenings of 1915. At meetings of the Council of the Royal Society held on 17 and 24 June it was resolved, "That the War Committee appointed on November 5 1914 with its Sub-Committees be discharged and that the Council constitute itself a committee for the purposes named in the original reference to the War Committee." At the meeting on 24 June the following were appointed members of the Sectional War Committee for Physiology:- Professor W. M. Bayliss, Professor A. R. Cushny, Dr. W. M. Fletcher (Secretary), Dr. J. S. Haldane, Dr. L. Hill, Dr. F. G. Hopkins, and Professor E. H. Starling (Chairman). At a meeting of the new War Committee on 15 July it was resolved that Mr. Joseph Barcroft, F. R. S., and Fleet-Surgeon R. C. Munday, R. N. (representing the Medical Department of the Royal Navy) be added to the Physiology Sectional Committee.

Apart from noting that the Barcrofts' holiday was spent at Malham, we have now only to report on Barcroft and Kato's work on the effects of functional activity in skeletal muscle and the submaxillary gland, as communicated to het Royal Society in November and published in *Philosophical Transactions B* on 20 December. The summary read as follows:-

"(1) When skeletal muscle is stimulated rhythmically for 15 minutes, the following effects may be observed:-

(1) The quantity of oxygen taken up is increased both during and after the stimulus, and five hours may elapse before the coefficient of oxidation returns to its former value.

(2) The blood flow is increased, as also is the exudation from the blood vessels. These, like the coefficient of oxidation, may remain abnormally great for several hours.

(3) The excised muscle, five or six hours after the stimulation, may be heavier, shorter, and of lower specific gravity than the unexercised one. Indeed, its properties may be so altered as to suggest the physical basis of the sensation of 'stiffness'.

(2) The length of time which is required for the products of activity to become oxidised suggests that special precautions are necessary to insure the condition of rest in which the basal metabolism of the muscle is obtained.

(3) The exudation from the vessels of resting muscle is just appreciable, that from the vessels of the resting submaxillary gland is inappreciable.

(4) When the submaxillary gland is under the influence of pilocarpine, the oxygen consumption, the exudation, and the hyperaemia increase, and for several hours do so relatively to the volume of saliva that is being excreted.

(5) Both in gland and muscle there tend to be two maxima on the curves of oxidation, hyperaemia and exudation, one when the activity is at its height, the other about an hour subsequently.

(6) The sustained increase of blood flow appears to be due to metabolic products. To them also is due the increased lymph flow;

their action may be partly direct and partly indirect, inasmuch as they produce a rise in local and capillary pressure."

To the above can be added some notes from p. 162 about the skeletal muscle experiments. "The full extent of the dilatation . . .", the authors wrote, "can best be appreciated when account is taken not only of the magnitude of the blood flow but of the nature of the blood which emerged from the vein. . . . The data are given in Table VII, from which it appears

(1) That the percentage saturation, even during the stimulation, when the muscle was using up more oxygen, was never under 50.

(2) That in the subsequent period it was usually over 80 per cent. saturated.

(3) After the hyperoxidation had passed off, it reached 90 per cent.

These figures are of course rough, nevertheless the picture of blood indistinguishable in tint from that in the artery, and rushing out of the muscle at four times its ordinary rate, was a striking one. Occurring as it did 4–5 hours after the exercise had been taken, it was a remarkable tribute to the activity of metabolic products." The extreme redness was not, however, a constant phenomenon in the experiments, and the continuing hyperaemia was most marked in those cases in which the nerve to the muscle had been cut some time previously to stimulation.

At the meeting of the Physiological Society held at King's College London, on 22 January 1916, J. B. made preliminary communications on the vascular and metabolic conditions in the kidneys of rabbits, first normal, and then injected with diphtheria toxin and uranium acetate respectively. In all three researches Margaret Tribe, one of the first women to be elected to membership of the Society under the new rule of 1915, had been a colleague; in the second one W. H. Harvey, and in the third one Hopkins, had also played a part. The results were as follows. The normal rate of blood flow was 2 ml. and the oxygen consumption 0.082 ml./g. per minute, while the oxygen saturation of the venous blood was 59 per cent. Two days after injection of diphtheria toxin the blood pressure was unusually low, the rate of blood flow averaged 0.42 ml. and the oxygen consumption 0.032 ml./g. per minute, the oxygen saturation of the venous blood was 47 per cent., and the venous blood was blacker than normal. The day after subcutaneous injection of uranium acetate in the dosage of 2 mg./kg., the average rate of blood flow was 2.4 ml. and the oxygen consumption 0.046 ml./g. per minute, the oxygen saturation of the venous blood 76 per cent. and that blood itself, as it emerged from the kidney, markedly redder than usual. "The histological examination of the kidneys showed that the spaces round the glomeruli were much enlarged, the glomeruli themselves being shrunk. There was some breakdown of the convoluted tubules, the other parts of the tubules being unimpaired. The blood vessels contained an abnormal quantity of blood, the corpuscles in many cases forming a lining to the vessels."

On 16 March J. B. sent in a report (which was not published until October 1918) to the Physiology Section of the Royal Society's War Committee on "the delayed effects of phosgene in rabbits, with special reference to the influence of muscular contraction." The work had been done at Cambridge, and the nine colleagues listed had included Lewis and Professor Boycott, F. R. S. The gist of the results was that on the day following exposure to phosgene the animals frequently suffered from a species of "shock" characterized by depression of the blood-pressure regulating and respiratory centres, death resulting from respiratory failure, and being accelerated by exercise.

Another report, forwarded to the Royal Society's War Committee in April by J. B., Lewis, and others does not appear to have been published. It dealt with the bradycardia, amounting to temporary stoppage of the heart beat, in gassed animals and stated that the fall in heart rate was abolished by section of the vagus nerves (see *Chemical Warfare Medical Committee Report* No. 4, 1918, p. 59, footnote).

In June the Government's Experimental Station was started at Porton, near Salisbury, Wiltshire, with Lieut. Colonel Crossley, F. R. S., as its Commandant and Superintendent of Experiments. From 27 to 29 June J. B. was at The Glen, Newry; he and his family later had their summer holiday on the waterways of East Anglia and at Midhurst, Sussex. Finally, so far as these notes on the year 1916 are concerned, on 14 October, in collaboration with Lewis, Cotton, Milroy, Dufton [1] and Parsons, he published a paper on "Breathlessness in soldiers suffering from irritable heart." It showed that the blood of some such subjects reacted more than that of normal

[1] Now Lady Moran.

people to a given addition of carbon dioxide, and suggested that the more marked lowering of pH went "far to explain the otherwise inexplicable breathlessness in certain patients who suffer from the condition described as irritable heart."

For the background to the first event which we shall record in 1917 we have to go back to June 1915, and to consult two Reports.[1] In that month of 1915 the Chemical Warfare Offensive Research and Development functions were transferred to the Ministry of Munitions as the Trench Warfare Department under General Jackson, and a Scientific Advisory Committee (the name was later changed to Chemical Advisory Committee) was set up with Hardy as the representative upon it of physiology. Soon after Pratt's appointment as Assistant Secretary in August 1916, the Committee considered J. B.'s appointment to Porton and some of the members doubted if, with his Society of Friends' attachment, he would be a suitable person for dealing with the unpleasant subject that chemical warfare then was. On 16 January 1917, however, at a further meeting of the Committee, J. B. was invited to take up duties as physiologist at Porton, and he accepted, thereafter going into residence and being in charge of the physiological laboratory there until the end of the war. In Mr. Pratt's Report it is indicated that this work was offensive, defensive, and medical in its character.

In March J. B., "who for some time had been assisting the Chemical Advisory Committee by physiological work at Porton and Cambridge, was made a member. The addition of a physiologist had, by that time, become absolutely essential in view of the large amount of work in hand in regard not only to the physiology and pathology, but also to the therapeutics, of gas poisoning. In April he was joined by Captain R. A. Peters, R.A.M.C., who was recalled for the purpose from France, where he had been serving with distinction.[2] Later he was joined by A. E. Boycott, J. Shaw Dunn, and G. H. Hunt, all of the R.A.M.C. Peters was Adjutant

[1] The first of these is the 1919 one on chemical warfare research during the 1914–18 war; it was prepared by J. Davidson Pratt, C.B.E., etc., who became Assistant Secretary of the Chemical Advisory Committee in August 1916, and later succeeded Young as Secretary. The second is the Report by Lieut-Colonel Crossley, F.R.S., who was Commandant at Porton during the 1914–18 war, on the development and organization of the experimental station there. Professor C. G. Douglas kindly sent me his abstract of the second Report, and Mr. Pratt's own abstract of the first one, together with certain additional information about J. B. which Mr. Pratt supplied.

[2] He was awarded the Military Cross and bar, and mentioned in dispatches.

at Porton to the end of the war and he has described (Peters, 1949) the growth of the Department of Physiology under J. B. "There is no doubt", said Peters, "that he was the unquestioned leader of all the work in that Department. We had some little difficulties as he was the only civilian in an entirely service establishment; but somehow we managed to build up a kind of aura round him as the mysterious 'Professor Barcroft', and he was accepted as a superior being. He was always making good suggestions, and was really behind the development of Shaw Dunn as an experimental pathologist. When we had done the work he collected the results and welded them into something worth while."

In summer he and his family took their holiday at Burnham Overy Staithe.

In October the Trench Warfare Research Department (as the Trench Warfare Department had been re-named some time previously) was reorganized and Thuillier was put in charge, as Controller, of the Chemical Warfare Department. At the same time the Chemical Advisory Committee was reconstituted as the Chemical Warfare Committee, with J. B., Cushny, and Leonard Hill as its physiological members. Shortly afterwards informal Sub-Committees were appointed, and these three members formed the Physiology one, with Hill as Secretary. The first meeting of the new Committee took place on 27 November.

There were no publications by J. B. in 1917, and the only specific indication about any of the work on which he was engaged is contained in *Chemical Warfare Medical Committee Report* No. 4, II, 1918. This section, written by J. B., G. H. Hunt, and Dorothy Dufton from the Porton and Cambridge Physiological Laboratories, was on "The treatment of chronic cases of gas poisoning by oxygen administration in chambers." Though the dates in the text cover the period from July 1917 to January 1918, the oxygen therapy had begun by the end of October, or beginning of November, 1917. The rationale of the treatment was that the symptoms and signs exhibited by the patients corresponded with those exhibited by dwellers at great altitudes, e.g., sleeplessness, nocturnal attacks of breathlessness and rapid heart beat after exercise, polycythaemia, acidosis and lowered alveolar partial pressure of carbon dioxide. Rabbits which had developed polycythaemia after exposure to chlorine or phosgene lost this sign in chambers containing 35–40 per cent. oxygen, and human subjects responded very satisfactorily to five-day periods in chambers containing 40–50 per cent. oxygen, with emergence some hours each day for the purpose of exercise. The chambers, which were the property of Cambridge University, were three in number with capacities of 10, 10, and 12 cu.m. respectively; they were made of plate glass in iron frames and were fitted with the necessary scrubbers for the removal of carbon dioxide and aqueous vapour.

In January 1918 the Director-General of the Army Medical Service, with the concurrence of the Controller of Chemical Warfare appointed a new Committee to function as a sub-committee of the Medical Research Committee (later the Medical Research Council). The duties of the new body were to prepare reports, based upon all the varied information received by the Chemical Warfare Department, and to submit these to the Director-General with a view to their distribution to those concerned; to make suggestions for further co-ordinated medical investigations that might seem desirable; and to advise the Director-General generally in respect of the scientific medical aspects of Chemical Warfare. The Committee consisted initially of Cushny (Chairman), Barcroft, Bayliss, Boycott, Edkins (Secretary), Fletcher, Haldane, Leonard Hill, Meakins, and Shufflebotham. Corresponding members at Porton were Shaw Dunn, Hunt, and Peters, in France Douglas, Elliott, and McNee, and in Italy S. C. Cummins.

The Committee began by taking over the report of the Physiology (War) Committee of the Royal Society, dated September 1917, and publishing it in January 1918. It was entitled, "Notes on the pathology and treatment of the effects of pulmonary irritant gases", and bore no names of authors, though various workers were specified passim in brackets in the text. Most of the items so attributed to J. B. have already been mentioned. Thereafter the Committee published a succession of further reports in 1918, Nos. 18 and 19 in 1919, and No. 20 in 1920. J. B. doubtless had much to do with many of these, but the only ones in which he was named as author or co-author were No. 4, II, 13–64, published in April 1918 and already mentioned in re 1917; No. 6, I and II, also published in April 1918, and to which reference has been made in the account of the year 1915; No. 12, published in October 1918; and No. 14, published in the same month, but dated 16 March 1916, and already referred to in the account of that year.

We are left, then, with only No. 12 which has not previously been mentioned. It was by J. B., G. H. Hunt, and Dorothy Dufton, and was concerned with the "Treatment of patients suffering from 'effort syndrome' by continuous inhalation of oxygen." Effort syndrome, defined as precordial pain and undue dyspnoea on exertion in patients free from any undoubted sign of organic disease, seemed to have similarity to the later effects of gas poisoning seen in 1916 in many patients, but it was found that oxygen therapy, which had proved beneficial in the cases of gas poisoning, could not be relied upon to improve the condition of patients suffering from the effort syndrome.

Certain further notes are needed to complete this account of J. B.'s activities during the first World War, and to begin with we may note that the high valuation which was put upon his work at Porton and elsewhere was acknowledged by his appointment to a Commandership of the recently instituted Order of the British Empire. [1] Next, we should present two examples of J. B.'s personal bravery, one at the front in France where it was on a par with countless others cited and uncited, the other in the quiet of a laboratory at night, where it was certainly unusual. With regard to the former, we may quote Douglas' account (Douglas, 1949); it reads as follows:-

"I was myself serving in France in the R.A.M.C. during this period, being seconded to the Directorate of Gas Services as Physiological Adviser, and Barcroft visited us a number of times for discussions about current problems or to take part in inter-Allied conferences in Paris on gas warfare. I have very happy memories of those visits, for the vigour and activity of his mind, his keen anxiety to appreciate the problems as we saw them in the field, the acuteness of his suggestions and his readiness at all times to help were a real stimulus to us all. One recollection I have, of a rather different kind, which stands out in my memory. On one of his earlier visits I was ordered to show him something of conditions nearer the line. So, among other places, I took him to an advanced dressing station in the vicinity of Loos. This was below ground but close to a cross-roads of dubious reputation since the range was accurately known to the Germans. When I got him there he insisted on standing in the

[1] It was instituted on 4 June 1917, and J. B. was appointed Commander on 3 June 1918.

middle of the cross-roads inquiring about points of interest around, while I, with one eye on German shells falling on some ruins farther up the road and the other on the entrance to the dressing station, was trying to reply to his questions and at the same time to calculate our chances of reaching safety if the Germans should lift the range of their guns. Perhaps the fact that Barcroft had chosen on this occasion to wear, of all things, a bowler hat may have been our salvation, for the sight of a man standing calmly in a bowler hat at a point where no ordinary mortal would voluntarily linger may temporarily have paralysed the Germans owing to the uncertainty and consternation created by such an apparition."

The other example, in 1918, was associated, indirectly, with a proposal to build a £1,000,000 factory for the making of shells filled with hydrocyanic, or prussic, acid. This had not unnaturally been suggested as an offensive agent, though the results of earlier trials in the field had been indecisive. To continue from Douglas (1949), "Tests on different animals of the toxicity by inhalation of this poison showed that there was a surprising difference of susceptibility in different species, the dog being particularly sensitive and the guinea-pig, goat and monkey being much less sensitive. If, therefore, an assessment of the toxicity were to be based solely on experiments on a highly susceptible animals a false impression of the toxicity to man might be gained. Barcroft, feeling convinced that man must be much less susceptible than the dog, decided to settle this point. He therefore went, unprotected by any respirator, into a respiration chamber with a twelve-kilogram dog and released into the air in the chamber enough hydrocyanic acid to give a concentration of about one part in two thousand. In just over one minute the dog was unconscious, and at the end of one and a half minutes was in convulsions and appeared to be in extremis, when Barcroft left the chamber having felt neither breathlessness nor any symptoms." He carried the "dead" animal out of the chamber and it was put aside, presumably for autopsy, burial or cremation at an early opportunity; in the morning, however, the laboratory attendant found it "bouncing about the lab complaining that its belly was empty and needed filling" (Douglas, personal communication, 1949).

From Peters (1949) come further details, namely, that J. B. did the experiment one night, after all his colleagues had left, helped only by a Corporal Carlile whom Peters had brought with him from the 60th Rifles and "who was a grand fellow and had been a stretcher bearer. "I think", added Peters, "that Barcroft must have thought we might have tried to stop him. We were just a little upset that he had done it this way, but quite understood why." The experiment was mentioned in the *Medical History of the War (1914–18), Diseases of the War, 2,* 1923, 466, but the full account was given by J. B., without mention of himself, in the *Journal of Hygiene,* 1931, *31,* 24–25. Three years later, in the eighth Stephen Paget Memorial Lecture, he referred to the greater susceptibility of the dog and explained it as follows. "The dog is capable of a much greater and more sustained degree of activity than most other animals. He can run down almost anything and pre-eminently he can run down man, from which it may be inferred that the maximal total ventilation of which the dog is capable is, for its size, greater than in man. The reason why the dog yields so quickly to an atmosphere of prussic acid is probably due to the power of his respiration; he takes a much larger quantity of the fatal gas; in short, he takes a bigger dose." When the poison is administered by injection, the minimal lethal dosage is approximately the same for most mammals that have been tested.

The only other notes about J. B.'s 1918 story are that he attended a meeting of the Medical Research Committee in Paris on 18 May [1], that he was elected a member of the Athenaeum on 3 June, that he and M. A. B. again took their holiday at Burnham Overy Staithe, and that during the year he brought out another enlarged and revised edition of Huxley's *Lessons in elementary physiology.* How soon after the Armistice he returned to Cambridge there appears to be no record, but we may fittingly link this Chapter and the next by reproducing a letter which he received early in 1919; it was written from 10 Downing Street on 10 January and read as follows:-

"Dear Mr. Barcroft,

I have only just been informed of your action in subjecting yourself to a dangerous and most painful experiment in order to obtain information which was of great importance, and could not otherwise be obtained.

[1] See Fulton (1946, 428). Harvey Cushing was present, and at the morning session the medical aspects of aviation, at the afternoon session gas problems, were discussed.

You were called upon to ascertain the immediate and subsequent effect on troops of a new gas, by comparing the effect on animals. Realising that experiments conducted in this way could not be conclusive, you voluntarily exposed yourself to a strong concentration of the gas for a period of half an hour, subjecting yourself to the certainty of severe pain and to serious danger of permanent ill-effects.

I understand also that on a previous occasion you went into a chamber containing a high concentration of prussic acid, and remained there until the dog that accompanied you became unconscious in order to show that the effect of the gas was less on men than on dogs.

I feel the most intense admiration for the gallantry and devotion to duty which you have shown by these two acts of outstanding courage, and I desire to express, personally, and as head of His Majesty's Government, my high appreciation of your brave actions, which obtained information of quite exceptional value.

Yours sincerely,

D. Lloyd George"

About the experiment mentioned in paragraph three of the letter we have read; about the other one the present writer has, unfortunately, no knowledge, but it seems equally typical of J. B.'s cold courage.

CHAPTER VI

1919–1925

After the Armistice of 11 a.m., 11 November 1918, there were priorities in the order of demobilization, students coming second after miners. So early in 1919 undergraduates began returning from the Services to Cambridge, but not until October were they present in more or less usual number, and even then they were a mixture of ex-Service men who would have come up in any case, of other ex-Service men who would not have done so but for Government schemes developed during the war, and of youths fresh from school. In addition, many of the ex-Service men were on specially shortened courses, designed to allow them to get a degree but at the same time to catch up a little on the time lost in action. Thanks largely to the keenness and mature attitude of those coming out of the Forces, this unique mélange worked out satisfactorily during the few years over which it persisted, and the traditions of Cambridge that were worthy of revival were successfully re-instituted.

A Readership in Physiology was established as from 1 January 1919, and J. B. was appointed to it as from that date. [1] "His teaching duties were thereby much reduced, and although somewhat tired by all the strains and activities of the war, it was not long before he was once more back in all his old peace-time fettle" (Roughton, 1949, *b*). The restoration was aided by a change which he made in his daily routine and which was obviously beneficial, as he kept to the new schedule thenceforward for the rest of his life. The change in question was the taking of a rest after luncheon, except on such occasions as attendance at an afternoon meeting or the like was unavoidable, and his new daily programme was as follows:- 7.10 Cold bath. 7.45–8.15 Work, preparing lectures, etc. 8.15 Breakfast. 8.45 Cycle to the Lab. 9 Begin work at the Lab. 1.10 Leave for

[1] According to Roughton (1949, *b*, 322), it was specially created for J. B. "in recognition of his outstanding work and the scientific position he had now reached." It became vacant in 1925 when he was appointed Professor, and it lapsed in 1926.

home. 1.30 prompt Luncheon. 2–3.30 Rest. 3.30 Tea by bedside. 3.45 Leave for the Lab. 4 Begin work. 7.15 Leave for home. 7.30 Change into a dark suit for supper. 8.45 Supper. After supper quiet time with the family, talking or sometimes correcting proofs, etc. 10 prompt To bed. Adherence in general to this schedule, plus his great facility for writing, explains how J. B. coped with a vast amount of very varied duties in the years from 1919 onwards. The facility for writing was an invaluable gift – he hardly ever needed to alter a written word and he appeared to write page after page with the greatest ease.

Another important easement was provided by the engagement of Sergeant Major Secker, R. A. M. C., as J. B.'s general factotum, head lab. man, and secretary; he was, in the event, to remain an invaluable personal aide to J. B. for the next twenty years or so (he is seen in Plate 33).

As a final background note, we may mention J. B.'s work as Supervisor in Physiology at King's College – for some time he was also the College's Director of Studies in Natural Sciences, but we can perhaps omit details of his duties in that capacity. The supervisions were at 5 p.m. and were attended once a week during term-time by all Kingsmen reading physiology; ten or so came to each supervision. From all accounts J. B.'s supervisions for the College, like his lectures and practical teaching for the University, were highly successful and left lasting impressions on those who were present at them.

With that general background, we revert to J. B. back in pre-war fettle in the spring of 1919. On 10 May four communications were made to the Physiological Society by him, Boycott, Peters, and Dunn, but as these communications appeared in expanded form in a single article in October they need no further mention here. At the meeting in Oxford on 12 July, he spoke on the nature of the respiratory centre and favoured the view that it was, like the ventricle of the heart, intrinsically rhythmic, but subject to modification by nervous and other influences.

Less than three weeks later, he and the two boys were in The Glen, Newry, for a holiday lasting the whole of August. M. A. B. stayed behind to nurse her mother, but some time after the latter's death on 6 August she rejoined J. B. and the family. The departure from The Glen took place on 1 September, and thereafter there is nothing to chronicle until October, when Barcroft, Boycott, Dunn, and Peters' paper, entitled, "Observations on respiration and circulation in the goat", was published in the *Quarterly Journal of Medicine.*

It was an account of determinations of the heart minute volume in non-anaesthetized goats by means of what J. B. called Zuntz', but what is nowadays called Fick's, principle. [1] The average weight of the animals was *c.* 24 kg. and the minute volume *c.* 3 l., but the major interest lay more in the technique, e.g., in the avoidance of anaesthesia, in the reduction in the amounts of blood needing to be withdrawn, and in the obtaining of the arterial and venous blood samples by left and right ventricular puncture respectively. Zuntz had passed a tube through the jugular vein into the heart and had put a cannula into an artery, procedures which have their lineal but more successful descendants to-day in cardiac catheterization and insertion of fine-bore tubes into the arteries of man, a general anaesthetic not being required. The reason for right ventricular puncture was the well-known difference in composition of the blood from different veins. "The classical example of this difference," wrote the authors, "is to be found at the confluence of the vena cava and the renal veins, the black flow from the legs forming a striking contrast to the red blood from the kidneys; the difference in colour is so marked as to be seen plainly through the wall of the venae in rabbits." [2]

On 15 October J. B. gave a lecture (see Barcroft, 1920, *J. R. Army med. Cps., 34*) at the Royal Army Medical College. The title was "Some problems of the circulation during gas poisoning", but in fact he dealt only with "that part of the pathology of poisoning with pulmonary irritants which concerns itself primarily with the circulation as evidenced by experiments carried out in the physiological laboratories of the Royal Engineers' Experimental Ground at Porton." In Part I he showed that in the lungs of gassed goats the cardinal feature, evident by the end of half an hour, was damage to capillary blood vessels in the zone where they were first exposed to the gas with only the delicate pulmonary epithelium to protect them. The more serious reaction was intracapillary thrombosis with

[1] The Fick reference is 1870, the Zuntz one in the paper under discussion was 1892.

[2] The phenomenon was first noticed by Claude Bernard in 1845 in dogs, and it was first described by him in 1858.

33—THE 'GLASS CHAMBER', 1920, WITH SERGEANT-MAJOR SECKER INSIDE

34—JOSEPH BARCROFT INSIDE THE GLASS CHAMBER DURING HIS EXPERIMENT, 1920

Facing page 113

complete local arrest of blood flow, the less serious was increase in capillary permeability leading to interstitial and intra-alveolar oedema. This oedema could be of such total amount that the lungs were four times their normal weight, yet surprisingly the arterial blood was fully or almost fully oxygenated. This was because the blood flow was more or less restricted to the still normal portions of the lungs. In Part II he showed that, through the nervous system's activity, the pulmonary blood pressure, etc., were kept more or less normal despite the inactivation of complete vascular areas. In Part III he explained why exercise should be avoided in gassed animals or human beings. "The moral, as regards gas poisoning is, that to the capillaries in the lungs are given the keys of life and of death, or some of them at all events. What Nature has closed let not man open. If Nature would cut down the activities of the patient to such as can be served by a limited quantitiy of good lung, let not the patient defeat his guardian angel by insisting upon exertion. For if he does one or both of two things will happen." The less serious is "that the circulation in the lung will open up and black blood will pass," the more serious "that the circulation in the injured lung will not open and insufficient blood will pass." In both conditions there will be oxygen lack for the more active man, in the second there is also the possibility of back pressure starting in the pulmonary artery and overburdening the heart. The treatment for the gassed patient is rest, warmth, and possibly oxygen therapy.

J. B. then added that the findings in gas poisoning were probably paralleled in broncho-pneumonia, etc. "We have learned," he went on, "some principles which may apply to lesions far removed from the lungs. And we have learned something beyond a study of lesions, something of the difference between the less mechanical normal and the more mechanical pathological, something as wide as pathology itself." [1]

Finally, J. B. thanked Majors Boycott, Peters, and Dunn of the R. A. M. C.; Colonel Crossley, C. M. G., for the constant facilities which he had afforded to physiological work in an organization which was primarily chemical; Lieut. Colonel Douglas, C. M. G., and Colonel Elliott, C. B. E.; and especially Colonel Cummins, C. M. G., and Colonel Sir William Horrocks, K. C. M. G., C. B., for the help given by the Army to an enterprise of the Ministry of

[1] For a full understanding of this the whole paper should be read. – K.J.F.

Munitions. In September 1920 J. B. was to say to the British Association, "The war has passed, and I, for one, have no wish to revive its memories." It is fitting, therefore, to quote here the detailed acknowledgements which he made to his war-time colleagues working in, or connected with, Porton.

Only one more dated item, of an entirely different character, comes into his 1919 story, and that is that on Saturday, 6 December, he sat by H. R. H. Prince Henry at the Founder's Feast at King's College, and proposed the toast, "Floreat Etona". There is, however, an undated beginning of importance to be chronicled. According to Roughton (1949, *b*), W. M. Bayliss, in the haemoglobin Chapter of his great book, *Principles of General Physiology* (1915), had in most polite fashion posed a number of questions as to which he – a non-worker on haemoglobin – was still in doubt. So in 1919 J. B. and A. V. Hill invited Bayliss up to Cambridge to discuss these problems with them, and this led, in the following year, to the appointment of the Medical Research Council Committee on the Properties of Haemoglobin. A. V. Hill (personal communication, 1952) wrote as follows when asked for further details. "My memory, for what it is worth, . . . is that J. B. had long agreed in not agreeing with Bayliss' scepticism of the chemical nature of the haemoglobin reactions with oxygen and carbon monoxide, and that I jestingly said to him, 'We had better form a haemoglobin society'. To Jo, being an Irishman, the most serious things were those said in jest, and he took it seriously and out of that emerged the idea of the Haemoglobin Committee of the M. R. C. – who wrote to the M. R. C. and suggested it, I don't know, but I expect he did." The alternative is that Bayliss did.

The next year, 1920, might well be called J. B.'s special oxygen one. In its first month he, Hunt, and Dufton published a paper on "The treatment of chronic cases of gas poisoning by continuous oxygen administration in chambers," on 20 January he took part in a discussion of oxygen therapy organized by the Section of Therapeutics and Pharmacology of the Royal Society of Medicine, and during the rest of the year he was largely concerned in one way or another with oxygen. The paper on its use in cases of gas poisoning was an amplification of observations already reported, and J. B.'s contribution to the Royal Society of Medicine's discussion was on not very dissimilar lines. The gist of it was that the duration of tachycardia and the dyspnoea after exercise in gassed patients, as also their raised red blood cell count, were brought towards normal by oxygen therapy. G. H. Hunt thereafter elaborated the dyspnoea story, and following speakers stressed the efficacy of oxygen treatment in cases both of gassing and also of other troubles associated with reductions in respiratory efficiency.

On the last day of the month, J. B. finished eleven years' service as an Honorary Secretary of the Physiological Society, and was succeeded in that office by John Mellanby.

Two days later, on Monday, 2 February, he began what later became known as the "glass chamber" or "glass box" experiment (see Barcroft, Cooke, Hartridge, Parsons and Parsons, 1920). The role played by the pulmonary epithelium in the process of respiration had for thirty years been a matter of controversy, and there were two views, (1) that the oxygen passed by diffusion, (2) that it was transferred by a secretory process depending on the expenditure of energy on the part of the lung-cell. Work by Krogh had shown that (1) was adequate in the resting animal, whereas Haldane and his school held that (2) was brought into play when the organism was in some special need of oxygen, e.g., in exercise, in cases of continuously low alveolar partial pressure of the gas, and in carbon monoxide poisoning.

J. B. conceived the plan of subjecting himself over a period to increasing oxygen lack in a chamber, and thereafter to measuring his alveolar partial pressure of oxygen, etc., under various conditions and to obtaining blood for analysis direct from his radial artery. He and Cooke in 1913, as we have already seen, had been the first to get blood direct from an artery of a human subject for blood gas analysis, and the construction of single plate-glass wards for the oxygen therapy of gassed patients had been a useful preliminary to the construction of the chamber in which J. B. was to live for his six-days' test. Thanks to Professor Walter R. Miles, a photograph (Plate 33) of it is available.

In this chamber, to parallel the conditions asserted by Haldane and Douglas (1912) to have produced oxygen secretion on Pikes' Peak, Colorado (14,000 feet), J. B. (Plate 34) underwent progressive anoxaemia through the liberation of nitrogen until for the last part of his sojourn he was living in an atmosphere in which the oxygen partial pressure was only 84 mm. Hg., corresponding to that at a height of about 18,000 feet above sea-level. Carbon dioxide and excess water-vapour were absorbed by scrubbers, and exercise, which according to Haldane and Douglas greatly accelerated the secretion of oxygen by the pulmonary epithelium, was carried out on Martin bicycle ergometers. An old bowler hat, with the crown mostly cut away [1], was adapted to hold in place the accordion tubing from a face-mask through which J. B. breathed on occasion during exercise.

On Pike's Peak the oxygen tension in the arterial blood had been determined by the indirect carbon monoxide method of Haldane, Lorrain Smith and Douglas, which is applicable to finger-prick blood and so avoids unpleasantness for the subject. J. B., however, as already noted, had determined to get blood direct from his left radial artery and, as he would need it intermittently and in quantity over a period of two hours, i.e., as Stadie's technique of arterial puncture (Stadie, 1919) would not be suitable, to have it withdrawn through a specially adapted burette inserted as required into the vessel. The procedure would involve subsequent loss of continuity in the artery, but that and the not inconsiderable strain of the six-day experiment he was ready to accept in his desire to settle the question of diffusion versus secretion. At the worst stage, as it turned out, his pulse rate was 86 instead of its usual 56, and he vomited, had a most distressing headache, and was unable to see an object clearly without concentrating on it.

The final part of the experiment, which came on the last day and occupied about two hours, must therefore have been an ordeal. His expired air was collected, his alveolar air sampled, and appropriate amounts of his arterial blood taken for analysis both at rest and during exercise at the low oxygen partial pressure obtaining in the chamber. [2] As the partial pressure of oxygen in his alveolar air at rest corresponded to a percentage oxygen saturation of 80 to 90 per cent. of his blood in vitro, and such blood is appreciably darker in colour than normal arterial blood, "the withdrawal of the first sample . . . provided a somewhat dramatic moment and was in a sense the climax of the experiment. The blood looked dark. The darkness might have been attributed to some extent to the artificial

[1] Called a "halo" in? the first published account of the experiment, a flippant article in *The New Cambridge* of 21 February 1920.

[2] For a special purpose blood was also taken later while he breathed oxygen from a Douglas bag while exercising.

yellowish light had it not been that the blood subsequently collected during oxygen respiration was amply bright."

This visual subjective evidence was confirmed, as we shall see below, by the objective determinations made on the blood samples. Meanwhile, as this is the biography of a man and not merely the story of a scientist, it is not out of place to think a little about M. A. B. during the time of this test on her husband. On its first day she returned from an operation on their second son, Robbie, and her diary also states that J. B. "became very poorly before he came out", so we can imagine that she had her anxiety, and we can feel grateful to her that on this occasion, as on several others, she appreciated the need for J. B.'s venturous experiments upon himself and did not gainsay them.

On 21 February J. B. gave the first account of his experiment to the Physiological Society, and he presumably told members the results of the objective determinations, namely, that the arterial blood in vivo had contained less oxygen, both during rest and during work, than had samples of the same blood exposed to alveolar air in vitro at body temperature. In other words, under the conditions of the experiment there had been no evidence of oxygen secretion in the lungs. Perhaps Haldane raised at this meeting the objections which he later published, namely, that no adequate acclimatization had developed under the laboratory conditions and that the arterial blood method, though at first sight more acceptable – as being more direct – than the carbon monoxide one, was in fact open to theoretical criticisms which did not apply to the latter. The first objection, in any case, was destined to be overruled by the Cerro de Pasco expedition's findings in 1921–2; with regard to the second, it was to remain as part of Haldane's attitude, though not to be shared by many other physiologists; most of them were impressed by the new evidence.

On 18 March J. B. attended the first formal meeting of the Medical Research Council Committee on the Properties of Haemoglobin; a number of informal conferences had preceded it. The terms of reference of the Committee were "to consider and advise the Council from time to time on the better coordination of investigations into the construction and properties of haemoglobin and connected problems." J. B. was elected Chairman by the other members of the Committee, namely, Professor W. M. Bayliss,

Mr. W. B. Hardy, Dr. H. Hartridge, and Professor A. V. Hill. Later in the year Dr. C. A. Lovatt Evans was added as Secretary, and Professor L. J. Henderson of Harvard as a Corresponding Member. The Committee was concerned at the outset with work on the physico-chemical conditions of the blood, its reaction, questions of oxygen and carbon dioxide transport, the problems of breathlessness, the affinity of haemoglobin for oxygen and the molecular aggregation of haemoglobin. [1] On 19 March J. B. left for The Glen, Newry, so a communication to the Physiological Society on 20 March, on "Reaction changes in the blood during muscular work", was made by his collaborators, T. R. and W. Parsons.

On 18 May the account of the glass-chamber experiment appeared in the *Journal of Physiology*, and it had one result of far-reaching importance, apart from its own intrinsic interest. For it brought into collaboration with J. B. one who at that time was only a student, but who nevertheless was greatly to influence the trend of J. B.'s future work. The student in question was F. J. W. Roughton, who was due to read a paper in ten days' time to the Cambridge University Natural Sciences Club, and who had as his subject the very problem of diffusion versus secretion which J. B. had set out to solve. Roughton, therefore, avidly read the account in the *Journal* so soon as it appeared, and all "was plain sailing until almost the end of the paper where question 2 was taken up. Here", wrote Roughton in 1949, "it at once struck me that a serious mistake had been made, as it must have struck any reader who was steeped at the time in the Copenhagen literature."

Roughton has elaborated this, in a note sent to the present

[1] This work, and its later development, was undertaken with the assistance of Council grants at a number of centres such as Manchester University and, later, University College, London, under Professor A. V. Hill, and Guy's Hospital under Dr. E. P. Poulton; the largest part of the research, however, was carried out in the Physiological Laboratory, Cambridge by, and under the supervision of, J. B. Among his colleagues and assistants were T. R. Parsons, H. Hartridge, F. J. W. Roughton, J. M. Duncan Scott, K. Uyeno, H. B. Taylor, C. D. Murray, M. L. Anson, A. E. Mirsky, S. Hecht and H. Wastl. Apart from a large number of papers which appeared in journals, the Committee was responsible for one official publication, namely, *M.R.C. Special Report Series* No. 72, "The acid-base equilibrium of the blood", an excellent account written by Lovatt Evans at a time when there was very great need for such.

During the years 1921–3 there were added to the Committee Dr. C. G. Douglas, Dr. H. H. Dale, Professor F. Gowland Hopkins, and Dr. J. H. Burn (who succeeded Lovatt Evans as Secretary). Dr. E. P. Poulton and Professor F. R. Fraser were temporarily added in 1921–2 while the report on acidosis was being prepared, and the services of Sir William Bayliss were lost through his death in August 1924. The last meeting took place in May 1932.

writer in 1952, in the following words. J. B. "had measured the pressure of oxygen in the alveolar air and in the arterial blood and had used the difference between these two pressures as divisor, the total quantity of oxygen absorbed per minute as dividend, then as quotient he thought he had obtained the diffusion constant of the lung. What he should have done was to have subtracted from the alveolar oxygen pressure, not the arterial pressure as he did, but some figure intermediate between the oxygen pressure in the arterial blood and the oxygen pressure in the mixed venous blood. To find out what this intermediate pressure should have been, required the use of Bohr's method of graphic integration and a knowledge of the output of the heart per minute."

With considerable temerity, because of their difference in age and status and because he had never before met J. B. personally, Roughton bearded him on the question on the stone stairs outside the physiology lab. J. B.'s response was instant: "Yes, that's a valid point. Now will you join me as my colleague and set me back on the rails again?" Roughton naturally leaped at the chance, and within the next two months they worked out together a method of getting the output of the heart (see Barcroft, Roughton, and Shoji, 1921); with the aid of that and Bohr's method of graphic integration, Roughton calculated out for J. B. a more correct value for the difference in pressure between the oxygen in the alveolar air and that in the blood. The value of the diffusion constant (oxygen absorbed per minute/this difference in pressure) then came out significantly lower than J. B. had stated. The correction of the error was quite an important matter at the time and J. B. made handsome acknowledgement of his indebtedness to his student colleague, both immediately and subsequently. August Krogh was a guest of the Barcrofts from 9 to 12 July – presumably he had come, en route to the Paris Congress, to discuss the glass-chamber experiment with J. B., perhaps also to hear Leonard Hill speak at the Physiological Society meeting on 10 July on "The capillary blood-pressure" (Hill, 1920). At this meeting, which took place at the London School of Medicine for Women, J. B. gave not only a communication on his and Roughton's work, but also a demonstration of their heart output method. They had to take up from Cambridge a Douglas bag and a Haldane gas analysis apparatus and sundry accessories, and together with Krogh and E. J. Cohn they carried this equipment uncovered through the London streets. As, however it was a Saturday afternoon, few people were about and the cavalcade did not attract very much notice.

If at this point we may anticipate in brief the remainder of J. B.'s scientific story, we can see how it was influenced by his generous attitude in 1920 towards the criticism of a previously unknown student. For the problem of measuring the heart minute volume probably led J. B. on to measuring the total blood volume, and the warm-weather increase which he observed in this latter on the way to the Andes brought him to his work on blood-depôts; consideration of the uterine veins in their capacity as a blood-depôt led him on to foetal physiology, and the latter carried over easily to his work for the Unit of Animal Physiology of the Agricultural Research Council. The effect on Roughton was equally determinant, for his co-operation with J. B. was one of the main factors which led later to his partnership with Hartridge in the measurement of the very rapid rates of reaction of haemoglobin with oxygen and carbon monoxide, and also to many other researches.

That, however, is enough of anticipation, and we must revert to 1920. The Paris reunion of Physiologists, since accorded the style of tenth International Congress though membership was in fact restricted to representatives of allied and neutral countries, took place from 16 to 20 July and was attended by Krogh, who gave a demonstration and a communication, but not by J. B. At the end of July the four Barcrofts and Ethel Beer crossed to Northern Ireland for their summer holiday; on 20 August J. B. left to attend the British Association meeting in Cardiff and to give the Presidential address on 24 August to Section I (Physiology).

The subject was anoxaemia, or "insufficient oxygen supply to the tissues", a factor in cases of gas poisoning, shock, etc. during the war and also a peace-time problem. J. B. said that no sentence embodied the problem more succinctly than that coined by J. S. Haldane, "Anoxaemia not only stops the machine but wrecks the machinery." All organs were affected, but in J. B.'s opinion the brain was the most sensitive. He mentioned uncomplicated anoxaemia as occurring in balloonists and aviators, in subjects (e.g. Haldane and Kellas) of low pressure experiments in chambers, and in victims of carbon monoxide poisoning. "To sum up, then," he went on, "what may be said of the permanent damage caused by acute anoxaemia, it seems to me to be as follows: No degree of anoxaemia which produces a less effect than that of complete unconsciousness leaves anything more than the most transient effects; if the anoxaemia be pushed to the point at which the subject is within a measurable distance of death, the results may take days or weeks to get over, but only in the case of elderly or unsound persons is the machine wrecked beyond repair."

With regard to chronic anoxaemia, he said that the distinction between stopping the machine and wrecking the machinery becomes so indistinct that it can be asked if the condition stops the machine in any other way than by wrecking it. Though on an average healthy man it begins to tell at above 18,000 feet, some people live and work at this height, the machine being kept going by a process of compensation. But such acclimatization is gained at the expense of the body's functional reserve, and the resting respiration resembles that of exercise at a lower level. "As a friend of mine, who has, I believe, camped at a higher altitude than any other man, put it to me, 'So great was the effort that we thought twice before we turned over in bed.' " While acute anoxaemia simulates drunkenness, chronic anoxaemia simulates fatigue.

In the next section he divided anoxaemia into three types, anoxic, anaemic, and stagnant, and noted that the anoxic was essentially a general as opposed to a local condition, and could be associated with adequate *quantity* of oxygen in the blood – a low oxygen *pressure* in it was responsible for the observed symptoms. Saying, "It is possible to calculate, as indeed has been done by my colleague, Mr. Roughton, what the amount of oxygen leaving the capillaries is", he showed in an arbitrary case the greater seriousness of the anoxic type.

With regard to the measurement of anoxic anoxaemia, he thought that the oxygen saturation of the blood rather than the oxygen pressure would be used, as the former was susceptible of direct measurement. In many cases of lung affection and of shallow respiration, Stadie's method of arterial puncture was indicated, but alveolar air determinations and the use of the dissociation curve would give a useful index in the cases of many normal persons, e.g., airmen at various altitudes.

In the rest of the address he dealt with the mechanism of anoxaemia, and the compensations for it. Showing that increased blood haemoglobin gives a little, but only a little, respite in the anoxic type, he stated that the only way of dealing satisfactorily with the condition is "to abolish it by in some way supplying the blood with oxygen at a pressure sufficient to saturate it to the normal level." Deeper breathing, a natural response, helps by raising the alveolar oxygen partial pressure, but "what Nature does not do should be done by artifice", i.e., by administration of oxygen. It had been tried on gassed soldiers during the war, and was being tried in clinical cases by Dr. Hunt at Guy's Hospital. It was also needed for aviators, and for some time past a light and efficient apparatus had been sought after by J. S. Haldane. "In the pages which I have read," J. B. concluded, "views have been expressed which differ from those which he holds in matters of detail – perhaps in matters of important detail. But Haldane's teaching transcends mere detail. He has always taught that the physiology of to-day is the medicine of to-morrow. The more gladly, therefore, do I take this opportunity of saying how much I owe, and how much I think medicine owes and will owe, to the inspiration of Haldane's teaching."

Presumably through pressure of work, J. B. did not return to Ireland, and it was not until 10 September that he was rejoined by his family. On that day a Cambridge friend told M. A. B. that "the sensation of the British Association was Mr. Barcroft." Not long afterwards, J. B. went off to examine in Cork and elsewhere in Ireland, and in Edinburgh, returning home on 3 October. Ireland was distracted by "the troubles"; in M. A. B.'s diary for 29 August is the note:- "Soldiers with fixed bayonets and steel helmets paraded the streets in Newry last night fearing Foster's shop might be set on fire. Dreadful times in Ireland. Seventy houses burnt down in Lisburn in retaliation for the murder of Inspector Swanzy last Sunday."

There is little else to mention in respect of 1920. The British Association address appeared, in various degrees of fullness, in the *Lancet* of 4 September, in *Nature* of 23 September, and in the *Scientific Monthly* of November. Professor Meakins dined with the Barcrofts on 6 October, and Professor L. J. Henderson came to stay on 3 December. The miners went on strike on 20 October, and J. B. paid visits to Porton in October and November, and so on. But one event is worthy of special note, and that is that in November Sir Charles Sherrington was elected President of the Royal Society, the first physiologist ever to attain that honour. Medals were awarded at the same meeting to Professor Biffen and to Mr. Heycock, whose name has appeared more than once in this story.

The year 1921 was in the main one of planning for, and finally of departure upon ,the expedition to Cerro de Pasco in the Peruvian Andes, i.e., of preparation for the direct settlement of some questions about the physiology of life at great altitudes. It began, however, with a twelve days' visit to Ireland in January, and with the appearance in that month of an article on "Anoxaemia as a factor in acute gas poisoning." This dealt with gassing by chlorine and phosgene in goats and men, and J. B. remarked that there was no single condition which so aptly illustrated the various types of anoxaemia, alone or in combination. He pointed out that a goat or man with blood oxygen saturation reduced to 85 per cent. for twenty-four hours shows no inclination for activity, but the goat will remain quiet, while the man may wrongly indulge in exercise. This kills the anoxaemic animal or man, as two examples show. A rabbit in such condition was apparently happy in a basket about eighteen inches high; then for some reason he jumped out, only to drop and expire as the result of the effort. "An officer, very slightly gassed, was sent to an aid post for examination and was thought, and thought himself, to be quite recovered. He started back to the line and came under shell fire *en route*. He ran to take shelter in a better place just ahead. He got there, sat down in shelter and rapidly died."

Death in anoxic anoxaemia uncomplicated by exercise is due to brain, probably respiratory centre, failure with perhaps some cardiac element. If exercise is taken, the sudden drop in oxygen pressure in the arterial blood increases the respiratory centre effect, but there is also a cardiac vagal effect, so that the brain suffers from stagnant as well as anoxic anoxaemia. In animals the vagal effect passes off as respiration ceases and the heart may beat again. Change of posture in gassed animals may also produce anoxaemia of the brain through lack of the normal peripheral vasomotor response. Unless a human gassing case shows some kind of cyanosis, oxygen is wasted on it. While the circulation is making a fight, cyanosis is plum-coloured and oxygen can be given as a preventive, but the presence of livid or grey cyanosis means that the circulation has failed and the respiratory centre is fast failing. Treatment is along three lines. Bleeding and infusion of saline combats stagnant anoxaemia by restoring the blood volume and blood pressure. Rest and warmth reduce the need for oxygen and for vasomotor reactions, and avoid vagal stimulation. Oxygen directly combats anoxic anoxaemia and therefore, if given early enough, wards off failure of the respiratory centre and also and onset of stagnant anoxaemia through heart failure. One or more of the three treatments should be applied as indicated in any particular case.

Early in April there was a miners' strike; on 11 June the *Lancet* published J. B.'s lecture on alpinism and he also heard that King's College would guarantee £ 700 from its research fund towards the expenses of the trip to Peru. "Alpinism" was one of a course of advanced lectures in physiology given in the Physiological Laboratory of St. Bartholomew's Hospital, where F. A. Bainbridge was Professor – he died later in the year. In the lecture J. B. had said that the effects of rare air upon the human body continued to fascinate (1) for their intellectual interest, and (2) for their practical importance. Ceasing to be the monopoly of a few mountaineers, they had become the limiting factors of the activities of airmen. Mountain sickness is in the anoxic types of anoxaemia, and mountaineers who had been at over 20,000 feet had told J. B. that alimentary trouble was the factor which places the real limit on the altitude attainable. From 15,000 to 18,000 feet there is a rising curve of "unsaturation" of the arterial blood and that is the real Everest. No pH measurements had yet been made at altitudes, only in experiments in chambers, where the alterations were insignificant owing to the loss of carbon dioxide being balanced by excretion of an alkaline urine by the kidneys. At altitude the strain on the heart (not synonymous with the work done by it) is increased through oxygen lack, and probably it is the nervous system which causes the increased rate at rest, and the palpitation with any exercise. As Haldane once said to J. B., "Over 10,000 feet everybody is a case of disordered heart action." In conclusion J. B. said that the effects of altitude upon the mind were perhaps the most interesting of the whole series. "I am sorry to say", he added, that "the change is always for the worse . . . I have yet to meet the man who becomes pleasanter to live with when he is at 12,000 feet altitude than at the sea-level."

On 2 July the *Lancet* published a letter from J. B. which it seems worth while to reprint here in full. It read as follows:-

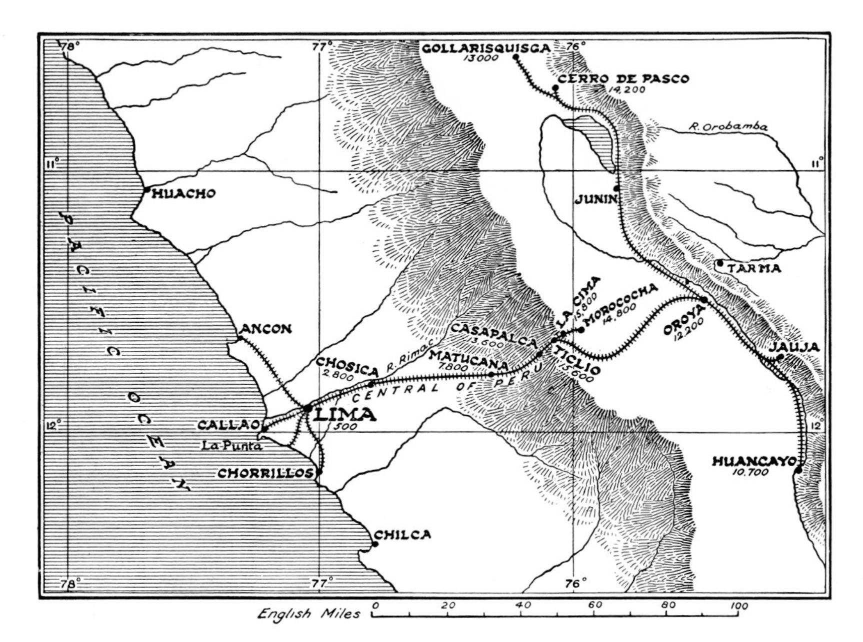

35—Cerro de Pasco expedition, 1921–2
Outline map of Central Peru. (Courtesy, The Royal Society)

36—CERRO DE PASCO EXPEDITION, 1921–2
Interior of mobile laboratory, Central Railway of Peru

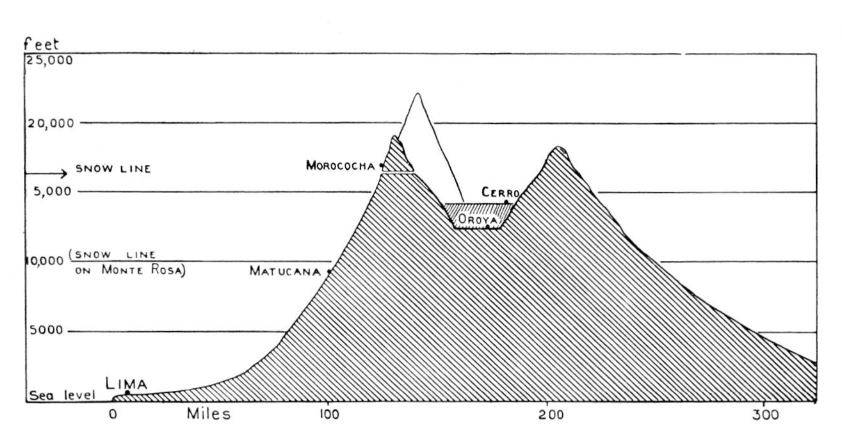

37—CERRO DE PASCO EXPEDITION, 1921–2
Profile diagram to show altitudes of places visited. (Courtesy, The Royal Society)

"The interesting leading article in your issue of June 25th on the subject of haemoglobin omits any statement, except the most general, of the reasons why haemoglobin is carried in corpuscles rather than in solution in the blood plasma, nor are these at all frequently discussed. It may not be out of place therefore to point out that a solution of haemoglobin has properties in some respects very different from those of blood.

"1. It is possible to obtain a solution of haemoglobin which, bulk for bulk, contains as much of the pigment as does blood. Such a solution is, comparatively speaking, viscous and therefore could only be driven along a system of fine tubes such as the capillaries by the application of considerable force.

"2. A concentrated solution of haemoglobin, as compared with blood, only passes through filter paper with difficulty, yet by a curious paradox the molecules of which this solution is composed pass through a collodion membrane that would be quite impervious to corpuscles. Hence haemoglobinuria consequent on laking of the blood.

"3. Owing to the viscosity of the solution, any effort to make it pass along a tube merely achieves the displacement of the central core of fluid. The arrangement of the haemoglobin in corpuscles, which are commensurate in size with the capillaries, ensures the forward movement of the whole contents of the capillary at approximately the same rate.

"4. The properties of haemoglobin as an oxygen carrier are extremely sensitive to properties of the solvent – e.g., its reaction, its partial pressure of CO_2, its potassium content, its temperature, etc. The segregation of the haemoglobin in corpuscles allows its exposure to the conditions more advantageous for it without imposing such conditions on the body generally.

"Without entering into any controversy as to the extent to which the corpuscle can be regarded in itself a living organism, rather than a suitable casing for the sixty-millionth part of one gramme of haemoglobin, the above facts are sufficient to illustrate the advantages which accrue to the organism by the trick of carrying large quantities of haemoglobin which is packed inside special corpuscles."

In her diary M. A. B. noted that on 16 July De Valera and the Prime Minister were trying to come to terms and that meanwhile a truce had been called in Ireland. On 20 July Professor (?L. J.) Henderson visited the Barcrofts, on 2 August the four of them left for St. Malo and Paramé, and they stayed on in Brittany until 6 September. Examining took J. B. to Scotland and Ireland before Cambridge term; late in October M. A. B.'s second brother, W. Valentine Ball, O. B. E., was appointed a Master of the Supreme Court, King's Bench Division.

On 17 November J. B. left Liverpool in the S.S. *Victoria* of the Pacific Steam Navigation Company en route for Peru, Professor J. C. Meakins of Edinburgh and Mr. J. H. Doggart of King's College accompanying him. Before giving details of that trip, however, it is as well to deal with four papers of which J. B. was co-author and which had gone to press before he left; three appeared in the *Journal of Physiology* on 18 November, the last in *Heart* in December. In the first paper of all Adair, J. B., and Bock stated that the corpuscle-free haemoglobin of different human subjects examined gave oxygen dissociation curves which were indistinguishable from one another, i.e., that the haemoglobin was presumably identical in all. In the second paper J. B. and Nagahashi described a direct method for measuring the oxygen pressure in human arterial and venous blood. The method combined various ideas of other workers and in principle was as follows. "Blood is withdrawn . . . by direct puncture; to this blood is exposed a small bubble of alveolar air at 37° C. until an equilibrium is reached between the blood and the bubble. The bubble is then analysed in a suitable apparatus." By such means readings accurate to within 2 mm. Hg. were obtained; in addition, the findings of Meakins and Davies (1920) were confirmed. The new determinations indicated that there could be a fifty-fold alteration in the volume of blood traversing the skin of the arm with appropriate change in the external temperature.

The next paper dealt with the method, demonstrated in July 1920 to the Physiological Society by J. B. and Roughton, for measuring the oxygen content of the mixed venous blood and the heart minute volume. The authors, namely, J. B., Roughton and Shoji, noted that the oxygen content of the mixed venous blood could be directly ascertained in animals, but had to be indirectly determined in man. Briefly, the new technique consisted in taking one deep respiration, followed by four normal ones, from a bag containing nitrogen, and then exhaling a sample of alveolar air, the partial pressure of oxygen being determined by use of a Haldane gas analysis apparatus, and the oxygen content of 1 ml. of mixed venous blood being ascertained by laying this value along the dissociation curve with certain corrections. The authors claimed that the method was simple and gave results accurate to almost 10 per cent.; the heart minute volume was calculated, on the Fick (1870) principle, from knowledge of the arterio-venous oxygen difference and of the consumption of oxygen per minute.

In the December paper J. B., A. V. Bock, and F. J. Roughton described their "Observations on the circulation and respiration in a case of paroxysmal tachycardia", the case being that of "F. J. R., a University student of 22 years", who had had attacks since the age of eleven years, including six, lasting from eight to twelve hours each, between 6 April 1920 and 8 May 1921. During one of these the arterial blood was 96.8 per cent. saturated but the basilar vein blood only 11 per cent., a degree of unsaturation as severe as that found by J. B. on top of Monte Rosa or by Barcroft and Nagahashi after exposure of the arm for fifteen minutes in the cold storage room. The heart minute volume fell from 5.61 to 2.8–2.1 litres per minute, while the heart rate rose to over 200 per minute, so the stroke volume fell from 77.5 to 12.9 millilitres. The authors concluded that the brunt of the reduction in cardiac output was borne by the skin.

We can now revert to the Peruvian expedition, on which J. B. and his two British colleagues set sail from Liverpool on 17 November. Its organization had not been begun until early summer when a group of British and American physiologists had secured the support of the various institutions to which they were attached; thereafter, financial provision had come from a dozen sources, and there were many other contributions, both in kind and in kindness, before the expedition was over. The American members were C. A. Binger of the Rockefeller Institute of Medical Research, New York; A. V. Bock of the Massachusetts General Hospital; H. S. Forbes of Harvard Medical School; G. Harrop of the Presbyterian Hospital, New York; and A. C. Redfield of Harvard Medical School. They left New York in the S.S. *Ebro* on 16 November, and were at Lima three weeks before the English party to get the mobile laboratory, etc., in readiness. The primary object of the expedition was research into the physiological conditions which make considerable muscular and mental effort possible at great altitudes, and the copper mining camps in the high Peruvian Andes seemed an ideal venue, for up to an altitude just short of 16,000 feet the special requirements – transportation, a native population, and a temperate climate – were simultaneously available.

J. B. kept a sort of personal diary for M. A. B.'s benefit from 18 November to 23 January, and it is a pity that it cannot be extracted at some length, for much of it is fascinating to read. It begins at 5 p.m. on the first day mentioned, when the S.S. *Victoria* was "just passing Land's End, which seems to be a very appropriate moment for the commencement of an account of my sea voyage." By the 21st J. B. had been appointed President of the Sports Committee, but the office was for long somewhat of a sinecure. On the 25th he wrote, "The lady that sits next me at table is a dry old stick – I can't help thinking that she is really very amusing if she would open out a little – at present she says almost nothing, wears rings on most of her fingers and never appears before twelve o'clock in the day." Within twenty-four hours she had justified J. B.'s diagnosis of her by producing an immortal retort, and his next day's note is as follows. "The old Bird who sits beside me at meals did not turn up till lunch time. The Captain began twitting her about not being there for breakfast. She said 'I have got up for breakfast on a few occasions in my life – but never without regretting it'." On Monday, 28 November, the party was kept busy measuring Professor Meakins' blood volume, while one of the crew whose pneumonia they had treated by administration of oxygen was getting well. On 1 December it blew hard, and J. B. "managed – and unmanaged – a three course breakfast." On 6 December, Founder's Day at Kings' College, the traditional toast "In piam memoriam" was proposed by the Captain, at whose table J. B. was sitting; the next day Havana was reached. Then on the 12th they began to pass through the Panama Canal. The last night at sea, 16–17 December, prompted J. B. to write that "of the many beautiful nights which we have had lately it is one of the most beautiful. The moon is just up and shining ever so brightly on the calm sea. Of course I can never leave a ship which I have been on without a pang and certainly I have got quite fond of this old barge which should go at 14½ knots and does go at eleven, but she has carried us through bad weather and now that we have arrived at our destination we are all in the pink of condition."

That destination was Callao (Plate 35), the port of Lima, where they arrived about 6 p.m. on 17 December; "in the distance were mountains, the foothills of the Andes, but they were covered with cloud. All round the steamer were boats with people shouting and launches buzzing about", and in one of the boats J. B. recognized Redfield, who came on board and stayed to dinner, leaving about half past nine. The next morning at 11.30 the party set off by train for Lima; J. B. got off at Mont Serrata, a suburb of that city, to inspect a long, bogied luggage van (baggage car) which had been given to the expedition by the Peruvian Corporation and which had been converted, under the Americans' direction, into a travelling laboratory; the conversion had been effected by carpenters whose services had been provided, without charge, by the Grace Line. The result (Plate 36) was "the most perfect laboratory of its sort that could be imagined." Further, there was a goods van which was fitted up as a store, and later a directors' coach was to be added to the train to serve as living quarters. A few minutes after J. B.'s arrival the apparatus which had come in the S.S. *Victoria* was safely delivered. Bock and Redfield and Harrop were all in great form and J. B. made the acquaintance of Binger and Harry Forbes. After dinner that evening he gave each member of the united Anglo-American party a schedule of work for the period up to 12 January, and everything was thoroughly talked over before they retired for the night; for Redfield and Binger, who left for Cerro de Pasco (Plate 37) at 6 a.m., it was a short one.

The following evening at about 5.30 p.m. the other six, plus the whole equipage (engine, store car, laboratory car, and about four passenger cars), left Lima for the hour's run to Chosica (2,800 feet); as there were neither bridges nor tunnels, J. B. and his colleagues "climbed up and sat on the roof, the better to take in the prospect." "Chosica," he wrote on 20 December, "is an outpost of Lima . . . Apart from the mountains which tower above one, there is a good deal of a much more subdued nature to admire. The two memories which I carry away are those of a violet acacia which bears blossoms as plentifully as a laburnum and of the long strings of ponies and donkeys. Some will be carrying milk, others vicuna skins. The harness of the ponies is most beautifully made." He must also have carried away a memory of the morning's work, for the time was spent doing pulse and respiration tests, on the station platform, "to the great interest and amusement of the congregation of onlookers."

On 21 December at 8 a.m. all six of the party left Chosica, the Americans expecting to go straight through to Cerro de Pasco, while the other three got off at Matucana (7,800 feet). Writing there some hours later in the heart of the Andes, J. B. felt that it had been one of the most memorable days which he expected to come his way. "The wonder of it all is quite impossible to describe. All the time we have been pushing up the river bed. The river is a rushing torrent which will give you some idea of the gradient of the line. When the torrent becomes a cascade, of course the gradient would become impossible and then we have to do a zig zag. Such a one is at St. Bartholmé; the station is in a sort of ravine with immense mountains towering up [and] huge cliffs overhead, your eye travels up these and suddenly you see high up the rock wall two railway lines, the train is taken off the engine [*sic*], put at the other end and you start off more or less in the direction which you came but always going up the face of the rock. After you have travelled perhaps an hour you look down and see the roof of St. Bartholmé station in the abyss below. We had what was very rare at Chosica, namely, a wet night, but the circumstances added greatly to the beauty of our journey, for dryness had left the atmosphere and now the more distant mountains were indigo wreathed in clouds, while the sun lit up the nearer ones in the most beautiful way. They appear to be entirely of granite, but with a yellow tinge something like the granite at The Glen rather than the blue of the Bessbrook granite. Sometimes the yellow borders on red. The various shades of colour passing into deep blue in the distance make a wonderful picture. As the ascent is made the vegetation increases. Here the mountain side is covered with tufts of grass and would no doubt be quite green were it not too steep for the water to lie . . . between here and St. Bartholmé we have seen some wonderful flowers. One cactus grew up like a pillar twelve feet high, I should think, with a single large bell-shaped cream-coloured flower at the top. Pepper trees are among the most common with their red berries; heliotrope, oleander, immense yuccas, figs, bananas and trumpet flower, are a few only of the things which can be seen from the window. At the station before this, Surco, the women were selling the most wonderful bunches of violets. No bunch I should think was less than nine inches across. I have never seen anything like them."

The next day was a quiet one. After breakfast J. B. wandered off at random and found in among the mountains a most attractive valley which he described Irish-wise as follows. "It was more like what you might find at home than anything I have seen. If the stream were clear instead of muddy and the vegetation had been brackens and whins instead of heliotrope and calceolaria, it might almost have been the Mourne Mountains – but for the size."

On 23 December the party left about 11 a.m. for Oroya (12,200 feet); they travelled with Dr. Crane, principal doctor of the Cerro de Pasco Company, in his car and this had two advantages. First, they avoided the sight of multiple vomiting in the ordinary cars, and secondly they were themselves with one who had had more practical experience of mountain sickness (locally styled *soroche*) than anyone else in the world. The train reached Ticlio (15,600 feet; only 200 feet lower than the summit, La Cima) about 5 p.m. in a snow storm – "as the saying goes, you can go from a glacier to a banana tree here between breakfast and lunch" – and thence dropped gradually down to the party's immediate destination, Oroya (12,200 feet). They were met by Mr. Colley, the head engineer of the Cerro de Pasco Company, and taken off – all in rather a piano condition – to his house. J. B. was soon sick, and put to bed. Then he was woken up and taken on a stretcher to the hospital, the swaying making him sick a second time. In the next bed to him in the hospital was Bock, who was somewhat more seriously affected by the rare atmosphere, and had epistaxis as an extra.

On the 24th J. B. was in good condition but Dr. Crane kept him in bed till late afternoon. Redfield, Meakins and Doggart had meanwhile gone on to Cerro de Pasco (14,200 feet). At 5.30 p.m. on the 26th J. B. left Oroya and until it was dark passed through a countryside of grass-covered limestone. About 9.30 p.m. he reached Cerro, where he was taken off, with a veto on any physical exertion, to the Company's hotel. There he found other members of the party "as keen as possible, but finding life a little bit of an effort. They have already obtained very important results. I did not feel the altitude much but was soon put to bed in the same room as Mr. Doggart and told to stay there for the next twenty four hours."

On the 28th, after breakfast, he "crawled down to the railway station", where the laboratory cars were, and came back up the hill with great caution. The following day he was considerably acclimatized and found himself swinging up to the hotel at the usual pace. "It was beautifully clear and a panorama of snow clad summits was visible in the distance. I took a little walk up the hill which overlooks this place and certainly I was rewarded for my pains. The mountains were an intensely deep blue except where covered with snow and for the most part steep and pointed like the Matterhorn." On that same day the party moved out of the hotel, though continuing to have meals there, into a luxurious nearby "cottage" in which all the rooms were electrically heated, there were beautiful pile carpets, and an immense fire in the sitting room.

The note for 30 December said that the day had "been uneventful except in the matter of work which is at present successful far beyond my highest expectations. Everyone is now in excellent form and the nerves of the party are all very good I am glad to say. So far there have been no temperamental troubles."

On the next day J. B., Professor Meakins, and Mr. Foran, the manager, set out on ponies after breakfast and rode up some of the adjacent hills, seeing mines which had been worked almost since the time of Pizarro. The amount of ore raised at Cerro, they learned, was 700 tons a day and was about a third of the total. In the evening the members of the expedition dressed up and went to the "party" given at the Smelter to see out the old year. "Though it would be regarded as remarkable in Cambridge the engine driver was one of the guests, and not too sober at that. He drove the engine in his dress clothes covered by his overalls. At 2.30 a.m. he reappeared in his overalls, a good deal more alcoholic, and announced that the train would start in ten minutes for Cerro de Pasco, and so we got home . . . . Regarded as a physiological demonstration of the degree to which the human frame can adapt itself to rare atmospheres this dance was very striking. With only about half the air in their lungs that these people would have had at the sea level they danced all the evening. . . . The ceremony of seeing in the new year was very striking. One of the hooters from the works was brought into the room and at midnight a terrific blast was blown on it which absolutely paralysed everybody: when the noise stopped everybody shook hands with everybody else and wished them a happy new year."

Monday to Wednesday, 2 to 4 January, 1922, were uneventful except for successful work. On 5 January J. B. decided that the party was overworking and needed a rest, so he locked the laboratory car and proceeded himself to enjoy what he called one of *the* days of his life. Redfield and Binger went off duck-shooting and bagged twenty-six ducks in Lake Junin. Jack Foran took the rest of the party off by car and train to twenty-five miles distant Gollarisquisga (13,000 feet), where "the general level breaks and you find that you are at the head of the almost precipitous wall of a valley thousands of feet deep. You look far down into it and see little towns, and across to the other side which is about the same elevation as yourself, and beyond is a magnificent range – snow clad in places and rising to about 21,000 feet. Then you know for the first time that you are on the roof of the world." J. B. was persuaded to stay overnight and he and Mr. Tweedie, the mine manager, rode on a pony and a mule respectively during the afternoon to a place about four miles away. "The ride was beyond all description – steep in places and not much road in others, but winding about the tops of magnificent valleys similar to the one I have described."

He returned to Cerro during the afternoon of 6 January, arriving in a storm of thunder and lightning and rain. The next day was the greatest one, as regards work, for the whole party, and J. B. was in the laboratory, with two slight breaks, from 7.15 a.m. to 10.30 p.m. But all went well, so all were happy. On the 9th there was a repeat performance and, if it went somewhat less smoothly, it still went excellently. The major items in the programme had been finished and all had gone beyond J. B.'s highest expectations, so now there remained merely two days of packing and minor duties.

On Thursday, 12 January, at 7 a.m. Jack Foran and all the party's other friends came down to the station to see them off. While the farewells were taking place "the station master was panting to get the train started . . . Ultimately the engine commenced to move only to find that our cars were not coupled on, so the train had to back up again in order that we should be attached," and there was much cheerful laughter. At Oroya there was another large party waiting to say farewell and bon voyage – they left there about eleven o'clock and reached Casapalca (13,600 feet) about 2.30 p.m. after enjoying a most lovely forenoon, with "bright sunlight illuminating the already bright reds and greys of the mountains, and heightening the brilliance of the glaciers on their summits."

Friday, 13 January, was described by J. B. as "one in a life time." After breakfast members of the party, with Mr. Campbell, head of the Casapalca mine, and Mr. Colley, chief engineer of the Company, set out from Casapalca on mules, which took them up 2,000 feet to just short of the snow line. Then, unfortunately, snow began to fall for the remaining 2,000 feet climb to the top of Mount Carlos Francisco (*c.* 17,500 feet). Every hundred feet farther up progress became slower, and for the last 800 feet or so it was very slow indeed – about ten steps and then a stop. After taking over two hours for the climb, they arrived at the top but falling snow hid the distant mountain panorama which they had hoped to see. So they climbed down about 30 feet of rock until they reached the snow, sat down on it, and in about five minutes had slid down the 2,000 feet up which they had so laboriously ascended. Five minutes' walk brought them to the mules, and in a further half to three quarters of an hour they were back in their hotel at Casapalca. At 4 p.m. J. B., Bock and Harrop went on down to Matucana on a railway "hand car" – they had to test some respirators there before rejoining the others, on the following day, on their way to Lima.

J. B. wrote that he could not attempt to describe what he saw during the 30-mile ride and 6,000 feet descent, but it was very different from the journey up. "Then it was sunshine, clear air and bright colours. Now it was infinitely grander. All the mountain tops were enveloped in cloud – everything was vast, sombre and majestic to a degree. The air got perceptibly warmer with every thousand feet we descended and the verdure more luxuriant. At 6.20 we had arrived at Matucana in the region of heliotrope and pepper trees. At 1.30 we had been 2000 feet above the line of eternal snow. The Royal Society Expedition to Peru had ended – for the rest it was merely packing and getting out."

The next morning it was good to get "some pretty solid air" into the lungs and they noted how their faces had reddened up after being purple at Cerro and Casapalca. They also remembered how it was at Matucana that they had commenced to feel dyspnoeic on exercise on the outward journey – now on return they felt full of breath, and what a blessing it was. About 4.30 p.m. they rejoined the other members of the party on the train, and went on with them to

Lima, where they stayed until Wednesday, 18 January, when they were driven down to Callao and embarked on one of the nicest boats in which J. B. had ever travelled, namely, the S.S. *Ebro* of Belfast, belonging to the Pacific Steam Navigation Company, for the voyage through the Panama Canal and on to New York. On 21 January J. B. was all happiness in a Palm Beach suit, the next day he was in blue serge, on the morning of 23 January he put on a thick tweed, and in the afternoon he found it none too warm on deck with a trench coat and fleece lining. So the climatic conditions deteriorated rapidly as they moved north. On the boat all the members of the party were kept busy working. Usually they met after breakfast and J. B. assigned to each a file containing the material on a particular subject. The member then abstracted the information and tabulated it, ready for J. B. to write it up the next day. That meant seven preparing and one writing, so J. B. did "little but drive the quill, or rather the fountain pen."

In Boston, on 27 January, he gave the Lowell lecture, presumably on the results of the expedition, though information on this point is lacking. On 2 February he arrived in New York, and on 11 February, at the Academy of Medicine, he delivered the sixth Harvey Society Lecture, his subject being "The raison d'être of the red corpuscle." It was summarized in the last paragraph in the following words:- "In the interior of the red blood corpuscle the haemoglobin exists in a world of its own; by this device nature has at a stroke increased the efficiency both of the blood and of the haemoglobin; it has saved the blood from possessing physical properties which the haemoglobin would otherwise have conferred upon it – increased viscosity, and an impossible osmotic pressure; it has saved the haemoglobin from being dissolved in a solvent (NaCl) of less than maximal efficiency and from functioning at a hydrogen-ion concentration in which the remarkable properties of haemoglobin as a respiratory pigment could not betray their maximal efficiency – such is the raison d'être of the red blood corpuscle." He appears also to have lectured on the Peruvian expedition in Philadelphia and elsewhere, and doubtless had much to do in discussing analyses of the data with his American colleagues, but details are lacking.

On 1 March he left New York in the *Homeric* of the White Star Line, and on 9 March he was met at Cambridge station by M.A.B. and Robbie; if he reflected on all that had happened since he last saw them, he must surely have been amazed, and at the same time very satisfied, by the measure of his achievement. Others felt its outstanding interest, and for the rest of the year he was called upon more or less monthly to talk about the Peruvian expedition. As it is obviously advantageous to consider all these lectures together, other items in the year's story will have to be taken up afterwards.

Towards the end of March he lectured at St. Mary's Hospital, presumably on the work in the Andes. On 11 April he addressed the Chelsea Clinical Society about it; on 20 May he spoke in King's College, Cambridge, and two days later lectured to the Philosophical Society in the University School of Anatomy. On 9 June he talked at the Royal Institution in London and early in September at the British Association meeting in Hull. On 3 October the venue was his hometown of Newry, County Down; on 2 November, presumably with the same subject, it was St. Thomas' Hospital, where he was entertained by friends who had assisted him in the glass box experiment of 1921; finally, on 15 December, he took part in a discussion, arranged by the Section of Medicine of the Royal Society of Medicine, on the medical aspects of life at great altitudes. On this last occasion, representatives of the Mount Everest expedition of 1922, in the persons of Dr. T. G. Longstaff and Mr. T. H. Somervell, also took part, and so did J. S. Haldane, so the scope was wider than the Peruvian experiences alone.

These various lectures, and the American ones which preceded them, are not available in extenso, so we have to make some composite account from reports in journals. At the same time, however, we must not trespass unduly on the full scientific account of the expedition, received by the Royal Society on 25 July [1] but not published by it until January 1923. So the account which follows is a reasonably limited one, though it serves also to pick up certain

[1] Professor Meakins arrived at 13 Grange Road on 23 April, and may have taken part, at that stage, in a consideration of the draft text. But documentation of this suggestion is lacking, and his main object in coming is given by a comparison of M.A.B.'s diary and *Lancet*, 1925, i, 319. For Dr. Davies went to live for a while in the glass chamber at a temperature of 90–95° F. in order to test the hypothesis, formulated as a result of findings on the way to and from the Andes, that changes in external temperature cause changes in circulating blood volume. Dr. Fetter, in the *Lancet* account, is said to have undergone similar incarceration. Presumably, however, some of the tests were done at some other time of year, for J. B. in 1925 said that "the season was one of snow". According to the same account, the blood volume was measured independently by Dr. Davies, Professor Meakins, and J. B.; the results confirmed the initial hypothesis.

points not yet mentioned, and not included in *Philosophical Transactions, B*, of 1923.

In the various lectures of 1922, though not covering all the ground in each of them, J. B. said that Redfield and Bock, and for a shorter while Harrop, had been with him in Cambridge prior to the expedition, and that it was there that "the scheme had been hatched, the methods standardised, and a number of controls carried out." Peru had been chosen for various reasons. On the one hand, water, electricity, transportation, etc., were freely available at all levels; on the other hand, there were on the spot not only a native Cholo population, indigenous in the mountain regions for generations and probably antedating the Incas, but also a number of American mining officials and engineers who had worked at Cerro and elsewhere for several years. With the members of the Expedition added, there were thus three groups of human subjects, differing in their conditions of acclimatization, available for study.

No researches were done on beings other than human ones, but J. B. reported effects of the diminished oxygen tension upon certain lower forms of animal life. At 12,000 feet there were cows which gave milk, and at 13,000 feet cows which gave little or no milk, though equally well supplied with fodder; "At 15,000 feet there were neither cows nor milk." Above 12,000 feet fleas, plentiful below that height, disappeared but lice accompanied man to greater heights and typhus was not uncommon at Cerro de Pasco.

The Cholos led a primitive, communal sort of life, many of them in chimneyless and windowless houses, "and some of their customs would hardly appeal to more civilized races. When a native was very ill, for instance, the date of his funeral was fixed without reference to his convenience, and an official [1] saw to it that he was ready to keep the appointment." The Cholos were short in stature, with sallow or purple faces, a number of them with clubbed fingers, and all with chest circumferences large for their heights. Remarkable were the loads which they could carry. A boy of about 13 would bring a load of ore weighing 40 lb. up from the mine, traversing a distance of *c.* 650 feet and ascending *c.* 250 feet in so doing, while an adult would carry up 100 lb.; a European was out of breath if he

[1] "Despenador", or "putter out of pain". The female form, "despenadora", according to Bensley's *Spanish and English Dictionary*, was a woman who was supposed to push her elbow into the stomach or breast of dying persons to relieve them of their agony.

carried his coat up a short incline. On the other hand, even the Cholos panted heavily and had to stop many times on the way up. Exercise on the flat, such as dancing or not too strenuous tennis, as opposed to climbing, was possible for Europeans.

Dealing with the more scientific aspects of the expedition's work, J. B. said that the lure of mountain sickness to the physiologist had originally lain in the fact that it was a disease to which a definite cause – ascending too high above sea-level – could be assigned, and which was promptly relieved on descending. With the cause now generally explained in terms of insufficient oxygen supply to the tissues, interest had shifted to the mechanisms of the body's adaptation, but the attractions for the physiologist were still the exactness of the conditions with which the body had to cope, and the ease with which those conditions were produced or abolished.

Secretion of oxygen by the pulmonary epithelium was not one of the means of adaptation at Cerro, though the blood of the natives there was 18 per cent., and that of the Europeans 15 per cent., unsaturated. The adaptation was in fact due (1) to increased total pulmonary ventilation, which raised the oxygen partial pressure and decreased the carbon dioxide partial pressure in the alveoli; (2) to increased expansion of the chest, marked in the natives, mild in the resident Americans, and not apparent in the visiting scientists; (3) to the increased red corpuscle count and blood haemoglobin; and (4) to an increased affinity of the blood for oxygen. The relative importances of these four factors remained to be determined; meanwhile, the individual variation in susceptibility to mountain sickness seemed to be related to individual variation in the diffusion constant, as Krogh had suggested it might be before the expedition set out.

Concentration was more difficult at Cerro; on the other hand, the activities of the resident mining staff showed that a fair amount of mental work could be sustained for long periods at 14,000 feet. One important point was that no member of the expedition slept well at the great heights. Some had short hours of sleep, and others, while sleeping the allotted hours, had fitful and broken rest. At the end of a month all of them were mentally exhausted. There is a further note which may well be added here, and that is that the ages of the members ranged from 25 to 49 years, i.e., J. B. was the eldest yet, as we have seen, he took his full share in the more strenuous activities, such as the exacting climb to the summit of Mount Carlos Francisco.

We can now revert to other items of the 1922 story subsequent to J. B.'s return to England, and the first of these is the publication, on 16 May, of a paper "On the hydrogen-ion concentration and some related properties of normal human blood." The experiments described in it had been planned by J. B., as part of a larger scheme, and had been carried out by him together with Bock, Parsons and Shoji before his departure in November 1921 for Peru. The manuscript of the paper was left with A. V. Hill when J. B. sailed, and Hill prepared it for publication and added a certain amount on the theoretical side. The findings cannot at all briefly be summarized and discussed here; those interested are therefore referred to the original.

J. B.'s summer holiday occupied most of September, apart from the time needed for the British Association meeting, and was taken at Rhosneigr, Anglesey. Thereafter, the next item of interest is a major one, namely, that on 9 November he was awarded a Royal Medal by the President and Council of the Royal Society for his researches in physiology, and especially for his work in connection with respiration. On 30 November he attended a dinner in London in order to receive his award and to make a five-minutes speech in reply. On 15 December, as already noted, he took part in a discussion at the Royal Society of Medicine on the medical aspects of life at great altitudes. J. S. Haldane, who also spoke, said that "he did not think that Mr. Barcroft's results had shaken the evidence furnished by the Pike's Peak expedition, that increased oxygen secretory activity of the lung epithelium was a main factor in acclimatization. And the fact that the Everest expedition had reached a height of 27,000 feet without the use of oxygen had considerably strengthened that evidence. In 1919 Meakins, Priestley and the speaker had pointed out that the diminishing oxygen saturation of the blood from an artery as altitude increased must be out of all proportion to the diminution in the mean oxygen pressure in the blood leaving the lung alveoli. It was this latter value only which was concerned in the question of oxygen secretion, and that they had measured on Pike's Peak. They already knew it was useless to measure only the percentage saturation with oxygen of blood from an artery."

On the following day a review by J. B. of Haldane's *Respiration* appeared in *Nature*, and it included the following. "No one who turns over the pages can be but impressed with the enormous advance which has been made in the physiology of respiration within the last thirty years, and the degree to which that advance has been due to Dr. Haldane's work and to the stimulating influence which he has wielded over the minds of others. . . . The reader cannot scan the pages without observing the large number of persons who have been privileged to collaborate with Dr. Haldane. To that company the book will mean something more than a mere recapitulation of his work or a history of the development and philosophic position, or a commentary on the action and reaction of abstract science on industrial research; it will mean something a little sacred, but something which one of them, at all events, finds some difficulty in putting into words."

On 18 January 1923 J. B. read to the Royal Society the report on the expedition to Peru, and it was published five days later. As the paper greatly amplified the account given in his lectures of the previous year, and as one set of observations (third paragraph below) led to his subsequent work on blood volume and blood depôts, it seems necessary to give the long summary in full. So here it is.

"Of the factors which might be held to assist in acclimatisation some at least appear to have little value at the altitudes at which we have worked (14,200 feet). Such are oxygen secretion, alterations in the vital capacity, residual tidal air, diffusion coefficient, and increased quantity of blood driven round the body per minute.

"The pulse, under basal conditions, beats at the same rate at 14,000 feet as it does at sea-level. It gives a greater response to exercise, however, the increase being most marked with light exercise; and, indeed, the ordinary conditions of life, as compared to basal conditions, constitute a degree of exercise which renders the normal pulse more rapid at Cerro than at sea-level. Inasmuch as the minute volume of blood is little altered, the increased pulse rate must be regarded, in the words of Schneider, as a signal of distress and not a form of acclimatisation. In some cases skiagrams showed an actual diminution in the size of the heart, in others they did not. Such an individual variation would indicate, along the lines laid down by Starling and his pupils, a corresponding individual variation in the efficiency of the heart. In the hearts, the fibres of which elongated in diastole to the same extent at Cerro as at sea-level, there would be a loss of efficiency; for with the same strain on the heart at each beat there are more beats. In the hearts which dilate less, the smaller elongation of the fibres goes to counterbalance the more rapid pulse.

"It had been our intention to make observations on the blood volume at high altitudes; this intention was not carried out, for a reason which probably proved to be more illuminating than our original programme would have been. There appears to be a temperature factor in the blood volume. On the voyage to Peru, and to a less extent on the voyage home, the blood volumes of three persons were observed to change with the external temperature; increasing in the warm climates. A similar increase has subsequently been observed in chamber experiments of two or three days' duration (Appendix I), in which the temperature factor was the only alteration of circumstance to which the subjects were exposed. The significance of the change in volume of the blood would appear to be that in hot climates much of the blood is in the skin; the circulation in the arm may in the most extreme cases be increased fifty-fold by a change of skin temperature. Under circumstances where the whole skin is affected, such as very hot climates, the increase in the vascular bed may be considerable, and the volume of blood increases to preserve the relation between the quantity of vascular fluid and the bed which contains it.

"There remain three principal factors which appear to have a positive influence in acclimatisation:-

(*a*) The increase in total ventilation, which usually raises the alveolar oxygen pressure 10 or 12 mm. higher than it would otherwise be.

(*b*) The rise in the oxygen dissociation curve, so that at any oxygen pressure the haemoglobin will take up more oxygen than before.

(*c*) The rise in the number of red corpuscles and correspondingly in the quantity of haemoglobin.

"These three factors may be regarded as independent variables and an attempt was made to appraise their relative importance. The attempt has necessitated an enquiry into the laws which govern diffusion in the lungs and the tissues. This enquiry makes it obvious that:-

(1) The colour of the blood in the lungs must be almost that of arterial blood, whilst the colour of blood in the tissue capillaries approaches that of the venous blood which emerges from the tissue in question.

(2) An explanation is found for the fact that, at high altitudes, the arterial blood darkens when exercise is taken, whilst it does not do so to an appreciable extent at the sea-level. It is also explained why the arterial blood should darken on exercise in lung complaints in which the permeability of the lung wall, or the surface of capillaries in the lung (see Appendix VI), is diminished – either will reduce the diffusion coefficient.

"Working from Bohr's method of graphic integration, it appears that fall of alveolar pressure tends to depress the region of oxygen utilisation in two ways:-

(1) It lowers the limiting percentage saturation which the arterial blood could attain if it achieved an equilibrium with the alveolar air.

(2) It increases the gap between this limiting saturation and the actual saturation which is attained in the lung. The equilibrium is not so nearly approached.

"Increase of total ventilation and rise in the oxygen dissociation curve each have two effects, and these in about the same degree:-

(1) They raise the point on the oxygen dissociation curve at which an oxygen equilibrium between the arterial blood and the alveolar air could be struck.

(2) They diminish the gap between the equilibrium and the actual degree to which the arterial blood is saturated with oxygen.

"The rise in haemoglobin value (§(*c*) above) produces little effect on the position of utilisation. It causes the arterial blood to be less saturated and the venous blood to be more saturated than would otherwise be the case. Inasmuch, however, as the average capillary pressure approximates to the venous and not to the arterial pressure, benefit accrues – this, however, is rather small, and it seems clear that the real advantage derived from increase in the red corpuscles is of a secondary character, as will appear.

"Concerning the mechanism of the increase in total ventilation, one possibility may be ruled out during rest, namely, increased hydrogen-ion concentration in the blood, for during rest the blood is no less alkaline than at sea-level. This is shown by the limited number of readings taken by the Dale and Evans' method. Indirectly it is shown also by the method of measuring the ratio of the free to the combined CO_2 in the whole blood. It is true that on the actual readings the difference in reaction was slight, but of two samples of blood exposed to 25 mm. oxygen which give the same readings by this method, that which contains the greater number of corpuscles will be the more alkaline (see Appendix II). As this result appears to be in conflict with the researches of Warburg, it will be wise to leave open the question as to whether the reaction of the blood is unchanged or becomes slightly more alkaline.

"By a process of exclusion, it must be supposed that the increased activity of the respiratory centre is the result – direct or indirect – of oxygen want on the centre itself. The fall of CO_2 in the alveolar air is the effect, and so also is the relative rise in oxygen.

"When exercise is taken, a given amount of exercise is found to produce a greater rise in the hydrogen-ion concentration in rare than in ordinary air, hence the urgency of the breathlessness which supervenes is due to the fact that there is not only a more irritable respiratory centre but a greater increment of hydrogen-ions, *i.e.* a greater stimulus acting upon it.

"Above the three main factors in acclimatisation ((*a*), (*b*) and (*c*) above) were provisionally treated as independent variables; in reality they are not so, for blood can be made artificially to resemble high-altitude blood, by shaking out the CO_2, centrifugalising and then withdrawing a portion of the plasma so that the blood is richer in corpuscles. Such blood has been found to give at the alveolar CO_2 pressure of the Andes (27 mm. CO_2 or thereabouts):-

(1) A reaction which is apparently almost unchanged, or even more acid as measured by the ratio of combined to free CO_2.

(2) A more alkaline reaction by the platinum electrode.

(3) An oxygen dissociation curve, which rises apparently out of proportion to the change in reaction.

"Herein would appear to be the essence of the acclimatory process. The possibility of the oxygen dissociation curve altering, owing simply to a loss of CO_2, appears to be ruled out (Appendix II). There was an increase in the haemoglobin value of the blood and in the red cell count in all cases. On making the ascent there was a marked increase in the number of reticulated red cells, after the descent these cells fell to below their normal percentage. In the natives the ratio of reticulated to unreticulated red cells was not greatly increased, but the absolute number of reticulated cells per cubic millimetre was about 50 per cent. greater than normal. We argue a hypertrophy in the bone marrow. There were no nucleated red cells. The increase in red blood corpuscles is such as to cause an absolute increase in the amount of oxygen in each cubic centimetre of blood in the majority of cases, in spite of the decrease in saturation.

"In the natives (3) the saturation of the arterial blood is 80–85 per cent.; in the members of the Expedition it was found to be 85–90 in most cases. The arterial blood, as withdrawn from the radial artery with a syringe, was always dark in appearance, as also was the colour of the lips. The cyanosis disappeared on breathing oxygen. The saturation of the arterial blood appears to be much the same as in many cases of pneumonia observed by Meakins. The 'oxygen want factor' in pneumonia is worthy of abolition by oxygen respiration, and must be regarded as an important factor accessory to the toxin.

"A number of mental tests of the ordinary type were performed at Cerro and at sea-level. These revealed no particular mental disability in the Andes. In our opinion, as well as in that of psychologists whom we have consulted, we have shown rather that the mental tests were inadequate than that our mental efficiency was unimpaired. Judged by the ordinary standards of efficiency in laboratory work, we were in an obviously lower category intellectually at Cerro than at the sea-level. By a curious paradox this was most apparent when it was being least tested, for perhaps what we suffered from chiefly was the difficulty of maintaining concentration. When we knew we were undergoing a test, our concentration could by an effort be maintained over the length of time taken for the test, but under ordinary circumstances it would lapse. It is, perhaps, characteristic that, whilst each individual mental test was done as rapidly at Cerro as at the sea-level, the performance of the series took nearly twice as long for its accomplishment. Time was wasted there in trivialities and 'bungling', which would not take place at sea-level.

"A number of tests were made for the purpose of discovering whether the pressure of oxygen in the blood was or was not higher than that in the alveolar air. In all cases they were so nearly the same that we attribute the passage of gas through the pulmonary epithelium to diffusion.

"Cyanosis, whilst always more or less evident at Cerro, increased upon exercise. Cyanosis is a darkening of the colour of the mean capillary blood in the area studied. This blood approximates in colour to the venous blood from the part observed. As exercise does not increase the oxygen consumption of the blood of the lips, and as there is no reason to suppose that it induces vaso-constriction in the lips, the reason for their cyanosis must be diminished saturation of the arterial blood which reaches them. Such diminished saturation is not accompanied by any fall in the alveolar oxygen, yet it is easily explicable on the diffusion theory.

"Some observations on mountain sickness are given; the principal contribution we have made is the observation that in our own party the proneness to 'soroche' corresponds pretty closely to the diffusion coefficient, those persons who had a low diffusion coefficient being the sufferers. Further research is necessary before any statement can be made as to whether [the] observation is due to more than coincidence. Such research is being carried out."

On 14 February J. B. crossed to Dublin to lecture at the Royal College of Surgeons of Ireland about the Peruvian expedition; on 21 March he and Uyeno published an extension of some observations included in Appendix III of the report on that expedition. They had found that the dissociation curve of concentrated blood was raised in relative absence of carbon dioxide, and lowered in the presence of excess of the gas, whereas the reverse occurred in the case of blood with a reduced red blood corpuscle count. On 26 March, the day of H. R. H. the Duke of York's marriage to Lady Elizabeth Bowes-Lyon, eighteen-year old Henry Barcroft, Exhibitioner-elect in Natural Science of King's College, left Marlborough College and thereafter worked with his father on the taking up of carbon monoxide by the splenic haemoglobin. This research headed the long series conducted by J. B. over a number of years upon "blood-depôts", and it is pertinent to note that the idea of such "stores of blood" was less novel than the functional proof which J. B. was to give. R. M. Wilson, for instance, in *The Hearts of Man* (1918), had put forward much such a concept, but his book appears to have made little impression on contemporary thought.

On 19 and 20 May Sir William and Lady Bayliss stayed at 13 Grange Road with the Barcrofts, the Cambridge meeting of the Physiological Society taking place on the Saturday. On that day, also, there appeared in *Nature* a letter from Bayliss on "Adsorption and haemoglobin." On 22 May Meakins came to the Barcrofts for a longer stay; he did not leave until 9 June. On 23 June *Nature* published letters from A. V. Hill and J. B. in reply to Bayliss' May one. Then in the second week of July J. B. went to be Sir Edward and Lady Schafer's guest at Park End, North Berwick, and while there he received a letter from Queen's University, Belfast, asking if he was agreeable to being one of five nominees for the Vice-Chancellorship. This gave him and M. A. B., who had meanwhile come north, much food for thought, but any decision was postponed until after the International Congress of Physiologists, which took place in Edinburgh.

It was the eleventh in the series, with an enrolment of 516 members, and the official part, lasting from 24 to 27 July, was preceded by an informal reception on the evening of the 23rd in the Upper Library of the Old College of the University, with the President and Lady Sharpey Schafer welcoming members and their wives, among them J. B. and M. A. B. The opening lecture on the following day was on "Insulin", and F. G. Banting's presence made the story revealed by Macleod even more vivid in the minds of his hearers. J. B.'s contributions to the programme were a "Demonstration of gas analysis apparatus as used in the Cambridge Medical Research Schools," and a communication, entitled, "The circulation in the spleen." The published abstract of the latter read as follows.

"A demonstration is given showing how small is the quantity of carboxyhaemoglobin in the spleen of an animal which has breathed CO. If rats are placed in 0.1 per cent. CO the blood in the general circulation becomes saturated up to 50 per cent. saturation in 24 minutes, and blood taken from the liver is indistinguishable from that in the general circulation; but the haemoglobin in the spleen requires at least another 25 minutes to become saturated to the same extent. Conversely, if rats have been in 0.1 per cent. CO till the haemoglobin of their blood and the haemoglobin of their spleen pulp are saturated to over 60 per cent. saturation, and are then exposed to ordinary air – in 45 minutes the blood will be only 30 per cent. saturated, whilst another hour elapses before the haemoglobin of the spleen reaches that figure. The spleen pulp would therefore appear to contain large numbers of corpuscles which are not circulating in the ordinary sense, and is in fact a sort of backwater in the circulation."

At the conclusion of the Congress M. A. B. and J. B. went via Stranraer to Larne, finding the journey through the Galloway country most enchanting, and then on to Belfast, where on the following day they went up to the University to interview the Secretary and the acting Vice-Chancellor, Dr. Sinclair. They saw over Elmwood House, the residence provided for the Vice-Chancellor, but were unfavourably impressed by its size and situation, and for those and other reasons J. B., after reaching The Glen, Newry, wrote declining nomination for the Vice-Chancellorship.

Following a fortnight's holiday at The Glen they returned to Cambridge, and J. B. and Henry went off to work at the Marine Biological Station at Plymouth; thereafter, from 30 August to 18 September J. B. was busy with government work at Scapa. Henry entered King's College on 11 October, and a week later J. B. went up to London to receive the Baly Medal of the Royal College of Physicians. This medal is awarded biennially, on the recommendation of the President and Council, "to the person who shall be deemed to have most distinguished himself in the Science of Physiology, especially during the two years immediately preceding the award, and is not restricted to British subjects." Previous recipients from 1903 onwards had been Langley, Pavlov, Starling, Emil Fischer, Halliburton, Haldane, Hopkins, Bayliss, Leonard Hill, and Dale. The medal is presented on the occasion of the Harveian Oration, and it is of interest that the Orator in 1923 was a fellow-physiologist, namely, E. H. Starling. In November J. B. was appointed Fullerian Professor of the Royal Institution for a period of three years, the duties being to deliver eight lectures each spring.

The final 1923 items are that J. B. and Henry's paper, "Observations on the taking up of carbon monoxide by the haemoglobin in the spleen", appeared on 28 December in the *Journal of Physiology*; and that the same number contained a "Note on the effect of external temperature on the circulation in man", with J. B. and E. K. Marshall, jr. its authors. The origin of the first paper was the observation that the blood volume of man varies with the external temperature, as first noted on the way to the Andes and subsequently confirmed by experiments in a glass chamber in which the air was artificially heated. This gave J. B. to imagine that the spleen had a depôt function, and led to these initial animal experiments. There is no need to give the conclusion drawn from them, for it has already been noted in dealing with the International Congress of Physiologists at Edinburgh.

The origin of the second paper was as follows. Uyeno (1923) had shown that a rise of external temperature causes a great increase in heart minute volume in narcotized cats, and a fall the reverse, but it was not certain if these circulatory effects were primary, or secondary to changes in the body temperature and metabolism. Using a simpler but at the same time more rapid method for determining the oxygen pressure in the mixed venous blood, J. B. and Marshall found that "in man exposure to cold till the point of shivering is nearly reached increases the minute volume while it slows the pulse, thus producing a large alteration in the systolic output;" that "exposure to warmth in the case of a person whose minute volume adapts itself quickly, raises the same by 3–4 litres – a quantity which probably is a rough measure of the blood flow through the skin"; and that "at low minute volumes below 8 litres the systolic output is susceptible of great alterations."

The first 1924 items which have to be recorded are publications by J. B. in collaboration with Duncan Scott and with Henry Barcroft respectively. The one by Scott and J. B. was probably the earlier in appearing; its subject was "The blood volume and the total amount of haemoglobin in anaemic rats", and it followed upon Scott's two previous studies of a certain form of anaemia (Scott, 1923, *a*, *b*). The authors found a fall in the blood haemoglobin percentage, while the blood volume per unit body weight remained practically normal. The chance observation, that the same was true in pregnant rats plus foetuses, is of interest as an early instance of J. B.'s concern with that gestational and foetal physiology which was later, for some years, to become his main field of study.

The work described in the second paper, which was published on 1 February, had been done by J. B. and Henry in 1923 in the Marine Biological Laboratory, Plymouth, and in Cambridge, and their object had been to see if the pigment commonly alluded to as haemoglobin in the worms was identical with that known by the same name in vertebrates; the worm they had mainly used had been *Arenicola marina*. The results indicated that the haemoglobin dissolved in the blood of this species was of the same general type as that contained in human blood, but different from it in detail. There were great individual variations in blood volume, but the oxygen capacity was much more constant, being of the order of 0.01 ml. oxygen per g. of worm. "This quantity is definitely less than the maximum the Arenicola is estimated to need during the time that the hole is sealed up at low water. Nevertheless, it is so nearly of the same order as to make clear the probable function of the pigment, namely, to act as a reserve store which the organism can use up when it has not access to sea-water." The findings on *Arenicola marina* and on a species of another genus of worm, *Nephthys*, supported the idea, put forward by J. B. in his Harvey Lecture of 1922, "that the haemoglobin in human blood is the survivor of a series of pigments to be found in the lower forms of life – a survivor selected because its properties are more suited to the needs of the higher mammals than are those of its fellows in the series."

On 12 February J. B. delivered his first lecture as Fullerian Professor at the Royal Institution, and Henry went up to London by motor-bike in order to hear it. Four days later, J. B. and five colleagues (Anson *et al.*, 1924) made a communication to the Physiological Society on "The relation between the spectrum of, and the affinity of certain gases for, vertebrate haemoglobin." They stated that "the following relation has been found to hold for the haemoglobins of Man, Horse, Cat, Sheep, Mouse, Rabbit, Hen, Pigeon, Roach, Lizard, Frog and Tortoise: If A be the position of maximum intensity of the α band in Angstrom Units and B that of the CO band, and if K be the relative concentration of O_2/CO dissolved in a solution which contains 50 % O_2Hb and 50 % COHb

$$\log K = .050 \ (A - B).$$

K is the measure of the equilibrium constant of the reaction and log K that of the free energy change. Therefore the displacement of this spectral band is proportional to the free energy of the reaction. The spectra of the haemochromogens derived from all the above bloods are identical."

In July appeared J. B.'s first *Physiological Review*, entitled, "The significance of hemoglobin." Near the outset he wrote that he would like "to give an account of its properties, to state where it first appears in the scheme of nature, to explain the precise purpose which it is there serving, and trace the successive devices which are invoked in order to make it meet the ever increasing demands which are put upon it through the ascent of the animal kingdom. Such a scheme is impossible. It is impossible to say where hemoglobin first appears, and even if we could do so it would not be easy to state precisely what it is doing there. Likely enough it would be difficult to draw any precise line between its function and that of some other pigment – its next door neighbor. Or it might have no function, that would be the most significant discovery of all for then we would have hit upon its accidental occurrence. We would know indeed that we had discovered a possible starting point for we could say: Here hemoglobin is found apparently as an accident, it serves no end, it apparently exists as a chance, but this may be a chance of which evolution has taken advantage. The opposite procedure must therefore be adopted. In the highest animals the significance of hemoglobin, or at least its principal significance, is fairly evident. How far back can we trace the pigment without losing our certainty of its function?"

At the end of the review he concluded as follows. "To summarize, then, hemoglobin consists essentially of an iron-containing portion which can unite with, and dissociate itself from, oxygen. By the coupling of protein to the hematin, the power of hemoglobin to acquire and part with oxygen is adjusted to the needs of living organisms so that either phase of the reaction may take place by the mere exposure of the hemoglobin to a suitable partial pressure of the gas. The properties so achieved are exploited in the mammalia in the following way. The hemoglobin is present in large quantities in the circulating fluid, where it is enclosed in corpuscles the inside of which is maintained at a suitable hydrogen ion concentration and which are at a suitable temperature. Adjustment of the reaction within the corpuscles enables the blood to alter its power of taking up or releasing oxygen and thus to adjust the properties of the body to those of its surroundings, e.g., high altitude. The remarkable power of hemoglobin in association with oxygen and bicarbonate to act as a buffer makes it possible for the tissues to produce carbonic acid on a large scale and yet not alter their hydrogen ion concentration to a serious extent. Lastly, hemoglobin by reason of the quantity of oxygen it can transport has made life on the great scale possible to the mammalia."

Before leaving this review, we may mention that another, on the functional significance of haemoglobin in the lower forms of animal life, had already been promised by J. B. for publication in Volume 5 of the journal.

The Barcrofts began their summer holiday late this year, spending 16 August to 1 September at The Glen, Newry, and then going on to the not far distant seaside resort, Newcastle, County Down. On 27 August, while they were still at J. B.'s home, Sir William Bayliss (Plate 38) died, aged 64; exactly a month later, *Nature* published an obituary notice of him, provided by J. B. The first part is so fine and well-written an analysis of Bayliss' contribution that it would be worth quoting for that reason alone. But it contains also some autobiographical notes by J. B., so a long extract is doubly excused.

It began with the remark a very competent critic made to J. B., that "Bayliss's book [1] is by far his greatest contribution to science – much more important than any of his individual discoveries is his statement of his point of view." "At the time," went on J. B., "I wondered whether or not it were so, and I have often wondered since. Bayliss's investigations into the electric phenomena of the heart and the salivary glands, into the conditions which govern the cerebral circulation, into the muscular movements of the alimentary canal, into the mechanism of vaso-dilatation, into the correlation of vaso-motor reflexes; his establishment of the existence of antidromic fibres in the mammal, his researches on the application of surface phenomena to physiological action, and the discovery of secretin – these were his principal discoveries.

"When all allowance has been made for the fact that most of this work was carried out in collaboration, it remains an extraordinary tribute to a man's point of view to say that the statement of it transcends such researches. Yet in support of my friend's statement I reflect that in another continent there are 'Bayliss Clubs'; these do not exist for the study of the specific subjects enumerated, but for the joint discussion by physiologists and chemists of so much of science as they have in common. The association of Bayliss's name with such societies is a tribute precisely to Bayliss's statement of his point. It is not merely that when one asked why the clubs were so called one received the answer, 'We discuss the sort of thing which is in Bayliss's Book,' but that when one comes to think the matter out, one finds it not a little surprising that such societies were not associated with other names; for it cannot be claimed that Bayliss was a pioneer in the investigation of biochemistry. His interest in

[1] *Principles of General Physiology.*

the subject – so far as may be gleaned from his published works – dated from about the commencement of this century – before which date the pioneer work in Great Britain had been done. Hardy had launched colloid chemistry in the 'nineties; Hopkins, before the eighteen hundreds were complete, was well forward with that series of isolations which adorn both organic chemistry and physiological science; and Halliburton had done the major portion of his work.

"Bayliss's great contribution was that he discussed the whole subject of biochemistry as a continuous whole, thinking out each point *ab initio*, and committing the record to paper, so that what he thought for himself he thought also for others. His method of approaching a subject was one which lent itself admirably to this procedure. The quality of genius differs from individual to individual, probably even more than its quantity. Among scientific men, the genius of some is of the artistic type; though possessing great certainty of touch their inspiration comes they know not whence. To the onlooker it appears almost to be an accident; that it is not so is proved by the fact that it crops out too often in the life of the same person. In others genius is of the mathematical type; with them the premises are grouped in a particular way and in their vision the conclusion flashes out.

"Bayliss's genius was not precisely of either type – at least if my own appreciation of it may be trusted. He took nothing for granted, he inquired with meticulous care into every step of an argument; if he found something which was not perfectly clear to him, he spared no pains to discover whether the thread of the argument was really broken or whether he had merely failed to follow it. In the end his mind became clear on the subject; to his own satisfaction he was able to pronounce either that he understood the matter and that it was thus, or that he failed to understand it because the thread, to the best of his judgment, was not continuous.

"Such a method is eminently calculated to exclude all forms of obscurantism, and indeed nothing was more foreign to Bayliss's philosophy than vague talk about 'vital force' or the like. Either a phenomenon was understood, in which case the explanation could be written down and placed on record in his book, or it remained for investigation. In the latter case it might fall into one of two categories, (*a*) that of being capable of explanation on the basis of current knowledge of the properties of matter, (*b*) that which awaited further discoveries into the fundamental conditions which govern material things. It was Bayliss's good fortune to be at the zenith of his intellectual powers at a time when important additions were made to the knowledge of several departments of chemistry and physics, such, for example, as of adsorption, of catalytic action, of interfacial phenomena, and of radiant energy. Each successive addition afforded to Bayliss a prospect of the removal of phenomena from category (*b*) (above) to category (*a*), and of their final elimination from the region of the unexplained. That was Bayliss's point of view – as I understand the matter; it was a point of view extremely stimulating to the student, not only because it led so directly to experimental investigation, but also because it led along a road which seemed so straight and so easy to follow.

"Could Bayliss have been given the choice as between a spectacular form of genius on one hand and a form which was readily intelligible on the other, I feel sure he would have chosen the latter. The spectacular had little attraction for him; simplicity was characteristic no less of his intellectual outlook than of his personal habits.

"I gladly concede to rising generations that to them Bayliss's statement of his point of view is his most important work, but to myself Bayliss – of course in conjunction with Starling – was pre-eminently the discoverer of secretin. The moment when the first drop of pancreatic juice was elicited by the injection of duodenal extract must, I think, have been the most dramatic in his scientific career. Possibly I take this view, because I was at a peculiarly impressionable age at the time, possibly it is accentuated because of a trifling incident which stamps it upon my mind. I had the good fortune to witness, not indeed the first successful experiment on the subject, but I think the second – that in which the first was to be either confirmed or refuted. The physiological laboratory at University College, London, was in those days peculiarly open to young physiologists – I imagine that it is not less so now. Some errand took me round there: the door of Bayliss and Starlings's room was open: an experiment was in progress. Bayliss held a flask in one hand, and with the other was in the act of introducing a tissue extract into the circulation from a burette, Starling was on his haunches, his eye on the level of a canula which projected from the animal: the extract went in: the blood pressure fell for the nonce: there was a pause and then – drop, drop, drop from the canula. There was no secrecy – all was explained without reserve, to a man who had published perhaps a couple of papers, who hailed from another laboratory, whose very presence might have been accounted an intrusion, and who had no possible claim on either the confidence or the genius of those who had made so great a discovery. Thus can generosity and understanding attract youth within the charmed circle of genius."

On 1 October there was published a fairly long paper by Anson, J. B., Mirsky, and Oinuma "On the correlation between the spectra of various haemoglobins and their relative affinities for oxygen and carbon monoxide." It began with the statements that "the spectra of the haemoglobins from different animals, and even different mammals, are measurably different. The relative affinities of these haemoglobins for oxygen and carbon monoxide are also different, and it turns out that certain properties of the chemical affinities and of the spectra are so related that by the use of a simple equation they may be deduced from one another." The summary of the paper read as follows:-

"1. A convenient calibration of the Hartridge reversion spectroscope is described.

2. For a number of different mammals the following relationship exists. If A be the position of maximum intensity of the α-oxyhaemoglobin spectral band, B that of CO haemoglobin, and K the equilibrium constant of the equation $CO + HbO_2 \rightleftarrows COHb + O_2$

$$\text{Log } K = 0.05\,(A - B),$$

A and B being measured in Angstrom units.

3. Log K is a measure of the change in free energy involved in the reaction.

4. The value of (A – B) called in the paper 'the span', varies from 43 to 56 Angstrom units in the mammals which we have observed. The variation in individuals in the same species is very marked.

5. The relation stated in § 2 is true of the recrystallised haemoglobins.

6. The cause of variation seems to lie rather in the specificity of the globin portion of the molecule than in the haematin portion.

7. Brown and Hill's observations on the effect of temperature on

blood have been treated on similar lines. The reaction being taken as

$$Hb_n + {}_nO_2 \rightleftarrows (HbO_2)_n.$$

If at temperatures T_1 and T_2, CT_1 and CT_2 represent the concentrations of oxygen in solution when the haemoglobin is half saturated in each case, and AT_1 and AT_2 represent the position of maximum intensity of the α-bands,

$$\text{Log}\frac{1}{CT_1} - \log\frac{1}{CT_2} = .049\ (AT_1 - AT_2).\text{''}$$

The authors thanked Professor A. V. Hill for his advice and help.

The next publication in which J. B. was concerned was a communication to the Physiological Society on 18 October on "The effect of splenectomy on carbon monoxide poisoning"; the co-authors were Murray and Sands, and the effect mentioned was significantly adverse. That ends the account of J. B.'s publications for the year, but there remains one other item for mention, namely, that on 8 November he was told he was to be appointed to a Foulerton Professorship in the gift of the Royal Society; such a Professorship was free from teaching duties and not tied to a particular institution. After full consideration, [1] however, J. B. decided to withdraw before the final election by the Council of the Society.

The first note in the 1925 story is that on 15 January he addressed the Manchester Medical Students' Club on the subject, "Recent knowledge of the spleen." The lecture, given in his best style, was later published in the *Lancet* of 14 February, and thereafter, in Professor Viktor Schilling's translation, in *Naturwissenschaften.* On 17 January he gave an account to the Physiological Society, at its St. Thomas' Hospital meeting, of spleen experiments done by himself, H. A. Harris, Orahovats, and Weiss.

At Manchester he mentioned the temperature effects on the circulating blood volume which had been determined during the voyages to the Andes and back in 1921–2, and the subsequent checks on these, carried out in the glass chamber on his colleagues, Drs. Davies and Fetter. Then he brought into the story Dr. Duncan Scott's work on the blood volume of rats, which had been done with the use of the carbon monoxide method. Scott allowed J. B.

[1] One result of acceptance would have been J. B.'s resignation from his duties at Porton.

to investigate the spleens of his animals, and J. B. found that, although the blood in the general circulation contained a very high percentage of carbon monoxide, the spleen pulp contained practically none. "This observation was confirmatory of one made by Heger [1] to which little attention had been paid – namely, that in some persons who died of rapid inhalation of carbon monoxide the haemoglobin of the spleen pulp was almost devoid of contamination with that gas." In the rest of his talk J. B. synthesized the results obtained to date by himself and Henry ("of the same ilk"), by De Boer and Carroll (1924), by Hanak and Harkavy (1924), by himself, Murray and Sands (1924), and by himself, Harris, Orahovats and Weiss (*Proc. Physiol. Soc.*, 17 January 1925). Together, the findings established the splenic blood depôt function in various animals, gave some first quantitative values of the organ's holdings in red blood corpuscles in the living state, and indicated haemorrhage and exercise as two of the conditions calling upon the spleen to part with its store to the circulating blood.

J. B. ended with a typical passage. "It is not intended that the views which I have put forward should compete with the current teaching about the functions of the spleen; rather they render it more intelligible. I have no wish, for instance, to deny that the spleen is an important cemetery for red blood corpuscles any more than I have to tilt against anyone expressing the view that London is the largest cemetery in England, but I think that, according to the above experiments, the blood volume should be regarded not as aliquot part of the body-weight, but as a physiological variable which is adjusted to the work required of it, and to the size of the 'bed' which it occupies, and of the spleen as being, not a 'ductless gland', but a definite part of the vascular system. It has a function entirely in conformity with its muscular structure, being in fact a reservoir of corpuscles at once fitted by its reticulum to detain them and by its musculature to expel them when required to do so. Finally we are enabled to arrive at an intelligible estimate of when and why the body is likely to 'vent its spleen'."

Apart from a fleeting visit by Krogh at the end of the month, there is nothing thenceforward to mention before 10 February,

[1] In 1894! Paul Heger, the picturesque and charming doyen of Belgian physiologists, was still alive and dynamic in the spring of 1925, and was doubtless pleased by this reference. He died later in the year, at the age of 79.

when J. B. gave his first lecture of the year at the Royal Institution. It, and the subsequent ones on 17 and 24 February and 3 March, were concerned with "The colour of the animal creation" and were later summarized in *Nature* of 9 May under the title, "The pigmentation of animals." J. B. discussed first the hue which a person presents, and said it was dependent upon two factors, pigmentation and complexion; as these were distinct in man, it was best to begin with the human skin and work backwards. Pigmentation due to melanin was uncontrolled over short intervals of time. Complexion varied with the thickness and consequent opacity of the epidermis, and with the calibre of the various vessels, arteries, capillaries, and veins, of the underlying dermis. Of the veins but little was yet known; about the capillaries much had been learned through the work of Professor Krogh and others during the post-war years. Changes in complexion could occur rapidly and were the expression of the play of the nervous system – in particular the sympathetic system – and of endocrine hormones upon the skin vessels. Later J. B. dealt with animals other than man, but a full review cannot be given here, and those interested are referred to the published article.

Between the second and third lecture the Barcrofts, together with countless others, were saddened by the sudden and quite unexpected death of the Right Honourable Sir Clifford Allbutt, K.C.B., P. C., F.R.S., Regius Professor of Physic in the University since 1892! Though in his eighty-ninth year, he was physically and mentally active right up to his death, and a remarkable central figure was lost from the Cambridge Medical School with his passing.

On 21 May J. B., Murray, Orahovats, Sands and Weiss published in the *Journal of Physiology* their paper on the influence of the spleen in carbon monoxide poisoning, i.e., an extended form of the communication made to the Physiological Society by three of the authors on 18 October 1924, and already referred to above.

In June J. B.'s mother, Mrs. Anna Richardson Barcroft, who had survived her husband for twenty years, was taken very ill and she died on the 19th, at The Glen, in her eighty-sixth year. The whole family went from Cambridge to the funeral, which took place on 23 June; the interment was in the Friends' burial ground outside the Meeting House at Grange, near Moy, County Tyrone.

On the 26th J. B. himself was 53; the next day, as on many occasions to which reference has not been made in this account, he went on a visit to Porton, but this time he took a cricket XI to play against the local team; though the Porton side was victorious, J. B. himself scored twelve runs. History does not relate if he used the bat in the special Barcroftian way that he developed as a scholar of the Leys School (see Chapter II)! The summer holiday this year was spent at Melton, near Woodbridge; prior to it, J. B. and Henry and John Wilder, a College friend of the latter, had brought the *Nancy*, a small barge yacht that J. B. had chartered at West Mersea, round the coast and up the River Deben.

In October appeared J. B.'s second *Physiological Review*, entitled, "The significance of hemoglobin in submammalian forms of life." It began by pointing out that within the previous twelvemonth the whole problem of "placing" haemoglobin in the chemistry of life had changed, partly through Keilin's work on cytochrome (Keilin, 1925), partly through Anson and Mirsky's work on haemochromogens (Anson and Mirsky, 1925). After tracing the descent of cytochrome and of haemoglobin, J. B. went on to consider the minor pigments, helicorubin, chlorocruorin, and actiniohaematin. Then he passed to the functions of haemoglobin and its related bodies, and devoted sections to haemoglobin as a catalyst, haemoglobin as an oxygen carrier, the identity or disparity of haemoglobins, haemoglobin as a store of oxygen, haemoglobin as a buffer, and the specificity of haemoglobin. The concluding paragraph read as follows. "The variations in such phenomena as the crystalline form, the solubility, and the spectrum have not yet been fitted into any scheme which correlates them with the functional purpose which hemoglobin serves in the respiration of the organism. Yet such variations have a significance of their own. This significance has less to do with the iron containing part of the molecule than with the protein, for there are many things which are true of hemoglobin that may also be true of all the other proteins of the body; in the case of hemoglobin they may be discovered because the globin possesses a label, the hem, on which the story writes itself and may be read by all who have eyes to see. Once that story has been read completely methods may be devised for the discovery of its applicability to proteins generally and in the revelation of this story, no less than in the evolution of the respiratory function, may lie the significance of hemoglobin in the invertebrates."

On the last day of October a paper appeared, by J. B., Harris,

Orahovats and Weiss, in the *Journal of Physiology.* Its subject was "A contribution to the physiology of the spleen", and it detailed the radiographic procedures used to determine the changes occurring in the size of the organ in the living animal, together with some estimates of the contribution made by the organ, on its contraction, to the circulating blood volume, e.g., 6–15 per cent. increase during exercise in the cat and the dog. The essence of the paper had already been included in J. B.'s January lecture to the students at Manchester, and this was the more detailed scientific account.

Not many days later Professor Langley fell ill with pneumonia, and on 12 November, aged 73, he died. There is little need to recall here all that he had done for the Cambridge Medical School both before and after he succeeded Michael Foster as Professor in 1903, or his work as Editor of the *Journal of Physiology*, or his researches on the structure and function of that which he named the autonomic nervous system. Suffice it to say that he had done extremely well in all three fields of activity, and that his interest in, and help to, one particular pupil, namely Charles Scott Sherrington, made that pupil speak of him, in 1935, with a gratitude undiminished either by the passage of time or by the very great distinctions which he had himself achieved.

In the second half of November the Cambridge University Press published *Part I Lessons from High Altitudes* of the new edition of J. B.'s book, *The Respiratory Functions of the Blood*, with an appendix by Major Hingston, I. M. S., Medical Officer to the Mount Everest Expedition of 1924. As we have already had long accounts of J. B.'s altitude researches which provided so much of the material for the book, we can content ourselves with the opening passages of Yandell Henderson's review of it in *Nature*, 1926.

"Whoever," he wrote, "reads this book – and every physiologist who deals at all with the haemato-respiratory functions must read it – will gain one certain result: he will conceive a sincere liking for the author, as the ideal companion under low barometric pressure. In a style intimate, as between comrades in adventure, Prof. Barcroft here sets forth his experiences in his various invasions of the regions of low oxygen, the Peak of Teneriffe, the Capanna Margherita on the summit of Monte Rosa, Cerro de Pasco in the Andes, and last but not least the glass chamber in his laboratory where for six days he breathed the oxygen down, and himself thus

L

virtually up, to the physiological equivalent of an altitude which proved too much of a strain even for his bold and cheerful spirit.

"Prof. Barcroft reminds us that the modern sport of mountaineering originated in such essentially scientific expeditions to the upper regions as those of de Saussure on Mont Blanc. It is quite proper, therefore, that the scientific treatment of the physiological effects of low oxygen, mountain sickness, and acclimatisation should retain something of the zest of a noble sport. In this field the investigator is himself the subject observed, and in his own person suffers discomfort and overcomes hardships as great as any explorer of a new country. Yet it is also in this field that physiology has most nearly emulated the precision of physics and chemistry. It requires literary art to bring out the sporting aspects of oxy-haemoglobin dissociation curves. Prof. Barcroft imparts 'human interest' (to use the journalistic term) even to the gas laws."

Henderson continued, "As it happens, although mountaineering is not a competitive sport, the physiology of altitude is just now almost as competitive as football or rowing between two of the universities of England." He then showed how Haldane's views had developed, and how J. B. had set out to test the one that included oxygen secretion in the body's acclimatisation to great altitudes. The rest of the review covered the less contentious remainder of the book, the popularity of which continues to the present day, if one can judge of such popularity by the impossibility of finding a copy available for purchase!

On 2 December J. B. applied for the post of Professor of Physiology, vacant through the death of Professor Langley, and on 8 December Mrs. Heycock told M. A. B. that opinion was unanimous in the labs., in King's, and outside, that he should be the next occupant of the Chair. The Board of Electors evidently held the same view, and at 3.15 p.m. on Wednesday, 16 December, J. B. telephoned M. A. B. to give her the news of his election. Sir Charles Sherrington, Professor Wilson, and Professor Starling went to the laboratory to congratulate him. His achievements so far chronicled can have left the reader in no doubt that the appointment was richly merited, and at that point we can fittingly end another Chapter of this biography of him.

CHAPTER VII

1926–1932

During the period with which this Chapter deals, J. B. more or less completed his researches on the circulating blood volume and blood depôts and began to be interested in pregnancy and the foetus; he also continued work on haemoglobin, and accomplished half of his tenure of the Cambridge University Professorship of Physiology.

Just at the beginning of the period, on 9 January 1926, he and M. A. B. were saddened by the death of Dr. George Herbert Hunt, Physician to Guy's Hospital, at the early age of 41. After education at Rugby, Christ Church and Guy's Hospital Medical School, Hunt had become Assistant Physician at Guy's in 1913, and then been on war service from 1914, gaining a mention in despatches in 1915. He was one of the first to describe the new complaint that became styled "trench fever"; later he returned from the front to work at the Royal Military Hospital, Devonport, and the Royal Victoria Hospital, Netley, Thereafter, he was associated with J. B. at Cambridge in the oxygen therapy of gassed men, and in the post-war years he continued to study the effects of such therapy upon ordinary patients at Guy's. In 1915 he had married Miss Rosie Strauss, who still lives at Great Shelford in the house that was once occupied by Sir Michael Foster, and who remains a personal friend of Lady Barcroft. [1]

On 11 February J. B. gave a very interesting lecture to the members of the Chemical Society, prefacing it with a frank acknowledgement of the incompleteness of his knowledge. "In making some remarks to-night," he said, "about one of the subjects dearest to my heart, namely, haemoglobin, I wish to disabuse you at the outset from any idea that my primary object is to inform you – far otherwise – haemoglobin is to me a query mark – a Will-o'-the-wisp –

[1] The George Herbert Hunt Scholarship of the University of Oxford was founded in 1927 to assist young medical graduates wishing to travel abroad for purposes of study. An election is made biennially.

something which one day you think you have grasped only to find the next that its real essence has eluded you."

Part I of the lecture dealt with new ideas of haemoglobin and of haemochromogens, and mentioned that Anson and Mirsky (1925), by regulation of the hydrogen-ion concentration, had obtained haemoglobin from globin haemochromogen. Part II was concerned with cytochrome, the spectrum of which was first described by McMunn (1886), but which had only become significant through the work of Keilin (1925), who had kindly agreed to give a demonstration. "There is reason to suppose, " J. B. said, that "it acts as a catalyst, in contrast to haemoglobin, which acts as a carrier, but pervading both the animal and the vegetable kingdom; it is far more widely distributed than either haemoglobin or chlorophyll. Not only so, but cytochrome appears in forms of life than which none are more primitive." In Part III, on the metallic porphyrin compounds, J. B. referred to the work of Robin Hill, and in Part IV he considered the equilibrium constants of compounds of haemoglobin with oxygen and carbon monoxide. He mentioned the discovery by Christian Bohr (1903) of the biologically so important *S*-shape of the oxygen dissociation curve of blood, and told how he and Roberts (1909) had obtained an approach to a rectangular hyperbola with solutions of haemoglobin of considerable purity, so that they and others believed that if complete purity were obtained the result would be a hyperbola. Subsequent work, however, by J. B. and his colleagues, and by Adolph and Ferry (1921) at Harvard, had reversed the situation, and Adair, in his recent Fellowship Dissertation presented to King's College, Cambridge, had indicated the probability of J. B.'s idea being wrong, in which case more dilute solutions than those used by J. B. and Roberts would need to be studied, and the technical difficulties would be considerable. J. B. and Dr. Selig Hecht, of Harvard, had in consequence recently passed on to the reactions of carbon monoxide and haemoglobin, using an almost audaciously simple method to estimate, without gas analysis, the concentrations of all the reacting substances in the equation $[Hb] + [CO] = K\,[HbCO]$. Between the limits of 0 and 25 thousandths of a millimetre of mercury pressure of carbon monoxide the curve was nearly, though not quite, hyperbolic in form. "It would seem," J. B. said, "that at last we are really in sight of the fundamental curve and in a position to push forward and to discover the effects on this curve of increasing the concentration of haemoglobin, of the salts, and of alterations in the concentration of hydrogen and hydroxyl ions in the solution."

Part V dealt with the velocity coefficients of the reactions of haemoglobin with oxygen and carbon monoxide, referred to inadequate pre-war experiments by J. B. and A. V. Hill, and went on to mention the amazingly successful work of Hartridge and Roughton (1923; 1925). In Part VI the importance of the protein was discussed, and in Part VII, on osmotic pressure and molecular weight, J. B. referred to Adair's (1925) osmometric determinations, each requiring a fraction of a year, at the Low Temperature Station at Cambridge; these indicated that the molecular weight of haemoglobin was about 68,000, but provided a final puzzle, namely, how to reconcile an equation $Hb_4 + 4O_2 \rightleftarrows Hb_4O_8$ with the form of equilibrium curve as obtained. J. B. had to admit that "we have now passed entirely into the domain of speculation" . . . "Yet so long as the physical basis of the inflexion fails to be understood the dream of the physiologist will be unfulfilled, for the inflexion of the curve is the biologically important fact about it."

On 20 February J. B. was made a Fellow of the Imperial Academy of Halle, founded in 1652; on 9 March he gave a lecture to the Medical School of Leeds University on "Some recent work on the functions of the spleen." It can be regarded as in the main a review of work done since his lecture at Manchester on 15 January 1925, when he "put forward in a preliminary way a view of the splenic function which was at once old and new. New because it did not figure at all in the then current literature and thought, old because it can be stated in words published by Henry Gray in 1854. These words are as follows:-

The function of the spleen is to regulate the quantity and the quality of the blood . . . the most satisfactory proof that we can possess is that the spleen really does contain, under certain circumstances, a varying amount of blood and that that amount is to such an extent as to justify us in concluding that the organ serves to regulate its quantity.' "

With regard to further experimental work, J. B. said that the previous work on cats had been extended to the dog and the monkey, the dog showing a greater, and the monkey a smaller, splenic contraction effect than the cat. In addition, the earlier, imperfect radiographic technique for estimating volume changes had passed, via an abdominal window technique, to the exteriorized spleen one, and the previous views about the effects of exercise and haemorrhage were in consequence not only validated, but made more quantitatively precise. Further, examination of the blood nervously expelled from the spleen after ligation of the splenic artery had shown that its average haemoglobin value was 115 per cent., so that 13.6 ml. of splenic pulp material corresponded to about 15.6 ml. of blood; the blood corpuscles so leaving the spleen were shown to have increased fragility towards hypotonic saline, but increased resistance to haemolysis by saponin. Finally, stimulation of the depressor fibres of the vagus nerve, and intravascular injection of considerable quantities of saline, had given rise to increase in volume of the spleen.

The lecture was published in the *Lancet* of 13 March, and in the next number appeared an annotation, entitled, "The functions of the spleen." which seemed to throw doubt upon the contractile importance of that organ in man and suggested that, "if Henry Gray had not died of small-pox at the age of 34 he might have secured that his essay, 'On the Structure and Use of the Spleen,' which won the Astley Cooper prize in 1853, should be as familiar as the 'Descriptive and Surgical Anatomy' of 1858. We should, then, as Prof. Barcroft points out, have known the essentials of all this without being told, for Gray clearly states the main point and, indeed, might with a great deal of luck have just been able to rise in Prof. Barcroft's audience and state it again."

J. B.'s rejoinder appeared in the *Lancet* of 27 March, and read as follows. "Sir, – Your leading article last week, dealing with my two lectures on the spleen, naturally raises the question: Why did not the view put forward by Gray in 1854, that the spleen was a reservoir for blood, become thenceforward part of the body of accepted knowledge? The answer seems to be in Gray's complete failure to comprehend the mechanism by which this function was carried out. Gray denied that the spleen was contractile, and, as it seems to me, attributed a 'connective' function to cells which are really unstriped muscle fibres. In justice to him it must be remembered that he lacked the now familiar methods of differential staining; acetic acid was his principal reagent. Even if the spleen were not a muscular bag one could conceive of its performing the rôle of a reservoir of blood as the result of nice vasomotor adjustments of relative calibres of splenic artery and splenic vein. The decade between 1850 and 1860 saw, if my memory is correct, the dawn of our present conception of arterial blood pressure, as measured by exact kymographic methods, and also of the conception of vasomotor nerves. These ideas in 1854 were evidently not sufficiently advanced to illuminate Gray's philosophy."

In April J. B. and his colleagues at Cambridge and in the Department of Therapeutics of Edinburgh University published a paper, "On the hydrogen-ion concentration and some other properties of the blood from two cases of autotoxic enterogenous cyanosis." Stokvis (1902) had been the first to draw attention to this form of cyanosis, but neither in his posthumous article, nor in publications about subsequent cases, had there been any report about the oxygen capacity and content of the arterial blood and the physico-chemical behaviour of oxyhaemoglobin. J. B. and his colleagues found that the oxygen saturation of the arterial blood was distinctly below normal, but that there was no need to assume under-ventilation of parts of the lungs, or short-circuiting of blood within the lungs, or impermeability of alveoli or vessels. The work on one of the cases had been begun in 1920, and most of the determinations had thus preceded the similar studies carried out in Van Slyke's laboratory.

On the 16th of the month Mr. Charles Heycock called on J. B. in his Department to ask if he would stand for election to the Provostship of King's College; he said that many in the College wished J. B. to accept, and that M. A. B. would be equally welcome as Provost's Lady. J. B. replied that, given certain conditions and with a sufficient backing from the College, he would be willing to stand. On 9 May, however, he decided that there was not enough support and withdrew his candidature.

It must have been about this time or a little later that J. B.'s term of office as Fullerian Professor at the Royal Institution came to an end. He was appointed in 1923, and his second series of lectures had begun on 13 April. On 1 May his obituary notice of Sir William Bayliss appeared in *Proceedings of the Royal Society, B*; it was a sympathetic and interesting complement to his earlier, more personal one, of which mention has already been made in Chapter VI.

While in general in this biography little reference has been made to outside happenings, it is fitting to recall such when they are of considerable importance, and in 1926, it will be remembered, the General Strike began on 3 May and finally ended on 17 May. There is a graphic excerpt in M. A. B.'s diary, in which a volunteer railway worker described his experiences in the Newcastle area in a letter to his mother, who was a friend of M. A. B. "We have some hot times with the trains," he wrote, "while passing through the mining districts with showers of brick-bats and lumps of iron. There is hardly a window intact in any of the carriages, and yesterday while shunting at Blaydon a crowd rushed the engine and a lively time ensued during which a good many heavy lumps of coal from the tender found their marks, and shovels and firing irons defended the footplate. We got away in the end without mishap and set off home at top speed in such high glee that I forgot about a level crossing and we went clean through the gates with no end of a bang, so I dont know whether they will let me drive again on Monday."

On 19 June, to get back to our story proper, J. B. was elected Membre correspondant de la Société de Biologie, Paris, and on Wednesday, 28 July, he and M. A. B. left Cambridge en route to the twelfth International Congress of Physiologists, which was to take place in Stockholm from 3 to 6 August. They went to Tilbury in Dr. Hartridge's car, as the two dogs with exteriorized spleens, which J. B. was to demonstrate to the Congress, could not go by rail. At Tilbury they joined a group of 32 others who had come from London, and just after noon went off in the tender *Ethel* to S.S. *Balder* (Swedish Lloyd, 1600 tons). After leaving the Thames estuary M. A. B. retired sick for 45 hours, and even J. B. went down on the following morning. All Thursday it was unpleasant, and there was fog at night, but on Friday it was fine and about 4 p.m. the party landed at Gothenburg. The next day, 31 July, they went on board the steamer *Pallas* for the voyage through the Göta Canal and on to Stockholm. The scenery was delightful and on Sunday, 1 August, the party landed to see the falls and power-station at Trollhättan, and the old castle and the church at Vadstena; there were also pauses while the steamer passed through the many locks en route. The next morning the voyage continued through the glorious blue water of the Baltic, dotted with innumerable islets that at first were rugged in appearance but later became softened with trees and shrubs. Then Stockholm was sighted, a "beautiful city in enchanting surroundings," Finally. about 6 p.m. the party landed, and J: B. and M. A. B. went off to the Hotel Kung Karl.

Professor J. E. Johansson was President of the Congress, and Professor G. Liljestrand Secretary, and the prelude to the meetings was an informal reception at 8.30 p.m. on this Monday, 2 August, by the Swedish physiologists in the building of the Swedish Medical Society. The formal opening took place at 10 a.m. the next day in the Concert Hall, Hötorgat; in the evening J. B. and M. A. B. went with Professor and Mrs. Krogh to dinner at the Liljestrands, and thence to Skansen (the open-air Museum in the Djurgården). At 8 p.m., at Bollnässtugan, there was a fascinating display of old Swedish country dances; the rich, though simple, hues of the dancers' dresses showed that the Swedes have an eye for colour that is equalled in few countries and surpassed in none. After the dancing refreshments were provided in a local restaurant on the usual hospitable Swedish scale.

On the morning of the next day, 4 August, J. B. spoke to a large audience in Lecture Room C in the City Hall on "The interpretation of observations on the spleen – new and old." In the afternoon, in the Physiology Department of the Caroline Institute, he gave a demonstration, in his name and that of J. G. Stephens, of the extracutaneous spleen. One of the two dogs brought from England had been run over and killed while it was being exercised the previous day, but the survivor attracted the keen interest of all in the crowded room, and the effect of exercise on the exteriorized spleen was convincingly shown. So much so, that a Congress Member said to M. A. B. later, "Your husband is a very renowned man – in fact he has been the great man of the day, indeed I might say the *very* great man!"

In the evening 690 Congress members and prominent citizens were present at a banquet given by the City of Stockholm in a superb setting in the City Hall. Evening dress was de rigeur and many also wore decorations. The guests were received at the entry into the Blå Hallen (Blue Hall) by the municipal authorities, and, when all had arrived, fanfares on the west balcony of the Hall gave the signal to pass into the Gyllene Salen (Golden Room.) After a wonderful dinner, and speeches by Gley, von Frey, and Starling, the Blue Hall and Gala Rooms were thrown open to the guests, and there was music in the former until after midnight. On the evening of Thursday, 5 August, J. B. and M. A. B. went with other Congress members by steamer to Saltsjöbaden in the Archipelago, where dinner was taken in the Grand Restaurant. The next day, at 11 a.m., they went in a party of some hundreds by special train to Uppsala for the closing meeting of the Congress. Thereafter they visited Uppsala högar (Old Uppsala) with its burial mounds, and also the Library and the Cathedral in Uppsala, before returning to Stockholm for dinner.

By 9 a.m. the next day, they and some other Congress members were approaching Copenhagen, "a beautiful picture in the early morning with numerous little sailing boats in the blue sea." After luncheon the party visited the Kroghs in their laboratory, and then went with them to tea in the Tivoli gardens. The following day J. B. and M. A. B. spent sightseeing, and then on 10 August they travelled some way across Denmark to the Kroghs' home at Lynoeshus Lynoes, where they stayed for three days, returning to Cambridge via Esbjerg, Harwich, and London on 14 and 15 August.

The only other notes about 1926 are that on 5 October J. B. demonstrated his spleen work to a Congress of Surgeons, that he ceased at Michaelmas to be Assistant Tutor in Natural Sciences at King's College, and that he published in *Ergebnisse der Physiologie* a long review, entitled, "Die Stellung der Milz im Kreislaufsystem." It consisted of a bibliography, introduction, five main sections, and a conclusion. The sections were (1) Is the spleen within the circulation?, (2) The size of the spleen during life, (3) The nature of the blood expelled from the spleen, (4) Causes of the spleen's contraction, and (5) The mechanism of the spleen's contraction. In view of the abstracts already given of J. B.'s papers and lectures on the organ in question, it is unnecessary to give a précis of this German review of the field.

The first note about 1927 is that at a special meeting, on 22 March, of the Manchester Literary and Philosophical Society, with Professor H. B. Dixon, Vice-President, in the Chair, J. B. delivered the Wilde Memorial Lecture, the subject being "Physiology of Life in the High Andes." From the summary in the Proceedings we can content ourselves with quoting two passages. The first of these stated that "Mountain sickness is a discovery of the New World; oddly enough it had not been found in the Alps. It might be thought that Alpinism [1] was of great antiquity, that persons in small numbers had been making ascents above the summer snow line throughout all time, but this appears not to be so. It was not until the New World

[1] The original reads "Alpvision", which I assume was "Alpinism" in the script – K.J.F.

was discovered that man betook himself to the high mountains. For this there is good reason; it is two-fold, firstly there is something [i.e., silver and copper] to go for, and secondly the climatic conditions are not so vigorous as to invest the peaks with snow and ice at levels below sixteen thousand feet. Whole populations in Peru live and work at an altitude as high as the top of the Matterhorn." With respect to this passage, it seems worth while to recall to the reader the historical section in Paul Bert's *La pression barométrique* of 1878, for in that section the literature on mountain sickness is mentioned at some length. In the second passage J. B. said, in relation to his own expedition to the Peruvian Andes, that "Never does a European become quite himself up there, he gets over his breathlessness and the palpitation of his heart to a large degree, but he never attains to real vigour either of body or of mind." It seems worth while, in view of this passage, to mention here that researches on the "Man of the Andes" had been initiated in 1925 in the Peruvian Medical School and that Dr. Carlos Monge (see Monge, 1948), who is now Director of the Institute of Andean Biology of the University of San Marcos, Lima, was finding himself about 1927 in some disagreement with J. B. "For our part," he wrote, "as early as 1928 we proved in the Paris Medical School that Professor Barcroft was himself suffering from a subacute case of mountain sickness without realizing it. His substantial error is easy to explain as resulting from an improper generalization on his part of what he himself felt and applying his researches to Andean man in general." Monge's own attitude is that "in order to judge life at high altitudes one must leave behind the orthodoxy of the texts and create a new human biology concerned with beings adapted to live in the high Andes." The present writer's object is not to influence the reader's judgment, but to acquaint him with J. B.'s work and any contemporary support for, or opposition to, it – hence this reference to Monge (1928); the Monge (1948) publication is mentioned here because the book has a wide circulation among those interested in bioclimatology, and there will not be any particularly appropriate place in which to refer to it later in this biography.

The next event of 1927 that needs a word or two is that on 26 June J. B. left, as a Delegate of the Royal Society, to attend the quincentenary celebrations of the Catholic University of Louvain, and that on 28 June he had conferred upon him the honorary degree of Doctor of Medicine – Her Majesty the Queen of the Belgians was one of the other honorary graduands. On 30 June he was back in Cambridge.

The family holiday this year was taken at Grasmere and Port Stewart.

We have now to record some further publications by J. B. and first we may mention "Étude des rapports entre la rate et la masse sanguine," which appeared in the second number of a new French journal, called *Le Sang Biologie et Pathologie*, and gave a review of work on the relation of the spleen to the blood in circulation; its relation to the quality of the blood would, J. B. hoped, form the subject of a later memoir. Between July and December another line of his work was given foreign publicity, for Julius Springer published a German translation of *The Respiratory Function of the Blood. Part I. Lessons from High Altitudes*; the translating had been done by Dr. W. Feldberg, who had come to Cambridge in 1925 to work with J. B. On 5 October, finally, there appeared in the *Journal of Physiology* papers by J. B. and J. G. Stephens, entitled, "Observations upon the size of the spleen," and by J. B. and L. T. Poole, entitled, "The blood in the spleen pulp." In the former it was shown that the exteriorized, innervated spleen of the dog contracted to half or one-third of its original size on exercise and even farther on death or severe haemorrhage, the contraction on exercise adding about one fifth to the circulating blood volume. The exercise effect might be preceded by an emotional paling and some degree of contraction; in any case the contraction came on early in both exercise and haemorrhage. The second paper stated that the spleen played "a considerable rôle in the increment of corpuscles both during asphyxia and during exercise, even though it may not be responsible for the whole phenomenon."

On 11 October J. B. was made an honorary member of the Caius Medical Society "in gratitude for the help you have given to the Club"; on 27 October he went to Lille to read a paper (see 1928) at "L'Institut de Commerce." He had, apparently, a wonderful time, but the only detail is that inter alia he went down a coal mine. He returned to Cambridge on 31 October.

On 21 January 1928 he and Henry went up to a meeting of the Physiological Society at which Henry demonstrated a new apparatus for arterial blood flow measurement, and in February J. B. published the short memoir, "Le groupement protéique dans l'hémoglobine", which he had delivered at Lille on 28 October 1927. Thereafter, there is no note until 7 May, when he was very busy preparing to take part in the Harvey Tercentenary Celebrations; six days later he was one of a hundred delegates who were received by the King at Buckingham Palace; they shook hands with His Majesty and then listened to the address read by Sir John Rose Bradford and to the King's reply.

Later J. B. went to Paris to attend the session of the Société de biologie held there on 25 and 26 May, and to speak at some length on "L'hémoglobine et son rôle biologique." A newspaper report on the réunion plénière said that "Cette manifestation a été marquée par la présence de sir J. Barcroft." Three days after the session was over he was still being fêted in all directions!

In the following month he experienced pleasure of a different kind in the appearance of *Part II Haemoglobin* of the 2nd Edition of his book, *The Respiratory Function of the Blood.* In the Preface, dated 3 April, he wrote as follows. "The present volume deals with haemoglobin regarded as a chemical substance; and here I would like particularly to point to the limited scope of this book. It makes no profession of dealing with the red blood corpuscle, or with the properties of blood. These will form the subject of another volume. Thus the consideration of many now classical investigations, such as those of the Rockefeller Institute and the nomogram of Prof. L. J. Henderson, is reserved for the present." The chapters of the book dealt in fact with porphyrins, haemochromogen, cytochrome, the specicifity of haemoglobin, specific oxygen capacity, the manufacture of haemoglobin, the nature of haemoglobin solution, the molecular weight and dissociation curve of haemoglobin, theories of the union of oxygen with haemoglobin, the kinetics of oxyhaemoglobin in dilute solutions, the interactions of carbon monoxide with reduced haemoglobin and of carbon monoxide and oxygen with haemoglobin, the effect of temperature on haemoglobin, and the biological significance of haemoglobin. Much of the newer work described had been assisted by the Medical Research Council not only with funds, but also with sympathy and advice, and J. B. gave a special word of thanks to the Council and to its Secretary, Sir Walter Morley Fletcher. The book as a whole was a timely review, welcomed by those who had been seeing the story unfold but were glad to have a synthesis by such an authority. It is, however, unnecessary to give here a detailed analysis of the volume, for older physiologists recall its appearance and younger ones, unless they are specializing in the particular field, probably do not need more than the notice given above.

August was also a pleasurable month, for the 5th was J. B. and M. A. B.'s silver wedding anniversary, and M. A. B.'s diary note reads: "*What* happy years we look back upon. Would that all the world were so happily married . . . We had a few friends for tea, Mrs. Leggett, M. Hammond, H. B. Stephen, Mrs. and Miss Digby, Peter Gaynor, and a Mr. Ede, and were quite a happy party." Perhaps in celebration, J. B. and M. A. B. took an extended summer holiday, from 21 August to 29 September, in Holland – particularly the Isle of Walcheren – and in Belgium. On 6 September, in the Bad-Hotel, Domburg, they met Werner Spalteholz, the distinguished Professor of Anatomy of the University of Leipzig, and his wife.

While they were on holiday, there appeared in the *Journal of Physiology* a paper by J. B. and J. G. Stephens, entitled, "The effect of pregnancy and menstruation on the size of the spleen," and another by J. B. and H. W. Florey on "Some factors involved in the concentration of blood by the spleen." The paper by J. B. and Stephens had had a forerunner in *Archivio di Scienze Biologiche* under the title, "Alterations in the size of the spleen during pregnancy in dogs." The introduction to this latter is of some interest, for it recalled that Miescher [1], in 1881, "made the observation that the spleens of Rhine salmon became smaller during the breeding season. This observation seemed less important than it otherwise would have been, because in the breeding season there is a general wasting of tissues in the salmon. The circumstances which led to the research described below were as follows. In the summer of 1926 we had three dogs, the spleens of which had been exteriorised for some weeks, all of these spleens reacted well to exercise. Towards the end of July it became necessary to choose which animals we should take for exhibition at the Physiological Congress at Stockholm. The spleen of the animal which at one time

[1] F. Miescher (1844–1895), Professor of Physiology at Basel, who was responsible for the local organization of the First Congress of Physiologists in 1889, had one of the most versatile and innovating minds in the history of our science, but published many interesting findings and thoughts in journals unlikely to come to the notice of physiologists.

seemed most promising, suddenly became very small, quite pale in colour and responded poorly to exercise. That is to say, it was obviously contracted and pale even during rest. This animal appearing anomalous was killed and the post mortem carried out by Sergeant-Major Secker revealed the fact that it was in an advanced state of pregnancy."

Experiments carried out since 1926 had shown that pregnancy caused a progressive diminution in size of the exteriorized spleen, with recovery after parturition. To this finding the paper in the *Journal of Physiology* added further details, e.g., that during "heat" the spleen of the bitch dropped to half its normal volume, and during pregnancy to an even smaller size, though even so the response to exercise was never completely abolished. The spleen surface also paled when the organ shrank, the onset of the pallor usually preceding the contraction. The shrinkage during heat and pregnancy seemed attributable "in the main to the necessity of supplying blood to meet the increased capacity of the vascular bed, caused by the dilatation of the uterine vessels."

The paper by J. B. and Florey discussed possible factors enabling the spleen to concentrate its contained blood, showed that ligation of the venous channels caused considerable concentration, fluid being drained off by the lymphatics, and suggested "that the very marked contractility of the splenic vein is a factor of importance in connection with the phenomena discussed." In view of all the new experimental findings since 1922 about the *animal* spleen, it is interesting to note that in January 1928 the famous American surgeon, William J. Mayo, had written of the *human* spleen as still "an organ of contradiction and mystery: in health of relatively unimportant function, in disease a menace of grave import."

The paper by Abeloos, J. B., *et al.*, the last of J. B.'s publications for the year, was concerned with the impression, given by a great number of determinations made in recent years, that the ferricyanide method of oxygen estimation (Haldane's constant pressure apparatus and J. B.'s differential one) had yielded lower results for the oxygen capacity of blood than the Van Slyke pump. The paper, as a first contribution, gave the results of a series of comparisons between measurements made with the old blood gas pump (a modification of the Barcroft and Roberts model of 1910) and others made with the Van Slyke constant volume apparatus (see Van Slyke and Neill, 1924). There was agreement in the analyses, for both oxygen and nitrogen, which they gave of haemoglobin solutions.

A week before this paper appeared, J. B. had been greatly saddened by the death, on 2 November, of Sir Hugh K. Anderson, Master of Gonville and Caius College, one of the two men who, as teachers, had first shown him the fascination of physiology. J. B. felt the loss to be irreparable, and said to M. A. B. that his best friend had gone.

For the beginning of 1929 we can make use of some notes from M. A. B.'s diary, and the first is that on 2 February George Pickering (now Professor of Medicine at St. Mary's Hospital Medical School) came to stay at No. 13 for a couple of nights. He was then a clinical student in London after a distinguished pre-clinical career in Cambridge, where he had been greatly impressed by J. B.'s powers as a lecturer; it was also through J. B. that Pickering, like so many others, first became interested in research. On 21 February Professor I. de Burgh Daly came from Birmingham to work with Henry and he also stayed two nights. The work was presumably on the mechanical Stromuhr, which Henry was to describe in the *Journal of Physiology* of 25 July; he was at the time George Henry Lewis Student of Cambridge University. Then on 8 March Sir Charles Sherrington stayed for a night on the occasion of an address to the Foster Club. In the evening the Barcrofts and he went to see the Victorian melodrama, "The Carpenter of Rouen", and had a good laugh.

Two days later Sir Charles wrote as follows from Oxford to his hostess. "Accept my hearty thanks for the kind welcome and hospitality. I enjoyed it all very greatly. Not least the remeeting of your son Henry and some talk from him about his apparatus and the results. After seeing some interesting things at the laboratory on Friday I caught – by your husband's aid – my train in the way trains should be caught, that is with 2 secs. to spare! In the way, in short, in which the 'Carpenter of Ruin' at the Festival Theatre would have caught it – melodramatically! It was pleasant to get some talk reminiscent of former days at Cambridge but I never enjoyed a glimpse of it more thoroughly than this last."

On 20 March J. B. and C. S. Robinson published in the *Journal of Physiology* a paper, entitled, "A study of some factors influencing intestinal movements." They had exteriorized a section of the intestine, in various dogs, for the purpose of studying the movements and had found that even when empty of food the small intestine is fairly active, displaying all the types of movement observed during the passage of food; exercise, emotion and sleep caused no noticeable change in the movements, and the passage of food etc. occurred even though a portion of the intestine 2 or 3 inches in length was inactive."

Another paper by J. B. in the same journal is mentioned below. Apart from these two, his publications for the year included six articles in the 14th Edition of *Encyclopaedia Britannica* on "Anoxaemia", "Blood", "Excretion", "Physiology", "Pigments of skin and hair", and "Respiration"; abstracts in *Proceedings of the Mayo Clinic* of two Mayo Foundation lectures; and two translations into German of 1928 publications. One of these, *Die Atmungsfunktion des Blutes. Teil 2: Hämoglobin*, was by Dr. W. Feldberg, the other, "Das Hämoglobin und seine biologische Bedeutung", was by G. Lemmel.

On 26 May about 50 members of the Physiological Society visited 13 Grange Road on the occasion of the Cambridge meeting, and thereafter there is no note until one comes to the preparations for the 13th International Congress of Physiologists, scheduled to take place in Boston, Mass., under the Presidency of W. H. Howell (1860–1945) from 19 to 23 August. About sixty French physiologists crossed in the *France* but the bulk of the European members went in the *Minnekahda*, embarking at London or at Boulogne on 9 August, and spending ten days together in a delightful "Pre-Congress" (Plates 42–44). Twenty-two countries were represented, and in a short while the whole party became as one in the one-class ship, as Starling had forecast in his memorable prophecy in Stockholm in 1926. Halcyon sunshiny days, with sights of porpoises, flying fishes, and whales added to the general happiness, and not long after the ship had docked on 18 August M. A. B. had a cable, laconically stating, "Magnificent crossing. Magnificent Congress."

It was magnificent in its size, for the enrolment rose to between 1600 and 1700; it was impressive in the general high level and number of the scientific items; it was interesting also through the attendance of at least two veterans of the first Congress of 1889, namely, Léon Fredericq and Louis Lapicque, and it was enlivened by the vivacious presence of Pavlov, whom Cushing described as "the most notable figure in this huge assembly"; finally, two social events in particular were most memorable, namely, the reception on the evening of 21 August and the dinner given by the Federation of American Societies for Experimental Biology on the following evening. The reception was at 9 p.m. in the Court of the Harvard Medical School. Building A was beautifully illuminated by soft cream lights, the Boston Symphony Orchestra assembled on the steps, "and under a gorgeous moonlight sky played as I had never heard them play before. The weather was perfect and the programme was particularly happy. I rather fancy that this incident will have impressed the foreign guests perhaps more than anything else that has been done" (Fulton). At the dinner somewhat over a thousand persons were seated in Memorial Hall, and between five and six hundred others were in rooms connected by loud speakers with the Hall. Cannon, who presided over the banquet, referred first to the guests of honour – Pavlov and Fredericq – and thereafter introduced Bottazzi, A. V. Hill, Frank, and Gley, each of whom replied. Gley's speech, which included quotations from French and English poetry, was most delightful and amusing, but it lasted nearly three-quarters of an hour! After the banquet members adjourned to the College yard, which was beautifully decorated with Chinese lanterns. An excellent orchestra played in full moonlight, the air was delightfully warm, and dancing continued until nearly 2 a.m!

At the closing session of the Congress on the afternoon of Friday, 23 August, Johannson, among others, spoke and in a short but very stimulating address he said, inter alia, that "It will be more and more evident that it is the actual searching for what we call truth, and not its presumed possession, which creates the cultured man. A general acceptance of this point of view might form the premise for that 'peace on earth' of which man has dreamt through all ages."

J. B. is named in the official publications as a member of the Congress, but there is no mention of him or of any of his research colleagues of the time giving a communication or demonstration. [1]

[1] This makes somewhat puzzling a reference in *Proc. Mayo Clin.*, 1929, *4*, 303, where he spoke of demonstrating at the Physiological Congress a dog which, apparently, had exteriorized spleen *and* intestine; his demonstration at the previous Congress in 1926 had been confined to the exteriorized spleen. Perhaps the passage should have read "Physiological Society" and not "Physiological Congress". A. V. Hill in 1952 had no memory or information about J. B.'s showing a dog with exteriorized spleen and portion of intestine at the Congress, whereas such definitely was demonstrated to the Physiological Society (see Barcroft and Florey, 1929, 188).

On 24 August most of the Congress members went to Woods Hole to visit the laboratories there and to get recreation ashore and afloat. J. B., however, together with A. V. Hill and Walter Fletcher, accompanied Alexander Forbes and his family to Naushon Island, which is near Woods Hole, and there they spent Sunday, 25 August. The next day, J. B., Hill, and Forbes started on a cruise to Maine on the schooner, *Black Duck*, the all-amateur crew including Edward B. Krumbhaar, Stanley Cobb, Allen Butler, Charles C. Lund, Eric Schroeder, and Stanley Cunningham. The party spent the night at Nantucket, and next morning Forbes thought J. B. had fallen overboard. In fact, he had gone to sleep on the deck, whither he had fled from the blankets and boots which A. V. Hill had thrown at him in the cabin. J. B. had "wanted to be allowed to snore in peace". From Nantucket they cruised via Portsmouth, N. H. (28 August) and Georges Harbor (30 August) to Swans Island, Maine (31 August), and on 1 September J. B. and A. V. Hill left Forbes and went on to Portland, Maine, whence they continued by car to L. J. Henderson's house at Morgan Center, Vermont, for a stay of several days.

From Vermont J. B., now without Hill's company, went on to Madison, Wisconsin, where he was the welcome house-guest of Walter J. Meek and his wife, and where he gave a lecture, entitled, "Observations on the physiology of the spleen." The date of the lecture was 13 September, and it was given before the Wisconsin State Medical Society because the fall session of the Medical School had not yet begun, whereas the Society was meeting at the time in Madison. J. B.'s paper was very well received by the members present.

Three days later he lectured at 7.30 p.m. in the Assembly Room of the Mayo Clinic, Rochester, Minnesota, on "Hemoglobin", and the next day, at the same time and in the same place, on "The spleen and the circulation". The first lecture, to judge from the published abstract which is all that is available, added a few more details about the development of his interest in the blood pigment in question, and included a more connected account of work by Keilin, by Anson and Mirsky, by Hans Fischer, and by Robin Hill. But it can reasonably be regarded as a variation on a theme, and therefore needs no longer analysis here. In the second lecture, likewise available only in abstract, he explained how he had wondered if the splenic contraction on exercise was peculiar to that organ or was a sample of a general visceral effect, and how this had led him to exteriorize portions of dog's intestine on the same side as the spleen. He had then found that, while the spleen tended to stay contracted, the intestine paled for about a third of a minute at the outset of exercise but regained its colour in about a minute. "One is going into a subtle field," he continued, "when one tries to differentiate an exercise syndrome and the mental activity which accompanies it. I believe, however, that the paleness of the intestine is due not to running but to the mental stimulus that prompts the running." He then reverted to the spleen, and stated that mental stress can keep the dog's spleen contracted for half an hour or longer. Various emotions could affect the organ to varying degrees, i.e., in a dog susceptible to cats the least contraction was caused by the smell of a cloth that had been in contact with a cat, the next greater by the sound of a cat, a greater still by the sight of one, and the greatest of all by the dog's bounding after it. Finally, he spoke of Stanley Cook's work in Cambridge on the haemosiderin of the spleen, and of the spleen's value in the animal's economy. On exposure to carbon monoxide splenectomized animals had been the first to die, then animals with other abdominal operations, and finally normal animals. So the presence of the spleen was a protection.

What J. B. did between these lectures and 2 October seems to be unknown, but on that date he gave a Mary Scott Newbold Lecture, the twenty-first in the series, at the College of Physicians of Philadelphia. The lectureship had been founded in 1917 by Mr. Clement B. Newbold, a prominent Philadelphian, as a memorial to his wife, and the first British lecturer had been Sir Robert McCarrison in 1921. In the spring of 1929 Dr. William J. Taylor (died 1936) the then Chairman of the College Committee on the Lectures, had invited J. B. to give one on 2 October, and on 30 April J. B. had replied, accepting and stating his appreciation of the distinction. The title of the lecture that he gave was "Alterations in the volume of the normal spleen and their significance." It need not be abstracted here, but it is perhaps worth while to quote the opening paragraph. "The work of three men", J. B. said, "whose names appear on the roll of this College, Pearce, Krumbhaar and Frazier, has to me been so great a source of inspiration as to make this evening one which will always stand out in my memory. The pleasure of discussing the

38—William Maddock Bayliss (1860–1924)

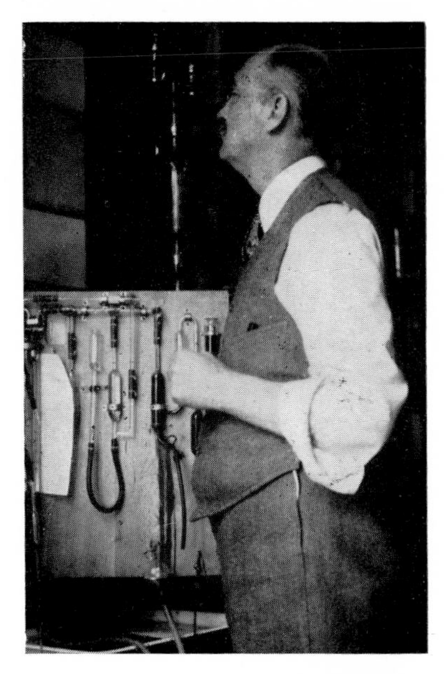

39—Joseph Barcroft at work, April 1928

40—Joseph Barcroft at work, April 1928

41—Joseph Barcroft driving off, 1929

42—S.S. *Minnekahda*, August 1929. Joseph Barcroft and A. V. Hill

43—S.S. *Minnekahda*, August 1929 Joseph Barcroft and August Krogh (1874–1949)

44—S.S. *Minnekahda*, August 1929. Joseph Barcroft and H. W. Florey

change of volume of the spleen in Philadelphia is as great as the sense of honor which I feel in being asked to do so by a society which numbers among its members some of those whose opinions on this subject are of outstanding authority. My own methods are perhaps different from most used by them and my only regret is that the occasion is that of a lecture rather than a medical exchange of experience." Writing in 1952, Dr. Krumbhaar regretted that he could not recall details of an event of so long ago, but modestly said that J. B. "was always more than kind to our work, the importance of which he consistently exaggerated; and this I felt was characteristic of his general attitude towards scientists." From a letter written to Dr. William J. Taylor on 7 October 1929, we can add that the visit to Philadelphia was for J. B. "a delightful occasion"; he asked Dr. Taylor to accept his thanks and to distribute them liberally to all concerned.

The climax, however, of the tour was provided by the lectures which J. B. delivered, under the Edward K. Dunham Lectureship for the Promotion of the Medical Sciences, at 5 p.m. on 7, 9, 11, and 14 October at the Harvard Medical School. The general subject of the series was "Some Features in the Architecture of Function", and the individual titles were "Integrative Adaptation", "The Constancy of the Internal Environment", "The Principle of Antagonism", and "Stores of Material". They were important because they rose above the ordinary presentation of research findings and attempted a more philosophical treatment. No published account appears to be available, but the lectures excited considerable interest, and they evolved finally into the book which J. B. published in 1934, and which has rightly been regarded as one of the more important in modern physiological literature.

Not long after the last Dunham lecture, he sailed for home in the *Baltic* and he was back in Cambridge on 28 October. A week later M. A. B., whose summer holiday had been spent with a "gall bladder" at home, went up to London for a cholecystectomy and appendicectomy by Lord Moynihan. We can complete this picture of the Barcrofts in 1929 by noting that Henry, as from 1 October, had left Cambridge for St. Mary's Hospital Medical School, and that on 23 October a paper, by J. B. and H. Florey, appeared in the *Journal of Physiology*. It was on "The effects of exercise on the vascular conditions in the spleen and the colon", but the summary did not add materially to what J. B. had said earlier in the year at the Mayo Clinic (see above).

We can begin the 1930 story with mention of three publications. The Mary Scott Newbold Lecture appeared in the January number of the *American Journal of the Medical Sciences,* "Some effects of emotion on the volume of the spleen" were reported in the *Journal of Physiology* of 27 January, and "The effects of certain anaesthetics on the volume of the exteriorised spleen" were described in *Archives internationales de Pharmacodynamie et de Thérapie,* P. Rothschild being co-author. Most of the results in the second paper had been revealed in the second Mayo Clinic Lecture of 1929, and all that need be added to the account is that "The known effect of adrenaline in producing contraction of the spleen has been confirmed in the exteriorized preparation, and a single injection of ephedrine has been shown to produce a contraction which passes off slowly, lasting over 60 and under 150 minutes."

The anaesthetic experiments were carried out on dogs with innervated or denervated spleens according as to whether central or peripheral effects were to be studied. To begin with, the results of administration of alcohol, to which the dog is strikingly resistant, were noted. In the dosage of 2 ml. per kg. via the throat, it had no obvious effect on the animal or upon the size of the innervated spleen; in four times that dosage, it caused signs of drunkenness, and definite contraction of the spleen. Chloroform-ether mixture caused contraction of the innervated spleen, the degree of the effect being related to the degree of nervous stress of the animal rather than to the depth of anaesthesia. Experiments to show the effects of alcohol upon the denervated spleen were too few to be conclusive; the effects of chloroform-ether mixture were less upon the denervated than upon the more normal organ, but here again the number of experiments was far too small by later-day standards, and the paper as a whole must be regarded as an indication of the field rather than an adequate exposé.

On 26 January, to turn to a different sphere, J. B. lectured to the students at St. Mary's, and his talk was described by hearers as "the best lecture ever delivered there." In March he was for a while in Holland and later had a week's holiday in Devon. Then on 10 April he went with other members of the Physiological Society to Belgium. So far as the present writer knows, this was the second time in the history of the Society that such a Continental trip had been arranged, the first time being in 1925. On the evening of 11 April there was a reception at the Royal Palace in Bruxelles for members of the Physiological Society and their guests, and the Harvey film was projected. At the special request of Their Majesties the King and Queen of the Belgians, informal morning dress was worn; J. B. had a long talk with the Queen, who presumably remembered him from 1927. The scientific meeting took place next day in the Department of Physiology of Louvain University, Belgian physiologists giving demonstrations before noon and Belgian and English physiologists (J. B. not one of them) giving communications in the afternoon.

May was marked in succession by Robbie Barcroft's twenty-first birthday, by a visit from Professor and Mrs. W. B. Cannon on the occasion of the former's Linacre Lecture, and by the Cambridge meeting of the Physiological Society; during the week-end a party of about eighty members and others visited 13 Grange Road. Dr. Herman J. Jordan, who was a house-guest for three nights, wrote on 13 May to M. A. B.:- "You can scarcely imagine the importance the scientific work of your husband has had for me and for my laboratory. After having read 'The respiratory function of blood' 1914 there came a fundamental change. We began to conquer new fields of our science with the method of Professor Barcroft to *think* science."

On 15 August J. B. and M. A. B. went off for a long holiday in Switzerland and Italy, passing from Wildersvil to Grindelwald and thence to Baveno. On 10 September they visited Isola Bella, and on 21 September left for home. The remainder of the year's items are mainly about their two sons. On 19 November Henry repeated one of his father's early successes by winning the Gedge Prize; in December Robbie passed his examination for military subjects No. 2, and also proceeded to the degree of Bachelor of Arts. On Christmas Day afternoon the Barcrofts attended the service in King's College Chapel and thereafter there was pleasant chat at No. 13 until bed-time, "J. B. imitating most excellently some of the early Friends of his youth." His power of mimicry has not yet been mentioned in this biography, but it was certainly remarkable, and his repertoire included an imitation of a speech by Pavlov, with the delivery interrupted at intervals through inefficient transmission via a loudspeaker. Whether or not the occasion was the dinner at the Boston Congress the present writer cannot say, but it seems possible; at all events, the imitation by J. B. was rated first-class by those who were fortunate enough to hear it.

New Year's Day, 1931, saw the publication of a paper by J. B. from the War Department, Experimental Station, on "The toxicity of atmospheres containing hydrocyanic acid gas"; it comprised experiments from the time of the war onwards, and reference has already been made to it in the 1918 story. J. B. stated that the fatal dose of a poisonous gas is best expressed by a toxicity-concentration time curve, and then went on to give such curves for different mammals and birds; he had found the dog the most sensitive of the mammals tested. Next he considered the mode and seat of action of hydrocyanic acid vapour, beginning the modern story with Lovatt Evans' (1919) paper, and going on to Warburg and Keilin's work, and to that of H. Taylor. The remaining headings were on the specific action of the gas inhaled in low concentrations, the toxicity of it to man when inhaled, the concentration necessary to produce unconsciousness, general comparison between mammals and birds, the concentration necessary to make pigeons vomit, indicators, and treatment. Older members of the Physiological Society will remember an allied demonstration by Barcroft and Taylor at Cambridge in which respiration failed in the cat via stages of pneumotaxis, apneusis, and gasping, in line with Lumsden's (1923, 1924) views on the respiratory centres and their activities.

At the end of January Robbie Barcroft was gazetted 2nd Lieutenant in the Cheshire Regiment, and on 20 February J. B. went to Oxford for the simulation of a mountain ascent in the pressure-chamber (Plate 45) installed in the Sir William Dunn School of Pathology; the experiment was recorded by M. A. B. as "most successful", but no contemporary details are available. Then on 25 February the *Journal of Physiology* published a paper by J. B. and J. J. Izquierdo (Plate 46) on "The relation of temperature to the pulse rate of the frog". Their object had been "to gain further knowledge of the point at which the nervous system commences to dominate the response of pulse rate to temperature and, if possible, to ascertain the nature of the nervous control if such were found to exist." The frog had been chosen as an initial species in a contemplated cold- and warm-blooded series. The excised heart in winter usually gave a linear relationship between the logarithm of the frequency of the sinus beat and the reciprocal of the absolute temperature between 5° and 20° C.; in the intact animal the results were irregular. In summer the frequency of the excised heart, as also of the heart of the intact animal, bore a nearly linear relation to the temperature. Results of experiments with atropine confirmed the view of those observers who regarded vagal tone as virtually absent in the heart of the resting frog.

On 12 March there was a visit to No. 13 by Professor and Mrs. Krogh and members of their family, from 18 to 27 J. B. and M. A. B. took a holiday in the New Forest, and two days before their return Robbie became engaged to Miss Betty Hermione Durancé Cartwright. On 24 April J. B. and Izquierdo published a paper on "The effect of temperature on the frequency of heart and respiration in the guinea-pig and cat," and J. B. and F. Verzár one on "The effect of exposure to cold on the pulse rate and respiration of man."

The former extended observations on the frog (Barcroft and Izquierdo, 1931; N. B. Taylor, 1931) to mammals; cats and guinea-pigs were used, but the conclusions given were about cats alone. Between 25° and 41° C. in deeply anaesthetized animals the pulse and respiration rates rose gradually with the temperature, but in lightly anaesthetized animals within the range from 33 ± 1.5° and 41° C. there were irregularities coincident with, and probably associated with, shivering and the general syndrome of "sham rage", and therefore? connected with cardiac sympathetic nervous activity. The irregularities were not abolished by atropine in dosage sufficient to paralyse cardiac vagal nerve endings. The paper by Barcroft and Verzár dealt with human experiments carried out in the cold storage room of the Marine Biological Station, Woods Hole, Mass., and with confirmatory ones done in the Physiologische Anstalt, Basel. The conclusions were that, "apart from spasmodic rises in the pulse rate associated with shivering, the pulse rate in man falls with fall of body temperature"; that "the spasmodic rises associated with shivering may amount to 40 p.c. of the original pulse rate"; that "the respiration shows marked summation of inspiratory movements during the rigors which had very deep and sustained inspirations"; and that "the oxygen consumption increases during the shivering fits by as much as 75 p.c. of its value during rest".

On 30 April J. B. heard that the Senate of Queen's University, Belfast, had decided that he should have conferred on him the honorary degree of Doctor of Science. Two days later the Physiological Society met at Cambridge, and E. P. Cathcart was a house-guest at No. 13 for two nights. Members always enjoyed the May meeting, partly because spring had come and the University, city, and surrounding country looked particularly beautiful, partly because there was invariably a good list of agenda, largely by the Cambridge workers themselves. This time there were three demonstrations and five communications by J. B. and/or visitors introduced by him, namely, Nisimaru, Brinkman, Margaria, Ray, Benatt, Greeson, and Goldschmidt. Two of the communications dealt with the mechanisms of the liver and of the skin, considered as blood depôts. Dinner after the meeting was served in the Junior Combination Room of Trinity College, and the next day, Sunday, about seventy-five members and guests went on the by now traditional visit to 13 Grange Road and its ever-attractive garden.

On 14 May J. B. dined, as one of two special guests, with the Colston Research Society of Bristol University; on 6 June he attended the funeral of an old friend, Colonel Charles Thomas Heycock, metallurgist, of King's College; on 26 June there was published his and Margaria's paper, entitled, "Some effects of carbonic acid on the character of human respiration". Since the work of Haldane and Priestley (1905) it had been known that inhalation of CO_2 increased the total ventilation, but no very simple statement could be made in regard to the frequency of respiration. J. B. and Margaria found that inhalation of the gas increased the rates of air inhalation and exhalation and shortened the time occupied by each phase; that the rate of inhalation of air at the middle of inspiration varied almost exactly with the total ventilation; that the above relation and all others measured were the same for an individual whether the hyperpnoea was produced by CO_2 inhalation or by exercise; and that the maximal total ventilation produced by exercise was nearly twice that produced by the highest concentration of CO_2 which could be breathed for a quarter of an hour. It seemed probable, thus, that CO_2 inhalation and exercise acted in similar ways, but that the maximal effect of the gas fell short of that of exercise.

The next event requiring mention is that on 10 July J. B. became Hon. D. Sc. of Queen's University, Belfast. After that there is a gap until 12 August, when he and M. A. B. went off for a holiday in Switzerland and Austria, visiting St. Anton, Oetz, and Innsbruck, and returning home via Zürich about 16 September. Ten days after their departure Henry became engaged to Bridget Mary, daughter of Arthur Stanley Ramsey, President of Magdalene College, and the late Mrs. Ramsey, and the announcement gave great delight to J. B. and M. A. B. From 23 to 30 September the British Association for the Advancement of Science held its annual meeting, the venue this time being London, and on Friday, 25 September, J. B. addressed the Section of Physiology on "The limits placed by altitude to physical exercise". The published account read as follows:-

"The work of Italian researchers has shown that man can live at an atmospheric pressure of about 110 mm. Hg. if he breathes, not air, but oxygen. At that pressure he can do little or no work. Recent researches by Barcroft, Douglas, Kendal and Margaria have, however, shown that at 170 mm. pressure breathing oxygen, man can step up 1,000 feet in an hour. As the work consisted of stepping on to a box, it was incidental that he stepped down as often as he stepped up. One hundred and seventy millimetres is a much lower pressure than that of the top of Everest. Therefore it follows that, given a supply of oxygen into the respiratory passages. the feat of climbing at the highest altitudes on the earth's surface is not impossible, and, apart from unknown difficulties in the terrain, the problem of climbing Everest is less one for the mountaineer than for the engineer. Not the engineer in general, but a particular sort of engineer, one who specialises in the apparatus of respiration, such, for instance, as the diving engineer or the technical chemical defence departments of the National Armée. The amount of oxygen necessary is about a litre and a half per minute. If an ascent of 5000 feet were made in five hours the oxygen actually absorbed by the climber would be 450 litres. Suppose he breathed half that amount on the descent:-

450
225
———
675: say 700 litres, say 30 cubic feet.

The problem then may be subdivided thus:-

1. How is a man to carry 30 cubic feet of oxygen?

2. If he 'rebreathes' it, how is he to get rid of the carbonic acid?

3. How is he to cope with the incidental difficulties proper to the use of apparatus such as the occurrence of water vapour, which freezes in inconvenient places?

4. An estimate of the margin necessary over and above the theoretical quantity.

"Seven hundred litres weigh approximately a kilogram, so that the weight of the oxygen itself is trifling, but the weight of an ordinary cylinder which would carry 30 cubic feet of compressed gas is too great. What, therefore, are the lightest cylinders into which it could be compressed? Were the problem one of providing a supply of air for a diver or a respirator for a soldier, a competent authority would sit down to face it on a basis of exhaustive experiment and extended drill. In the end I have little doubt that he would solve this problem and with less expenditure than is entailed in the equipment and expenses of successive expeditions to the Himalayas – expeditions which cost not only money but a toll of valuable lives."

So much for the correct scientific attitude of a physiologist with wide experience of great altitudes. It seems, however, to the present writer that the other side has to be considered, namely, the determination of the mountaineer to climb and, at personal risk if necessary, to attempt to respond to a challenge which he feels it imperative to answer. The older among us can advise the younger, and can do our best to assist them if they decide on a course despite the risk, but perhaps we must halt there. Maybe it is better to experience some of the wonders of such great altitude and to die in attempted achievement in the full power of youth than to reach an old age without ever having risked. Mallory, at all events, in the 1924 Everest expedition, "was in no mind to be finally thwarted, . . . he was absolutely possessed with the idea of climbing Mount Everest, . . . and his was not so much bull-dog tenacity, or sheer hard determination to conquer, as the imagination of the artist who cannot leave his work until it is completely, neatly, and perfectly, finished. Mallory was himself the very embodiment of the 'Everest spirit'. And to get him away from Everest before Everest itself had hurled him back you would have had to pull him up by the very roots of his being" (Younghusband, 1926). With Irvine he made the final attempt to reach the summit, and we do not know if they

45—Blackboard drawing made by Joseph Barcroft at the 14 March 1931 meeting of the Physiological Society at University College, London

46—Joseph Barcroft and Jose Joaquin Izquierdo

succeeded. Odell went to the top of a little crag, at about 26,000 feet, to watch and "there was a sudden clearing above him. The clouds parted. The whole summit ridge and final pyramid was unveiled. And far away on a snow slope he noticed a tiny object moving and approach the rock step. A second object followed. And then the first climbed to the top of the step. As he stood intently watching this dramatic appearance the scene became enveloped in cloud once more. And this was the last that was ever seen of Mallory and Irvine. Beyond that all is mystery . . . Where and when they died we know not. But there in the arms of Mount Everest they lie forever – lie 10,000 feet above where any man has lain in death before. Everest indeed conquered their bodies. But their spirit is undying. No man onward from now will ever climb a Himalayan Peak and not think of Mallory and Irvine" (Younghusband, 1926).

. . . .

Reference to three further publications concludes this account of J. B.'s activities of 1931. The first was a letter about uteroverdin, written by R. Lemberg, J. B., and Keilin from the Biochemical and Physiological Laboratories and the Molteno Institute, Cambridge, and it appeared in *Nature* on 5 December. A note about a 1932 publication on the substance in question will reveal the ultimate importance of the work in J. B.'s full story; here we can be content with a résumé of the letter. Lemberg had recently isolated oocyan – the blue-green pigment of the shells of many birds' eggs – and had characterized it as an ether-soluble pyrrol pigment closely related to the bile pigments. Uteroverdin, another substance of the same class, was the green pigment of the dog's placenta, examined in 1871 by Etti, but not then properly identified from the chemical aspect. It is a transformation product of the blood pigment in the extravasates of the dog's placenta, and Lemberg *et al.* remarked that they did not know how the decomposition of haemoglobin in this instance – and in other cases of blood extravasates in the uterus – led to such pigments instead of to bilirubin. "It has not, up to the present", they ended, "been possible to demonstrate an enzymic formation of uteroverdin by placenta tissue or tissue extract, any more than in the case of bilirubin."

The second publication was by J. B., Benatt, Greeson, and Nisimaru on "The rate of blood flow through cyanosed skin," and was an account of work done to test Wollheim's (1927) claim that the subpapillary venous plexus should be considered a "blood depot". As Grab, Janssen and Rein (1929) had put forward a similar claim for the liver, J. B. *et al.* thought it desirable "to consider more closely the fundamental basis on which rest the conceptions underlying the term blood depot. To be a blood depot," they went on, "an organ must clearly contain important quantities of blood which are unnecessary, or at least temporarily unnecessary, for its own metabolism and which can be transferred to other organs in order to meet their needs." With respect to the human skin, their experimental results were rather irregular because of certain technical difficulties, but there was a general agreement on the following points:-

"1. That after a considerable quantity of CO has been inhaled rapidly the blood in the uncyanosed hand does not reach its maximum content of CO for some minutes – more than 4, usually not more than 9.

"2. That under the same circumstances the curve for CO content in the cutaneous blood of the cyanosed hand [cyanosis produced by cold] lags behind that of the uncyanosed hand. The rise in the curve is slower, the summit is later and less high and the descent postponed. This lag seems to be of the order of 10 min. It indicates that a considerable number of corpuscles must tarry in the vessels of the cyanosed skin for at least that length of time."

The third publication, by J. B., Douglas, L. P. Kendal and Margaria, was on "Muscular exercise at low barometric pressure," and the experiments had been done in the pressure chamber of the Sir William Dunn School of Pathology, Oxford, in order, in the main, to test the possible usefulness of oxygen at altitudes such as the summit of Everest. The authors found, as J. B. had already related to the British Association, that it was possible to climb at the rate of about 1000 feet an hour in a chamber in which the barometric pressure was 170 mm. Hg., provided the subject breathed oxygen at that pressure; further, that 170 mm. Hg. appeared to be nearly the limiting pressure for the performance of such work, that the metabolism appeared to be no greater than normal, and that an ascent of 5000 feet in 5 hours and subsequent descent should not require more than 1.2 kg. of oxygen.

An interesting comment upon this work is to be found in Fulton (1948, 52–4). Yandell Henderson, in 1917, had apparently been the first to realize that, if aeroplanes were to ascend too rapidly to a great height, the flying personnel would be in danger of decompression sickness, or – in other words – of developing "bends". The aeroplanes of that day, however, could not climb sufficiently rapidly for the danger to be more than potential, and the first recorded instances of pain being experienced at low barometric pressures were in fact, reported in the paper by J. B. and his colleagues in 1931. Margaria suffered from it within 25 minutes of beginning "climbing" at the equivalent of 30,000 feet, and the pain was bilateral, though climbing had been on one leg only; the pain also persisted to some extent for some days. Kendal, a younger subject and in good training after a climbing holiday, experienced acute pain in both knees while exercising at the equivalent of 36,000 feet. "Like good scientists," the authors "recorded what had happened and allowed themselves a minimum of speculation. While they did not recognize the pain as that of the bends, they were aware that the phenomenon was peculiar and required explanation." It was not, however, until 1938 that the first acute case of decompression illness, recognized as such, was described by Boothby and Lovelace in the *Journal of Aviation Medicine.*

To the lay reader the most interesting part of J. B.'s 1932 story will probably be his trip with M. A. B. to South America and back, i.e., the period from 16 July to 24 September. Before that, however, he and various colleagues published nine papers, of which some account must be given; we should also note, as an item of family interest, that on 23 February Robbie sailed for India.

Two papers appeared in January, the first, with Nisimaru and Ray as co-authors, being entitled, "Observations on the time taken for corpuscles to traverse the liver." The object of the research had been to see if there was any store of stagnant blood in the liver such as had been found in the spleen and in cyanosed skin, and the conclusions were as follows. "The time spent by a red corpuscle in traversing the liver is small relative to that which may be spent in the spleen or the skin. Although the liver is a store in the sense that it contains large quantities of blood which can be transferred to some other site, it is not a store in the sense that the blood is out of the circulation. The above conclusions correspond with the structures of the liver, the skin and the spleen respectively. In the vessels of the liver there are no considerable diverticula from the general current in which blood can lie. The spleen pulp and sub-papillary venous plexus provide situations aside from the general stream." The second paper, by J. B. alone, was on Claude Bernard's dictum, "La fixité du milieu intérieur est la condition de la vie libre", and the essential points had been given in one of the Dunham lectures at Boston in 1929. The subject as a whole can best be discussed in connection with the publication of J. B.'s book in 1934.

In February he and Margaria published an account of "Some effects of carbonic acid in high concentration on respiration". It had been found that in anaesthetized cats the gas "tends to produce a certain characteristic type of respiration which may be either faster or slower than the rhythm which existed previously depending upon the initial rhythm. In cats with the vagi cut, and especially under dial hypnosis, high concentrations of CO_2 will produce the train of symptoms observed by Lumsden and resulting from successive sections of the brain, and also by Taylor as the result of HCN administration: pneumotaxis, apneusis, gasping, standstill."

Four papers appeared on 7 March. The first, by J. B., Khanna of Lahore, and Nisimaru of Okayama, was on "Rhythmical contraction of the spleen", the second, by J. B. and Nisimaru, was on the "Cause of rhythmical contraction of the spleen." In the former it was reported that there was no truth, in so far as the cat was concerned, in the idea that were two essentially different rhythms. Usually the contractions took 25–50 seconds to arise and disappear, but if the spleen was in a bad condition or the general blood pressure was low, the rhythm was often over 60 seconds. In the second paper a variety of causes of splenic rhythm in the experimental animal were detailed; perhaps the most interesting finding was that it occurred in the excised and perfused organ as strongly as in that of the intact animal; for further details the reader is referred to the original account.

The third paper, by J. B. and Nisimaru, was on "Undulatory changes of blood-pressure" in cats. The authors concluded that the waves of $\pm$ 45 seconds duration were due principally to the rhythmic contractions of the spleen; they were those described by Roy, Bunch, Strasser and Wolf, and Bayliss and Bradford. Shorter waves, of about 7 seconds' duration, occurred during asphyxia, and these were the ones described by Traube, Hering, and Mayer. Concerning the origin of the waves described by Bottazzi and by

Wood the authors were in doubt, and they also left for a future paper a discussion of waves of under 25 seconds' duration in the cat. The fourth March publication, by J. B., Nisimaru, and Puri of Lahore, was on "The action of the splanchnic nerves on the spleen." Experiments on cats had shown that stimulation of the major splanchnic nerve resulted directly in contraction of the spleen, followed by rhythmic contraction; there was a similar indirect effect through secretion of adrenaline by the adrenal gland. Stimulation of n. splanchnicus minor (i) sometimes produced direct and indirect effects on the spleen, at other times only an indirect effect. The authors failed to find connections between n. splanchnicus minor (ii) and either the spleen or the adrenal glands.

On 26 April, J. B., Nisimaru, and F. R. Steggerda [1] described "The effects of intestinal rhythm on general blood-pressure" in the cat. They had found waves of 25–50 seconds' duration, but less marked than the somewhat similar splenic ones. Removal of the spleen and adrenal glands, as also denervation of the intestines, did not prevent the appearance of waves. The next publication, by R. Lemberg and J. B., on "Uteroverdin, the green pigment of the dog's placenta", appeared a week later. The details about the substance itself are of considerable interest; though it was discovered in 1830 by Breschet, no work had been done on its chemistry since 1871, and in the preliminary stages of the new researches the authors had had valuable help from Keilin. More important, however, is the fact that, according to Roughton (1949, *b*), the studies on uteroverdin formed the quiet opening of J. B.'s great pioneer work on foetal physiology. "In taking up such an outstanding new line when he was" [nearly] "sixty years of age, he has been likened to the Russian physiologist, Pavlov, who did not begin his classical work on conditioned reflexes until he had passed well into the afternoon of his scientific life."

So much for the initial spate of publications of 1932. We must now give an account of another line of activity. A body known as the Ibero-American Institute of Great Britain has recently been created, with H. R. H. The Prince of Wales as President, and Mr. Philip Guedalla as Hon. Director, to facilitate lecture-visits by English scientists and men of letters to the Argentine and Brazil, and

[1] Dr. Steggerda, now Professor of Physiology in the University of Illinois, Urbana, Ill., has often told the present writer how much he appreciated his time with J. B.

N

thereby to counteract the effect of similar visits by French scholars, which were giving the impression that science and culture throve across the Channel more than they did in England. Mr. Guedalla went to Cambridge and discussed the problem with the Vice-Chancellor, Lord Rutherford, and Sir Humphry Rolleston, and in consequence, on 20 April, the Vice-Chancellor wrote to J. B. and asked if he would consider a lecture-tour to Rio de Janeiro and Buenos Aires: full expenses would be paid for him, and half-expenses for M. A. B. A week later, after J. B. had discussed the matter with Mr. Guedalla, they had decided to go, Sir William Bragg, the physicist, and his wife accepted a similar invitation.

On 24 May Mr. Guedalla, after going over details with the General Manager of the R. M. S. P. Co., sent the following itinerary for J. B.'s approval. July 16. Depart from Southampton in *Asturias*. July 31. Arrive Rio de Janeiro. August 14. Depart in *Almanzora*. August 19. Arrive Buenos Aires. August 29. Depart in *Desna*. September 24. Arrive Liverpool.

The next note is that on 7 July M. A. B. answered a trunk call from London for J. B., and was told, "The Prince of Wales wishes to have a command interview with Professor Barcroft to-morrow at York House at 2.45." M. A. B. asked if it would mean frock coat, etc., and was told, "Oh no, just lounge suit, quite informal." So she said, "Oh, he has a new blue suit, I will put him into that," and heard much laughter at the other end. The next day J. B. duly arrived at York House, and had a long chat with the Prince, who spoke about Argentina and Peru, and impressed J. B. as being very well informed. He asked J. B. to convey to the Argentines a message of his good will towards them.

J. B. and M. A. B. left Cambridge early on 15 July and went via London to stay the night at Salisbury; at Waterloo they had a word with Mr. Guedalla and said they hoped they would not ruin his cultural mission. The next day they left early for Southampton and went aboard the M. V. *Asturias*. At the first stop, Cherbourg, they picked up some of the Argentine students who had recently visited England. One of them, Alfredo Lanari, had been in a group that went to J. B.'s laboratory and saw two dogs, with their spleens exteriorized, at rest and during exercise. "We were accustomed," he wrote in 1948, "to the distance which prevails in the Argentine between the students and professors, and the simplicity and friendliness with which Dr. Barcroft treated us surprised us . . ." During the voyage Lanari gave J. B. lessons in Spanish pronunciation so that he could deliver at least one lecture in that language. In return for the daily hour's tutorial, J. B. said jokingly that he would help Lanari in his diving during the ship's swimming tournament. He advised him to overventilate before diving and in consequence Lanari was able to last out a little longer than any other male competitor. However, "a girl, maybe she had a spontaneous or emotive hyperventilation syndrome, got the prize."

On 18 July the ship stopped for two hours in Corunna, and after tea for two hours in Vigo, in an "exquisite setting of sunshine and blue sky." On the 19th they sailed up the Tagus to Lisbon, and on the 21st J. B. called M. A. B. at 5 a.m. so that she could watch the approach to Madeira. By now it was very hot, and it continued so for the rest of the voyage. On the 29th they arrived in Bahia early in the morning, and it looked wonderful. Despite this natural beauty, however, and despite its 375 churches, it was described by the stewardess as "the wickedest city in the world." At 11.30 the ship left for Rio de Janeiro, and in the evening J. B. and M. A. B. accepted an invitation to dine with the Argentine students. On 31 July they rose and enjoyed the "beauties of Rio as we entered the magical harbour. Paradise! 365 Islands! Bluest of Water! Pretty Boats! Miles of Mountain Scenery! Everywhere loveliness met our gaze."

In the absence in England of our Ambassador, J. B. and M. A. B. were met by his Secretary, Mr. Noble, and by the Secretary of the Ministry of Education, and during their stay they were guests of the Ministry in the Gloria Hotel, with exquisite views over the bay. On shore there were palm trees and roses everywhere, and unfamiliar bird-notes greeted their ears. Two days later, having learned of their arrival from the newspaper, the Professor of Physiology 'phoned, and in consequence J. B. spent the afternoon at the lab. The next day he and M. A. B. spent at the Botanic Gardens at Bavia. On 6 August Sir William and Lady Bragg arrived, and four days later there were portraits of Sir William and of J. B. in the daily paper. The next day, after nearly a fortnight in Rio, J. B. gave a lecture. Perhaps the revolution that was in moderate progress elsewhere in the country had delayed matters academic until this Thursday, 11 August. It, presumably, also accounted for the fact that the lecture began nearly an hour after the scheduled time. For the original audience, as the harassed Professor explained, had been arrested, and they had had to get another one together to listen to J. B.!

Excursions to Copacobana and elsewhere gave M. A. B. material for wonderful written memorials of the time in Rio and its surroundings, but can scarcely be reproduced at length here. We must content ourselves with noting that on 15 August she and J. B. sailed, reluctantly, away from Rio on the *Almanzora* and that, after a couple of hours' break in Montevideo on 18 August, they continued on to Buenos Aires, which they reached the next day (Plate 47). They were met by numerous reporters and photographers and, what was more important, by Dr. A. E. Houssay, the Professor of Physiology, and his assistant, Dr. Biasotti, who had studied in Harvard. The British Embassy kindly sent a car and a courier who saw the Barcrofts' luggage through the Customs and delivered the Barcrofts themselves safely at the City Hotel. There Dr. Castex, the Professor of Medicine, called about 9.30 a.m. and invited them to luncheon on the following day so that their programme could be arranged. Our Ambassador, Sir Ronald Macleay, also called, but by that time the Barcrofts had gone out. In the afternoon Professor Houssay showed J. B. his laboratory, probably the most progressive scientific one in Buenos Aires; he and his staff also told J. B., in somewhat halting English, of the work done by each of the thirty or more researchers! Then J. B. was taken for a drive round the city, and after that was introduced to the Dean of the Faculty; he also had to read his lecture in Spanish and have it altered.

On Saturday, 20 August, after some rearrangement of the plans for the return voyage to England had been effected, J. B. called on Sir Ronald Macleay and had a pleasant chat, chiefly of a general nature. Then he and M. A. B. went off to their luncheon with Professor Castex and his wife, the co-guests including the Macleays, the Houssays, and Professor and Mrs. Greenwood; after luncheon J. B.'s programme was discussed and decided. Sunday afternoon was spent in sightseeing, mainly en route to and from Tigre, and M. A. B.'s diary mentions the fresh spring greenery, the pink peach blossom, and the oranges on the trees.

During the morning of Monday, 22 August, J. B. was shown round the Radiological Institute, from 3 p.m. onwards he watched

47—The Barcrofts on the dockside at Buenos Aires, 1932

48—Joseph Barcroft with local scientists, including A. Dustin and A. E. Houssay, at Buenos Aires, 1932

Facing page 194

Professor Houssay perform three operations, and at 6.30 p.m. he attended a conference, at which the President of the Republic was present, in the Academy of Medicine; apparently he projected one of his films on this occasion. The next morning, at 10.30 a.m., he and M. A. B. were "whisked off" by Professor Houssay, and at 11 a.m. he began his lecture on oxygen to an audience of about 300 in the theatre of the Department of Physiology. "He read his first two pages in Spanish and was warmly applauded, Professor Houssay then took up the reading and between them they finished the lecture", which "was pronounced a great success." In the afternoon J. B. and M. A. B. were shown over the Institute of Bacteriology and Public Health by Professor Sordelli, and in addition to the animals usual in such institutes saw a considerable collection of snakes. "There was," wrote M. A. B., "an audible noise in the house, due to the snakes rattling their tails", and the visitors were shown how this was done.

The next day at 9 a.m. J. B. went off to visit the Faculty of Medicine, returning at noon to prepare for a British Chamber of Commerce luncheon. Just before it took place "an enormous basket of pink sweet peas, blue ribbons, and asparagus fern" arrived for M. A. B. with the compliments and best wishes of the members of the Chamber. The guests of honour at the luncheon were the Right Honourable Lord Vestey and J. B., who sat on the left of the Chairman, Sir Herbert Gibson. At the appropriate moment the Chairman introduced the guests, reminding members that the first representatives of British science and culture who had come out on a similar mission to that of J. B. had done so exactly a year previously, and had been Lord Moynihan, Sir Almoth Wright, and Dr. Freeman.

J. B. replied:- "I thank you for your kindness in extending to me this invitation to your hospitable board; and I accept it as an expression of goodwill to my colleagues – to the fraternity of scientific men in England. Perhaps it is inevitable that as I stand here I should feel that the occasion demands a few words on the position of science; perhaps it is inevitable that such a discussion should involve the growth of science within my own memory, perhaps it is inevitable that the development of science with which I myself have been concerned should take a prominent part in the picture before my mind.

"In my student days the nature of matter was dismissed as being of two sorts, crystalloid and colloid; though these words had become classical, they conveyed little and crystalloid meant no more than what it obviously said, colloid meant the rest – things which like glue had no obvious structure.

"The colloid world moved first and in my early graduate days Sir William Hardy laid the basis of what has become a great field of knowledge. In those days the new knowledge demanded new words – it all seemed very curious, very abstract, very theoretical, very remote from the practical applications of everyday life. And now after thirty five years where do we stand? I have only to look to the south of my laboratory to see the next building, presided over by Sir William himself, in which his labours have reached fruition along one intensely practical line – the preservation of food, a subject than which none is more important to the every day life of a nation only able to grow a small percentage of the food which sustains it.

"But the word 'colloid' has been on the lips of people in England in another connection – we have heard a good deal of colloid fuel. How long a road has been travelled between the days when 'colloid' expressed the idea that a substance had no tangible structure and to-day when it is used to express the very simple idea of a suspension of impalpably fine coal dust in a fluid matrix of oil. Whether colloid fuel will or will not fulfil the hope of its adherents is a matter on which I have no opinion, but the progress in scientific thought and work of which it is a tangible expression is one of the great facts of our time.

"Of course the study of colloid touches industry at innumerable points, dyeing, tanning, etc., but these I pass over because I, as a biologist, am thinking rather of the relation of scientific investigation to the process of life.

"About crystalloids I will say but little. The great expansion in the study of crystalloids is an even more recent occurrence than that of colloids and you have lately listened to the greatest living authority on the subject. I will only say this, that some of the interstices into which that study has ramified are entirely foreign to anything which might have been looked for. Such a problem as to why a vitamin should have a specific effect on the body has been attacked from this angle and apparently not without some success.

And if the south window of my room in Cambridge looks into a laboratory devoted to the preservation of foodstuffs, the north window looks onto a site allocated to the study of crystalloids, including I hope those aspects of the subject which are concerned with the relation of foods and poisons to the human body. Again, nothing in my student days was regarded as more purely abstract than the electrical phenomena exhibited by living matter, and the application of electrical methods in the study of life. There were those who would have had one believe that in the electric organs of fish we had found something as near to fundamental living matter as we were likely to attain. A few days ago at Rio de Janeiro I was shown an electric fish which was said to have lived in the same tank for thirty years, and I could not but think of the progress which had been made in that time in the study of life. An example of the extent to which electrophysiology has broadened from a purely abstract subject to one which has very practical applications is furnished by the growth of knowledge about the human heart. The issues involved are sufficiently practical to have an important bearing upon the everyday subject of life insurance. Thirty years ago the prospect of a man's heart giving out prematurely was judged almost entirely by the stethoscope – that is to say by the noises which could be heard when the organ beats. I speak feelingly on this subject because my own heart in those days evidently made the wrong noises; in any case I had to pay more than the normal premium and moreover my company would not insure me beyond 55 years of age. The question now asked is not so much what can be heard in the heart, but what will it do? To answer this question tests of quite a different character have been elaborated. That has principally been the work of the late Sir James Mackenzie and Sir Thomas Lewis, work which has involved the nicest electrical measurements, and although the tests now given are extremely simple, the experimental edifice which they crown is of the most laborious and exact character. Full advantage was taken by the State at the end of the war of the new cardiology, to the considerable financial advantage of the taxpayer. But we are not at the end of finding out what the heart can do. It speaks a language. That language has been learned by my colleague and friend Professor E. D. Adrian, who most kindly slipped into my bag on leaving home a gramophone record in which the language of the heart is recorded for those who would like to hear. It is a simple tongue, something like the Morse code for electrical signalling yet in a sense even simpler than Morse, which of course consists in dots and dashes. But the language of the heart consists only of dots, tappings of an almost infinitely small electric current which Dr. Adrian picks up and magnifies by wireless; what it says is conveyed simply by the rate at which the dots follow one another. At each beat a record goes to the brain stating the strain which is put on the heart. At present it requires a surgical operation to reach these currents but doubtless the time will come when that can be dispensed with and, when the expert doctor of the Insurance Company can hear what the heart tells the brain at each beat, he will doubtless be able to make an even more accurate prophecy of its probable efficiency than at the present time. But after all the body of man is but the vehicle of his mind. The study of the mind may be undertaken from both ends. Considered as a machine, as a sort of complicated telephone system we may try to build up its mechanism, or taking the machinery for granted we may consider its powers, of what it is capable.

"A complete knowledge of this machine is still far beyond our ken. I am sure the first person to say so would be Sir Charles Sherrington, the wonder of whose work is one of the milestones of the scientific thought of our time. In my student days the machinery of the mind was understood to about this extent, that if under appropriate circumstances you put a piece of blotting paper on one leg of a frog it would kick it off with the other. Now we know that there are nervous outfits, of the most complicated and self-contained character, for the conduct of the nicest and most delicate movements. I have with me a film which Professor Sherrington has kindly lent me, showing at work the machine which is responsible for the whole of the movements involved in ordered walking, and the remarkable thing is that these movements would be taking place incessantly unless that machine was presided over by a higher one which threw it out of action when not required.

"And from the other standpoint, that of the capability of the mind, progress has reached the point at which the question may be asked with some hope of a favourable answer. Do we understand enough about the mind to check the terrible wastage of human energy we see taking place around us? Of this wastage a great part is caused by persons taking up occupations for which they are fundamentally unsuited. A sort of sample branch of this great subject is being studied in England, on a more or less homogeneous category of boys entering for the Navy, with the hope of finding out to which branch of the naval services they are most suited.

"Here I come to a word about organisation; in my young days there was none. A man in whom the urge to research was sufficiently strong yielded thereto if he could see some way of keeping body and soul together. But it is evident that research on the grand scale such as is required for the study of industrial fatigue, vocational efficiency, tropical diseases and the like must have some organisation adequate in influence and finance. That charge has been undertaken in England by an authority no less high than the Privy Council and under its aegis the physical, chemical and in part the biological interests are placed, as Sir William Bragg told you, but those subjects of which I have principally spoken to-day, subjects on the borderline of biology and medicine, are like medicine itself under a different department of the Privy Council, namely, the Medical Research Council, and no review of the growth of biological science in England and its Colonies would be complete without some reference to the beneficial activities of that body."

On Thursday, 25 August, J. B. spent the morning with the physiologists, and perhaps this was the occasion on which he demonstrated one of his operations to them. He and M. A. B. then had luncheon at the Jockey Club as the guests of Sir Herbert Gibson, and after that visited a Country Club and an Art Gallery; thence J. B. went on to the Department of Physiology, where he projected the film lent by Sir Charles Sherrington and reproduced the sound records, made by Professor Adrian, of? the activity of the depressor nerve in the rabbit. The next day he and M. A. B. were shown over the "Anglo Frigorifico" slaughterhouse and canning factory, etc., and on the Saturday they visited La Plata and the Armour Meat Refrigerating Company's plant. Luncheon at the Jockey Club was followed by a call at the fine Government House and some talk with the Governor, and a most enjoyable day closed with a visit to the wonderful Museo de la Plata. On Sunday, 28 August, they lunched with Sir Robert and Lady Macleay, and began to prepare for their departure. This took place on the Tuesday, following a farewell Faculty of Medicine luncheon, and the projection by J. B. of a spleen film at 6 p.m. at the Medical School. Various Argentine friends came to see the local steamer off at 9 p.m. for Montevideo, and J. B. and M. A. B. waved their handkerchiefs until they could no longer see those friends on shore. M. A. B. must have had some difficulty in waving, as she was carrying a beautiful pot of cyclamens presented by the Houssay boys, and three snakes in bottles, presented by the Bacteriological Laboratory! After all their activities of the past few days, she and J. B. were glad to turn early into their luxurious berths and to enjoy, the sea being beautifully calm, a restful night. They carried away from Buenos Aires "delightful memories of days packed with incidents, hospitalities, and interest of all kinds, and felt that the world contained no kinder people than those they had met in the Argentine." We in our turn can feel that they had done all that a cultural mission should have in improving international relations, and in evidence of this there is, inter alia, the fact that J. B. was elected to honorary membership of the Biological Society of Argentina and of the National Academy of Medicine.

Montevideo was reached at 7 o'clock on Wednesday, 31 August, and J. B. and M. A. B. transferred to comfortable quarters on R. M. S. P. *Desna* (twin-screw, 11,500 tons gross) for the voyage home. On Thursday there was a glorious sunset, with the 'Milky Way' and 'Southern Cross' looking very beautiful thereafter, and on Saturday they reached Rio, which they did not leave until late on Monday, 5 September. On the following Friday the chief event was the sight of a whale sounding in the distance, on Sunday they observed a large school of flying fish skimming over the surface of the water, and they were also interested in the guano-covered St. Paul's Rocks near the Equator. On the following Wednesday, 14 September, they saw the first commercial Zeppelin on its flight from Germany to Pernambuco, had a clear view of Cape Verd Islands twenty-seven miles away, and finally watched the eclipse of the moon in the evening from the vantage-point of the Captain's bridge. The next day Teneriffe came into view, though that view was somewhat marred by mist, soon after breakfast. Then on 20 September, just before breakfast, they reached Lisbon and passengers were able to go ashore until noon; among the mail was a letter from Netta Barcroft giving news of David's engagement to Miss Georgiana (Georgie) Norman. Two days later the Scillies were faintly visible, and finally, on the afternoon of Friday, 23 September, J. B. and M. A. B. were moving up the Mersey, among unaccustomed clouds and smoke, to dock at Liverpool. They spent the night at Chester, and next evening Henry welcomed them home in Cambridge. All together, their time away had been a very wonderful experience, presumably well recompensing them for their necessary absence from the fourteenth International Congress of Physiologists, which had taken place in Rome from 29 August to 3 September, and which had been greatly enjoyed by those present.

Two days after their return, Henry left to take up duties as Lecturer in Physiology at University College, London, under Professor Lovatt Evans; on 10 October F. A. Meakin arrived for a visit; on 28 October Sir Charles Sherrington and Professor Adrian shared the Nobel Prize for Physiology and Medicine; on 30 October Dr. Camis came to dinner at No. 13. The next note is that four out of five of J. B.'s remaining publications for the year appeared in the 18 November number of the *Journal of Physiology*. The first of them was on "The effect of some accidental lesions on the size of the spleen", and it stated that contraction of the organ could accompany necroses of the skin, caused either by friction or by unduly high temperature. The contraction could come on before the skin had been broken and could pass off before the necrosed area had "dried up", provided it was suitably dressed. Finally, the effects could be observed in denervated as well as in innervated spleens.

The second paper, entitled, "Alterations in the size of the denervated spleen related to pregnancy", dealt with points left outstanding by Barcroft and Stevens in 1928. It showed that the spleen of the bitch contracts during "heat", pregnancy, and lactation, and that denervation abolishes the "heat" and pregnancy contractions, but leaves the lactation one undiminished. Presumably, therefore, there was a large humoral element in the causation of the last-named, while the other two were nervous.

The third paper, on "The volume of blood in the uterus during pregnancy", was written in conjunction with P. Rothschild, and the work described was in effect the major way by which J. B. passed on from his blood-depôt researches to the later ones on the physiology of the foetus. It was done on three genera, but only the results in the rabbit were described. The authors stated that "during the resting condition the genital organs contain less than 2 c.c. of blood. They become appreciably more vascular from the fifth or sixth day onwards, and about half-way through pregnancy contain about

10 c.c. of blood, Up to this point the embryos are of negligible weight. By the twentieth day the embryos weigh only 5 g. and the generative tract of the mother contains about 15 c.c. of blood. The maximal quantity of blood, about 30 c.c., seems to occur about twenty-eight to twenty-nine days and the quantity falls rapidly before parturition. The significance of the arrangement of vessels is discussed, especially in reference to the possibility of intra-uterine haemorrhage due to pressure on the veins. The quantity of blood in the generative organs on any particular day does not bear so near a relation to the number of foetuses as does the total weight of the embryos. The quantity of blood in the genital organs seems to be closely related to the combined weights of the foetal placentas up to the twenty-fifth day when the latter seem to cease growing."

The fourth paper, by J. B. and F. R. Steggerda, described something very different, namely, "Observations on the proximal portion of the exteriorized colon", observations which the authors believed to be a worthwhile addition to information derived from the use of other techniques. The work had been done on three dogs, and the summary read as follows:- "From 2 to 3 weeks after the colon and caecum had been exteriorized, the water content of faeces began to diminish along with the return of activity and tone of the exteriorized parts. There is a typical series of movements, consisting of caecal contractions, followed by anti-peristaltic waves and then a type of kneading contractions in the colon. These series usually occur at intervals of about 30 minutes. There is evidence of an occasional slow, deep, progressive wave in the colon. We found anti-peristaltic waves in the colon of the dog, appearing at the rate of five and seven a minute. There is evidence of a gastro-colic reflex, appearing within a few minutes after feeding. Movements were observed after the administration of magnesium sulphate and morphine, which differed from the normal in both frequency and intensity."

It may be suitable at this point to make reference to the only other 1932 publication by J. B., namely, that entitled, "Stores of blood", which appeared in the *Veterinary Journal* in October and November. It was a useful summary of the knowledge which had accumulated about blood depôts (spleen, uterus, liver, skin) during the decade that had elapsed since, so to speak, J. B. had started the ball rolling; it also contained some more general considerations. As, however, there have been many notes in this biography about individual contributions to the story, it is perhaps unnecessary to give a précis of the paper here; the older among us can remember its value as a contemporary review of the work in a new field by the pioneer in that field, and that is really the measure of its significance.

On 29 November, to pass to quite different matters, David Barcroft and Georgiana Eleanor Norman were married at St. Columba's Parish Church, Omagh, Co. Tyrone, Netta Barcroft being one of the four bridesmaids, Alex. Richardson of Moyallon the best man, and the Reverend John Barcroft, M. A., of Mellifont, one of the three officiating clerics. David Barcroft had returned to Newry, Co. Down, a few years previously after eighteen years of practice in Sloane Street. On the same day as this happy event took place, the Dean of Dromore (the Very Reverend Henry Biddell Swanzy, of St. Mary's Rectory, Newry) was fatally injured in a car accident. So once again gladness and sadness came more or less simultaneously to the Barcrofts.

On 12 December, to round off the 1932 story, Bryan Matthews entered the glass chamber in the Physiology Laboratory at Cambridge to test his invention for keeping warm at great altitudes, and on 22 December J. B. presided at the King's College Association dinner in London; his brother-in-law, W. Valentine Ball, responded. Later reports stated that J. B. had been the best Chairman ever and his speech a model of what such an oration should be. Finally, it is worth noting that 1932 was the year in which Pharmacology at Cambridge became a Sub-Department of Physiology.

It seems reasonable, with the end of 1932, to conclude another Chapter of this biography, even if the end-point is not so well-defined a one as was the case with some of the earlier Chapters. The indication in this instance is the passing-over of the blood-depôt studies into the foetal physiology ones, and the transition was not so sharply marked as to be obvious at the time. In retrospect, however, it is more apparent.

CHAPTER VIII

1933–1937

This Chapter deals with J. B.'s concluding years as Professor of Physiology at Cambridge University, and the story opens with the publication, on 16 January 1933, of a paper by himself, W. Herkel, and S. Hill on "The rate of blood flow and gaseous metabolism of the uterus during pregnancy." It described work designed to answer a question left open by J. B. and Rothschild in 1932, namely, whether the large amount of blood found in the uterine vessels of the rabbit towards the end of pregnancy was stored or in active circulation. The answer demanded measurements of the uterine blood flow, and any further discussion required some knowledge of the extent to which that blood was utilized by the uterus. The paper dealt only with the period between the fourteenth and twenty-eighth days of intrauterine life – the last two days of pregnancy presented, the authors stated, some rather baffling problems which would have to be the subjects of further enquiry.

The summary and conclusions of the 1933 paper read as follows:-

"1. The blood becomes appreciably concentrated in its passage through the uterus.

"2. The blood flow through the uterus increases in volume in proportion to the increase in the vascular bed and anticipates the growth of foetal tissue.

"3. The blood flow in the rabbits' uterus attains a maximum of about 30 c.c. per minute.

"4. The oxygen used by the pregnant uterus and its contents is less than 0.1 c.c. per minute up to the eighteenth day; within the next two days it undergoes a tenfold increase, corresponding to foetal growth. After that time the oxygen used increases much more slowly and at a rate proportionately less than the growth of the embryos.

"5. The oxygen saturation of the venous blood which is from 80 to 90 p.c. on the fourteenth day falls to 25 to 45 p.c. by the end of pregnancy.

"6. The function of the extensive venous reservoir in the broad ligament is discussed (*a*) in relation to its possible function as a blood depot, and (*b*) as an insurance against stasis or intra-uterine haemorrhage caused by local pressure."

Six days after the appearance of this paper J. B. was back for the evening with one of his older loves, namely, the effects of altitude. For he dined at Clare College and had a most interesting discussion with Everest climbers and others, whom M. A. B. succinctly lists as follows:-

"Priestley who went with the Shackleton and Scott party to the South Pole, went as far up Mount Erebus as any man had ever done, and for three days and nights lay out in his sleeping bag in such a blizzard that he could not stand up or get food.

"Odell who got nearer the top of Everest than any man who has ever returned.

"Courtauld who was for many weeks under the snow.

"Scott who went to look for him and did not find him and who is Secretary of the expedition just starting.

"Bryan Matthews whose skilfully devised apparatus for keeping warm by means of layers of copper gauze over the mouth and nose will be one of the great 'tests' of the present trip."

On 17 February a more personal event occurred, namely, the marriage of Henry Barcroft and of Bridget Mary, elder daughter of Arthur S. Ramsey, President of Magdalene College, and of the late Mrs. Ramsey. It was solemnized in Coton Church, where J. B. and M. A. B. had been married thirty years previously, and the senior of the two officiating clergy, namely, the Reverend Canon S. T. Adams, had also officiated in 1903. The organist was Dr. A. W. Wilson, uncle of the bride, the best man was Dr. Geoffrey Barber, and the ushers were Stawell Meakin and Robbie Barcroft. The guests included David and Georgie Barcroft, who stayed at No. 13, and Mollie Barcroft and Muriel Richardson, who stayed at the Garden Hotel. The reception, attended by two or three hundred persons, took place in the Hall of Magdalene College.

On 6 March it was forty years since M. A. B. had first come to Cambridge, and guests at the Sunday tea-party the day before had included Professor and Mrs. Langdon Brown and Professor and Mrs. Adrian. Towards the end of the month J. B. and M. A. B. went off for a week's holiday, and thereafter there is no item to be reproduced from the latter's diary until 7 May, when there is an entry:- "J. B. *very* pleased with his goat experiments this week. I wish he was as satisfied with his false teeth." On 13 May the Physiological Society held its customary spring meeting in Cambridge, and the next day about seventy members and guests visited 13 Grange Road; in addition Henry and 'Biddy' came to lunch, and Betty and Robbie were staying in the house. So M. A. B. must have been busy! Sir Charles Sherrington had been prevented from coming by the illness of Lady Sherrington, who in fact died on the day of the scientific meeting.

After this strenuous week-end J. B. had to get ready for another trip to the United States. He left Cambridge for Liverpool on 2 June, and sailed the next day in M. V. *Georgic* for New York City; he shared a three-berth cabin with A. V. Hill, but the latter's berth was round a corner so, as J. B. wrote with memories of 1929 in his mind, "he cannot throw boots at me." The invigorating North Atlantic made J. B. look "ten years younger" in a few days, according to the stewardess, and certainly he felt much fitter for it. On 10 June the ship reached Boston, and Millikan, Margaria, and a Dr. Edwards came on board to see J. B. and stayed a few hours. Then early on 12 June he was welcomed in New York by Dr. and Mrs. Van Slyke. He spent the morning in the Rockefeller Institute, and at luncheon met Drs. Rufus Cole, Mirsky, Cecil Murray, Sendroy, H. M. Evans, and Peyton Rous. In the afternoon he went to the offices of the Rockefeller Foundation in the hope of getting further details of the death of Sir Walter Morley Fletcher, the first Secretary of the Medical Research Council. On the pier in the morning he had merely heard that this friend and colleague of many years' standing had died; he learned now that it had happened on 7 June, in Sir Walter's sixtieth year.

In the evening the Van Slykes, with whom J. B. was staying, gave a dinner party at which the other guests were Dr. and Mrs. Rufus Cole and Dr. and Mrs. Evans; later the Sendroys dropped in, also an ornithologist named Murphy, who had purchased Lord Rothschild's collection of birds, and his sister. The next day a luncheon was given in J. B.'s honour by various people who had been at Cambridge and some others; they included Drs. Murray, Binger, Van Slyke, Sendroy, Mirsky, and Murphy. Later he had tea with Dr. and Mrs. Peyton Rous, and thereafter a quiet evening with the Van Slykes.

On Wednesday, 14 June, he lunched at Cornell University Medical School, and after dinner went on by train to Toronto, where at noon the following day he was met by Drs. Best and Taylor, and an hour later lunched with Drs. Fitzgerald, Banting, Best, Taylor, Frazer (Professor of Bacteriology), and others. After visits to the laboratories in the afternoon and a dinner party at the Bests' house, he left at 9.30 p.m. for Chicago, which brings us to the explanation of this short American trip, namely, J. B. had been one of seventy-five distinguished scientists chosen by a thousand American ones to be invited to Chicago on the occasion of the holding of the World's Fair in that city.

By about 8.30 p.m. on Friday, 16 June, he was established in the Harvard-Yale-Princeton Club of Chicago, and Drs. Carlson and Hastings picked him up there at 5 p.m. On the following Monday he went with Dr. and Mrs. Hastings to the former's Club, and dined with them and Dr. Edwin Cohn on a verandah which commanded a magnificent view over Lake Michigan. Thereafter they went on to the official reception at The World's Fair. The following morning J. B. found that he had to pay Federal Income Tax on his honorarium, the authorities placing him in "the same category as actresses, who were not allowed to deduct their travelling expenses from their emoluments for the purposes of income tax"! At 2 p.m. he addressed a meeting of the American Association of Science, his subject being "The conditions of foetal respiration", and his volunteer projectionist Dr. Crandall, from Dr. A. C. Ivy's Department.

The substance of the address was published on 4 November in the *Lancet*, and J. B. said that it was a résumé of work carried out by Adair, himself, S. Dickinson, R. H. E. Elliott, R. E. Havard, Herkel, F. G. Hall, A. St. G. Huggett, A. B. Keys, E. F. McCarthy, Roughton, and M. Talaat. After drawing a partial parallel between the problem of the developing foetus and that of Everest climbers, and paying tribute to the earlier work of Huggett (1927) and of Haselhorst and Stromberger (1930; 1931), J. B. went on to say that "there is no research which purports systematically to have followed the possible alterations throughout the whole course of pregnancy", and then went on to describe the recent work done in Cambridge on goat foetuses of from seven to eighteen weeks, full term being twenty-one weeks. Space is insufficient to detail anything further except the summary, which read as follows:-

"It seems to be proved: (1) with regard to the *mother*, (*a*) that from about the middle of pregnancy onward, the dissociation curve shifts to the right, and (*b*) that the shift may be accounted for by an increase in the hydrogen-ion concentration of the maternal blood; (2) with regard to the *foetus*, (*a*) that, on the whole, from about the same time, the dissociation curve of the foetal blood at the relevant pressures of oxygen falls to the left of the normal position, and (*b*) that the shift is not due to abnormal alkalinity of the foetal blood, for this is no more alkaline than that of the normal goat; (3) that the characteristic dissociation curve of foetal blood is due to a specific form of haemoglobin.

"Again, it seems proved that during the latter part of pregnancy the blood of the foetus is richer in base than that of the mother.

"It is proved", finally, "that the quantity of carbonic anhydrase in the foetal blood is small as compared with that in the maternal blood, especially in the early stages, but the precise significance of this fact cannot be stated with certainty (Roughton)."

After the lecture J. B. went to Ivy's laboratory, where he met an old friend, Dr. Walter Meek, and then motored with Ivy ("probably the first authority on the physiology of the gall-bladder") to the latter's house for supper, following which his host drove him round the industrial areas of the city. Of the prevailing smell from lard-refining, etc., J. B. wrote that "A little goes a long way and a good deal goes a longer way". Ivy brought J. B. back to his Club by a drive along the lake front, and after that J. B. went to the Stevens Hotel, where he met the Kroghs. On his way home, by accident but to their mutual pleasure, he encountered Dr. Walter Miles and his wife.

The following morning he lectured at 10.20 a.m. in the Field Museum, cutting short his talk so that Krogh, who was next on the list, could begin at the scheduled time. In the evening he was visited by Dr. Carlson. On the morning of the next day, 22 June, he finished packing, called on Krogh for an hour's talk, and then heard A. V. Hill's lecture, "which was very good." He was then driven by Carlson to the University of Chicago, where a luncheon in his honour was attended by Drs. Hastings, Griffith-Taylor, McLean, Margaria, Flexner, and others. After luncheon he went round the laboratories until 4 p.m. "The finale," he wrote to M. A. B., "was quite worthy of the occasion. I showed the spleen films to a most appreciative audience and was in quite my best form. So it all went excellently and I could not even commence to repeat the nice things which were said to me, even if I remembered them, which I don't."

He left at 6.30 p.m. for New York, and on 30 June was back in Cambridge, having crossed tourist class in S.S. *Olympic*. All together, he had had a delightful time, not having been too rushed, and not having found it too hot for enjoyment. While he was away, there had been a pleasant piece of family news, for Henry had passed the Cambridge 2nd M. B. examination.

Towards the end of July J. B. went to Ireland for a few days. His main reason for going was to receive the honorary degree of Doctor of Science from the National University, Dublin, but he also visited The Glen, Newry. His doctorate diploma was signed by Mr. de Valera, as Chancellor of the University, and the other recipients of the same degree were Sir Edward Sharpey-Schafer, Dr. Rufus Cole (in absentia), Professor Dean Lewis, and Professor T. H. Milroy. On 1 August J. B. was back in Cambridge, and a fortnight later he and M. A. B. left for a month's holiday in Austria and Switzerland, visiting inter alia Salzburg, Alt Aussee, and St. Wolfgang, and getting home on 16 September.

The end of the Long Vacation was also the end of building work at the Physiology Laboratory, and J. B. found that the new lecture theatre was just right for the seating of his two hundred and forty students. On 16 October, the day after the laboratory had got into its new working order, the Tutor of St. Catharine's College called to see J. B. and to ask him if he would be willing to become Master. Presumably the answer was in the negative, or there was a hitch in the further procedures, for there is no subsequent note on the subject in M. A. B.'s diary. Four days later J. B. was elected President of the Philosophical Society, and Sir Henry Dale stayed overnight at No. 13 on 10 November.

That concludes the relevant items extracted from M. A. B.'s diary for 1933, but one further, important note needs to be inserted into the year's story, and it concerns the assessment of nominations received for the Nobel Prize in Physiology and Medicine. On p. 258 of Liljestrand's history of this Prize, it is stated that "Other studies on circulation proposed for awards include the investigations of J. Barcroft on the function of the spleen. According to these, one purpose of the spleen is to regulate the volume and contents of the blood. By tests on various animals it was shown that the spleen contains blood which is shut off during rest periods but which during times of work or other strains can be added to the blood already in circulation. These findings, which have since been fully confirmed by other workers, have been of considerable importance to the study of the reserve supply of blood and were found to merit a prize in 1933 and 1936." In 1933. however, the Prize was awarded to T. H. Morgan "for his discoveries concerning the function of the chromosome in the transmission of heredity", and in 1936 – if we may for convenience anticipate – to H. H. Dale and Otto Loewi "for their discoveries relating to the chemical transmission of nerve impulses."

Items for the year 1934 begin with the death, on 23 January, of another old friend of J. B., namely, Sir William Hardy, F.R.S., Director of Food Investigation, Department of Scientific and Industrial Research; like J. B., he had been a keen yachtsman; he had also been a near neighbour of the Barcrofts, for he had lived in No. 5 Grange Road. A month later Professor E. B. Verney stayed the night at No. 13; he had accepted the post of Reader in Pharmacology in Cambridge, which meant giving up the chair at University College, London.

February 28 saw the first of J. B.'s publications for the year, an article on "Some forms of apparatus for the equilibration of blood." It described forms of saturator which aimed at the attainment of considerable accuracy with a smaller quantity of blood than was required in extant accurate methods. A month later J. B. and M. A. B. had a week's holiday at Fowey. Then, on 12 May, Henry and Professor B. A. McSwiney, of Leeds, came to No. 13 for the Cambridge meeting of the Physiological Society – McSwiney had been most helpful to J. B. in designing the new Physiology Laboratory. The day of the meeting was also, apparently, the day of publication of J. B.'s new book, and on the following day (Plate 51) the Barcrofts held the usual open house party for members of the Society and their guests, this year a total of over a hundred. So it was a busy and eventful, but also gratifying, weekend.

The new book, which was dedicated "To my Wife", was one of the more arresting ones in modern physiological literature, namely, *Features in the Architecture of Physiological Function*. It originated through a remark made by Sir John Rose Bradford during an address which he gave to the Cambridge Medical Society in or about 1928. He said, so nearly as J. B. could remember later, that "The difference between physiology as taught now and in my youth is that now the student is given principles: then he was only given facts." J. B. commenced to wonder what those principles were, and the list, as it occurred to him then, was much the same as the headings of the 1934 book. In the meantime, however, there had been a preliminary exposition in the four 1929 Dunham Lectures at Harvard, and one of these – "The constancy of the internal environment" – had been expanded into the *Biological Review* of January 1932, with the title, "'La fixité du milieu intérieur est la condition de la vie libre.' (Claude Bernard)." "At the outset," to continue the story in J. B.'s own words, "I had regarded the body as a noble building on the principles which it exhibits as unconnected features in its architecture. It became clear that the features were far from independent. The highest functions of the nervous system demand a quite special constancy in the composition of its intimate environment. The stability of the internal *milieu* almost compels the principle of the storage of materials and of integration in adaptation. Again an easy stepping stone to integration is the practice of the body to have more than one way of doing many things. But parallel mechanisms may express themselves not only in integrative but in antagonistic processes. Moreover, increased functional activity may be achieved either by heightening the efforts of units already functioning or by marshalling a greater number of units: and so we arrive at the 'all-or-none' relation. It seemed almost as though there had emerged an approach to physiology from an unusual angle: not from that of mere structure, whether the structure of organs or of chemical formulae, but from the principles of function." He then went on to acknowledge the sympathetic encouragement of friends, notably Sir Charles Sherrington and Professor E. P. Cathcart, and the help of Professor Adrian, Mr. Matthews, Dr. Winton, Dr. Keys, and a host of other workers in the Cambridge Laboratory.

With but minor changes, the first three Chapters of the book were a reprinting of the 1932 *Biological Review*, and the final passages read as follows. "Just as an army, after the tedious ascent through a mountain defile, may arrive at and deploy over the open plateau of the summit, so it is not unnatural that the slow and laboured course of evolution should be broken at intervals by sudden and rapid developments. Such would appear to be the sequence before us; by degrees throughout the ages the constancy of the internal *milieu* became controlled with ever-increasing nicety till ultimately this control was perfected up to the point at which man's faculties could develop and he could attain to an understanding in terms of abstract knowledge of the world around him. Each century, and now each decade, add emphasis to the antithesis between the complete insignificance of man when considered as part of the material universe and the astounding ascendency to which his intellect has attained in comprehending the universe in which he is placed. Of that intellectual ascendency, 'la fixité du milieu intérieur' appears to be the, or at least a, condition; of that intellectual ascendency – 'la vie libre' is no inapt description."

Chapters IV – VI dealt with the body's "Stores" (certain proximate principles, oxygen iron and copper, and blood), and Chapters VII – IX with the theme, "Every adaptation is an Integration." They appear, therefore, to have been expansions of two more of the Dunham Lectures. The titles of the other Chapters were respectively, "The 'All-or-None' Relation", "Units", "The Principle of Antagonism" (the title of the remaining Dunham Lecture), "The Principle of Maximal Activity", "Duplication", and "The Chance that a Phenomenon has a Significance". It is not possible here to analyse these Chapters and to make adequate quotations from them – the book is available and should be read by all interested in the science of physiology and its wider implications. It is, however, worth while to give a few extracts from reviews and thereby samples of contemporary reactions, and also a tribute of a much later date, which will stress the continuing value of the book.

One reviewer wrote that "the high spot of interest in this fascinating book is the section which supports the view that 'every adaptation is an integration'." Another referred to the whole as "a brilliant and stimulating survey of life which is unique among physiological monographs . . . Of Dr. Barcroft it may be said . . .: 'He has made familiar things seem new'." A third wrote, "Specialization has developed to a point where, but for this book, one might have feared that no one man could appreciate the kernel of the problems fashionable in more than a few of the many branches of physiology.

Professor Barcroft shakes himself clear of the deluge of impersonal reports on what new methods can tell us about bits of animals, and wonders what are the things it would be really interesting to know about in connection with how the body and its components work . . . To the physiologist the book is a joy for its novel points of view, its innumerable happy ways of expressing them, and the vitality of constructive and critical thought; for anyone who has forgotten nearly but not quite all his physiology there is no book which will so surely revive his interest in it and bring up to date his information about most of those branches of the subject which, for the moment, seem to matter." Finally, there was a French review which opened, "Chaque oeuvre du professeur de Cambridge est une joie pour le lecteur. Il y trouve nombre de faits précis, nouveaux, dont beaucoup sont des acquisitions personnelles de l'auteur; il les voit présentés d'une manière originale et vivante qui ajoute à leur intérêt et oblige à réfléchir; enfin, de leur groupement se dégagent quelques idées générales, directrices qui dépassent même la physiologie expérimentale."

The tribute of a much later date is the one which was paid by August Krogh in 1948, and published the following year. He said, "I am not going to try and characterize Barcroft's scientific work – that will be done much better by others. But there is one book by Barcroft to which I want to draw your attention. That is a book on the Architecture of Physiological Function. The title is very characteristic of Barcroft, but perhaps not the best title to get people to read the book. I would suggest that it is a book which gives an integration of physiology of such a kind that it ought to be read by everyone who is going into experimental work in physiology. It gives the general ideas which cannot be obtained from any other book in existence." It is pertinent, perhaps, to note that an Honours B.Sc. student to whom the present writer suggested reading the book in 1952 was inspired by it in the way suggested by Krogh, and wished to know if there were any similar books, J. B.'s one having so greatly impressed him. So, after a generation, the stimulating influence of J. B.'s original-mindedness continues through his published work.

One final point may with relevance be made about the book, namely, that it inevitably reveals much about the author's own personality, career, and outlook upon things in general. The layman may well find it somewhat of an effort to cull these extras from the preponderating mass of more technical matter; the scientific reader, on the other hand, will find the extras not only fascinating per se, but contributing in no small measure to his enjoyment of the essential parts of the work.

We pass on now to Tuesday, 5 June, when, in response to an invitation sent in March, J. B. delivered the eighth Stephen Paget Memorial Lecture at the Annual General Meeting of the Research Defence Society, the requested subject being, "Experiments on Man", and the venue the London School of Tropical Medicine and Hygiene. The Society had been founded in 1908 by Stephen Paget, under the Presidency of Lord Cromer, to make generally known the value and the necessity of experiments on animals; the restrictions imposed on them by the Act of 1876; and the great saving of human and animal lives already obtained by means of such experiments." The Act 39 and 40 Vict. regulated the conduct of animal experiments in the interests of the animals concerned, while at the same time giving some protection to licensed experimenters. J. B., through the general restriction of his talk to human experiments, largely kept off the contentious ground of animal ones, though certain implications in respect of the latter were unavoidable and he began by saying that the human experiments that he was to describe would have had to be conducted under the Act had man been regarded as a "vertebrate" in the sense of that Act.

The researches which in fact he mentioned included inhalation of prussic acid gas, and work on sensation, the higher faculties, trench fever, and yellow fever. He finished the lecture as follows:- "Roughly then, let me sum up. Purely objective experiments do not as a rule demand the use of man; in a great many cases the relevant information can be obtained on animals. Experiments on sensation and on mental performances must usually be carried out on man himself. As regards the communication of disease, if animals show symptoms of the malady they can be used at all events to clear the ground; if they do not, resort must be had to the human experiment. The considerations with which I opened this discussion brought back to me some recollections of the Great War. But a greater war is constantly being waged. It becomes dramatic when nations clash or when capitals are wiped out as was Rio by yellow fever. The dramatic element is due to the concentration of the fatalities in a small area, but disease is waging war to-day against mankind; less dramatically because its victims are diffuse in space, but no less certainly. The proof that plague could be communicated to men, was according to the text book statement first supplied by Whyte, who injected himself with blood taken from a plague-patient. I leave it to the judgment and conscience of my hearers to decide whether if to-day the matter could be settled with a high degree of certainty on rats, marmots, monkeys and the like, such an act, in any case one of heroism, would not verge on unjustifiable suicide? The second instance quoted was an injection of the disease into a condemned criminal. Having regard to the great number of experiments which usually are essential to the proof of anything, having regard to the paucity of condemned criminals, and having regard to the obvious abuses to which such a course is open, I again leave it to your judgment whether, if the relevant information can be acquired from animal experimentation, we should have recourse to the use of criminals. Personally I am against the use of criminals. The third instance quoted was a deplorable accident in Vienna in which workers in some unaccountable way became infected from the germs of a culture.

"I do not leave it to your judgment whether in the face of death around us we are to fold our hands and wait for accident to enlighten us. We of the Research Defence Society are pledged to the combat; we believe we have open minds; we believe that research is a most potent weapon, therefore we are pledged to research; we are pledged to certain methods of research – namely, animal experimentation – because we think that many problems can be solved most rapidly and most humanely by that method; but we welcome no less any other method which will be of use, any other weapon with which the war may be waged. We welcome criticism, but we judge it according to its constructive value. With the policy of waiting for the illuminating accident, with the policy of folding of the hands, with the policy of wrapping the talent in a napkin, we have nothing to do, but all legitimate methods, all useful criticism we welcome 'so that by all means we may save some.' "

On 6 August J. B. and M. A. B. went off for a month's holiday in Norway, visiting Norheimshund, Ulvik, and Balestrand. On the fourth day J. B.'s fortune, told by someone in the hotel, included the forecast that he would be knighted within a year. On 2 September he and M. A. B. were back in the United Kingdom, and on 6 September he took part at Aberdeen in the Symposium, arranged by Section I of the British Association, on "Some recent advances in the physiology and pathology of the blood." J. B.'s contribution was on the "Respiratory function of blood in the foetus" and, in as much as it added somewhat to the account which he had given in Chicago in 1933, it is worth while to quote from the précis published in *Nature* (see *Anon.*, 1934), which in some ways is more informative than the brief official *Report*.

"At the beginning of gestation", it read, "the placenta is large relative to the size of the foetus, but the growth of the foetus soon catches up with the placenta, and by term it may well be that the foetus has outgrown its commissariat. The matter has been investigated quantitatively by measurement of the oxygen content of maternal and foetal blood. Several compensatory mechanisms seem to have been adopted to cope with the relatively poor conditions of oxygen supply to the foetus. (i) The maternal blood becomes more acid, thus being enabled to part with its oxygen more readily. (ii) The haemoglobin of the foetus differs from that of the mother in that it has, under identical conditions, a distinctly greater affinity for oxygen. (iii) In certain animals (for example, rabbit) the maternal and foetal blood vessels are anatomically arranged in such a way as to ensure maximum diffusion of oxygen from the maternal blood to the foetal blood. The extraordinary efficiency of these arrangements is shown by observations on the oxygen content of the blood returning from the uterus to the venous system of the mother. As pregnancy advances, the content sinks until at term the blood is almost denuded of oxygen. Even so, the oxygen in the foetal blood feeding the foetal organs does not reach a level as high as would be found in the arteries of a man on the top of Mount Everest; it is doubtful indeed whether the foetal oxygen level would be enough to maintain consciousness in the born animal. The foetus, however, appears to be better off, in that the oxygen consumption of its tissues, per unit weight, may be only about a third of the oxygen consumption per unit weight after birth."

On 13 September the Barcrofts were at last back home in Cambridge, and four days later appeared J. B.'s fifth publication of the year. It was entitled, "A case of deficient acclimatization to low oxygen pressure", and the co-authors were R. H. E. Elliott, F. R. Fraser, Herkel, B. H. C. Matthews, and Talaat. The subject had been Matthews, then "26 years of age, height 6 ft. 1 in., weight 12 stone, of active habit and physically strong." He had been exposed to diminished oxygen pressure from approximately 6.15 p.m. on 12 December 1932 until approximately 12.30 p.m. on 16 December. The chamber was the one used by J. B. himself in 1920, but with a scrubber that was infinitely more efficient as regards water vapour. The greatest "height" reached corresponded to 21,000 feet, and Matthews acclimatized very poorly, though why he did so it was not easy to say. His alveolar oxygen partial pressure fell to about 30 mm. Hg., while his carbon dioxide one remained above 28 mm. Hg. The figures for his total metabolism also fell, and his oxygen dissociation curve at 40 mm. Hg. carbon dioxide partial pressure and even at that obtaining in the body was shifted considerably to the right. Blood, obtained by puncture from his femoral artery at the time of his emergence from the chamber, was not more than 65 p.c. saturated with oxygen, he was intensely cyanosed and in an indifferent mental condition, and for some days after the experiment he became unduly hyperpnoeic on exercise and was appreciably hysterical. An interesting footnote by Barcroft on p. 372 stated that "with regard to Matthews's psychological condition at the end of the experiment the following episode seems relevant. Three samples of alveolar air were taken by him before leaving the chamber. Matthews said in substance: 'I can vouch for the third sample because the tap of the alveolar air tube into which it was collected is so much *simpler in construction* than those of the other two tubes.' Actually the tap was not *simpler in construction,* it was merely greased with a more transparent lubricant; the pregnancy of the remark is not lessened by the fact that few persons, in the ordinary course, would grasp details of mechanical construction more surely and rapidly than Matthews."

On 13 October Professor L. J. Henderson of Harvard was an overnight house-guest at 13 Grange Road; on 20 October he returned to give a lecture that evening and to stay for some time. Two days after his return, there was an occasion of some pageantry, namely, the opening of the new University Library by H. M. King George V, accompanied by H. M. Queen Mary. King's College and Clare College had generously given up playing-field space for the Library's site, and half the cost of the building had been defrayed by the International Education Board, founded by Mr. John D. Rockefeller Jr. Rockefeller money had also been given towards constructional work in four biological laboratories, so the day as a whole was very much in the nature of an acknowledgement of large-scale American generosity.

At noon Their Majesties arrived at Cambridge station from Sandringham, and twenty minutes later they were at the Library, where the Chancellor, Mr. Stanley Baldwin, awaited them. He presented the Chairman of the Library Syndicate (Professor A. Hutchinson, Master of Pembroke College), the Registrary (Mr. E. Harrison), the Librarian (Mr. A. F. Schofield), and the architect (Sir Giles Scott). Then the procession moved on to the long and narrow Reading Room – as long as the nave of nearby Ely Cathedral – and, after Their Majesties had taken their places on the dais and the National Anthem had been sung, an address of welcome was read and presented by the Chancellor, and His Majesty graciously replied. The King, according to M. A. B.'s note, "looked frail enough but his voice was strong when he read his address. Queen Mary, a statuesque figure, missed little that her roving eye could see, and we all were most impressed by her comely appearance." After the King had spoken, there were presented to Their Majesties those who were to receive honorary degrees later in the afternoon (i.e., the American Ambassador, the Provost of Eton College, Professors Henderson and Landsteiner, Bodley's Librarian, and the Hon. Secretary of the Bibliographical Society), the Heads of the four Science Departments for which buildings had been erected under the Rockefeller scheme (i.e., Professors Seward, Stanley Gardiner, Barcroft, and Engledow), the Secretary to the Library, the Engineer for the Construction, a representative of the builders of the superstructure, and the Clerk of Works. Their Majesties left just before one o'clock for the station and their return thence to Sandringham.

The University's guests were entertained at luncheon in three Colleges, namely, Gonville and Caius, Pembroke, and Corpus Christi. The Vice-Chancellor, the Master of Pembroke, and the Master of Corpus respectively proposed the healths of the honorary graduands, and there were replies by the American Ambassador (Mr. Bingham), the Provost of Eton (Dr. James), and Professor Henderson. At Pembroke emphasis was laid on the contribution of the Rockefeller Trustees to the erection of the Library, and at

Corpus on their immense benefaction for the furtherance of the biological sciences. J. B. and M. A. B., like Professor Henderson, were among the guests at Corpus Christi.

In the degree ceremony in the afternoon Professor Henderson was introduced as the great analyst of the blood, not content with observing its colour and action, but instructing us as to its very substance and nature. "*Demonstravit enim*", said the Public Orator, "*quibus elementis constet sanguis, duobus scilicet ita sollerter compositis ut aequum tenorem servet nequid nimis sit acidi neve alkalini.*" Dr. Karl Landsteiner, of the Rockefeller Institute for Medical Research, who had been awarded a Nobel Prize in 1930 for his discovery of the human blood groups, was acclaimed as a signal example of an emigrant who had gained distinction in an adopted land. After the degree ceremony, receptions were held in the new buildings of the Agriculture, Botany, Physiology, and Zoology Laboratories and in the evening there was a special dinner in King's College; the healths of the University's guests were proposed by the Provost, and the Vice-Chancellor of Oxford University and General Smuts replied. Gonville and Caius College also put on a special meal, and M.A.B. dined there while J. B. and L. J. Henderson were being entertained in King's.

Four days later L. J. Henderson said goodbye to his host and hostess, and J. B. went to Reading to give a talk to the Berkshire Pathological Society. He took this opportunity to visit the distinguished neurologist, Sir Henry Head, F.R.S., now "a hopeless invalid entirely paralysed except in his head – fortunately he retains all his mental faculties." On 29 October J. B. applied for, and was granted, a sabbatical term after Christmas in order that he might have time to operate on his hundred pregnant ewes; he had no intention of going away from Cambridge, but foresaw so heavy a programme of research during his remaining years as Professor that this expedient was necessary.

Two publications in November and two in December round out this account of J. B.'s 1934 activities. One of the November ones, "Conditions of foetal respiration", appeared in *Revista de la Sociedad Argentina de Biología* and began as follows:-

"Foetal respiration in the mammalia or in those forms which have been studied principally, namely the rabbit and the goat, takes place under certain limiting conditions.

"1. The placenta and the foetus develop at different times, the former before the latter.

"2. The mechanism of foetal respiration is the following:

(*a*) The maternal blood imparts its oxygen to the foetal blood by diffusion in the placenta.

(*b*) The foetal blood coming from the placenta mixes with other foetal blood coming from the tissues of the foetus. This mixture goes to the heart and is distributed to the body. (The finer points in the mechanism of this mixture, which insures to the head blood of greater oxygen content than that which goes to the body generally, are passed over here as being but an incident in the general scheme.)"

"The present paper," J. B. then added, "consists in a detailed and, where possible, a quantitative restatement of the general positions put briefly above." That was correct even if the specialist reader could discover some points either not previously mentioned at much length or else less particularly stressed; there was also mention of recent measurements of the blood flow through the foetal heart but, as they were the subject of the experimental work described in the second November publication, it is more convenient to pass straight on to that article, written by J. B., L. B. Flexner, and T. McClurkin, and entitled, "The output of the foetal heart in the goat."

The object of the research had been to measure the quantity of blood which passed through the foetal heart at various stages of development, and, after preliminary trials with other methods, reasonably accurate determinations had been obtained with the use of a cardiographic technique. The conclusions were as follows:-

"1. During the latter half of foetal life:

(*a*) The ratio of the blood flow through the heart to the weight of the body varies little. It is of the order of 0.12–0.18 c.c. per g. of foetus per min.

(*b*) The oxygen used by the foetus also remains constant at about 0.0025 ± 0.001 c.c. per g. per min.

"2. The quantity of blood which flows through the foetal heart is, relatively to the body weight, the same before and after birth.

"3. The oxygen used by the foetus, relatively to the body weight, increases on birth to perhaps four or five times the prenatal value."

The most interesting of the findings was in this last sentence, and in the previous paper J. B. had written:- "To what is this rise due?

Clearly it must be due to activity in various forms such as muscular tone, the secretion of juices and so forth. It would appear therefore that even soon after birth the oxidation may be divided into two categories, one which is demanded by a purely vegetative existence, the other which is the expression of activity, and the researcher is left to guess what meaning the term 'basal metabolism' may have under such conditions."

The first of the December papers, by J. B. and seven colleagues, was on "Conditions of foetal respiration in the goat", and its conclusions had been anticipated in earlier publications of the year, so it need not concern us further here. The second, by J. B. and four colleagues, was on "The utilization of oxygen by the uterus in the rabbit", and contained an account of work done chiefly to clear up some points left over from the research of J. B., Herkel, and Hill (1933). It gave the saturation of the uterine venous blood of the rabbit from the eighteenth day of gestation onwards and the marked rise occurring within 24 hours from parturition; it also provided data relating the foetal weight to that of (1) the whole placenta and (2) the foetal placenta at different times during pregnancy.

The reader may by now be feeling a little over-saturated with foetal physiology and ready, at least temporarily, for a complete change of topic. Fortunately, such is available in a newspaper cutting, dated 24 December 1934, which M. A. B. pasted into her diary. Though it deals with the English weather on Christmas Eve, that weather was for once worth reporting. "Haycarts on the roads", it stated, "strawberries and raspberries in gardens, and roses and primroses in hedgerows are now to be seen in many parts of Devon and Cornwall, where the temperature, which is well above the average for this time of the year, has produced a crop of spring flowers and fruit out of their season." Even were there more items available for the 1934 story, and there are not, that would surely be the note on which to end it!

The new year, destined to add greatly to J. B.'s already very high prestige, began with the routine-free Lent term sanctioned by the University, and to mark his "leave of absence" he put a notice on his door in the lab., saying, "Professor Barcroft is away from Cambridge for all purposes except research." During this "absence" and during the corresponding ones in 1936 and 1937, a member of J. B.'s staff was appointed Deputy Professor, and he himself was a guest-researcher in a laboratory presided over by one of his subordinates, a *vice versa* situation, as Professor Roughton later wrote, which appealed to his Irish love of paradox. On 11 January M. A. B. noted that J. B. "is thoroughly enjoying his work and the leisure to do it; he is finding more and more interesting facts about the foetuses in his sheep."

On 23 January he broke off for a short while to go to London and to introduce a discussion on haemoglobinuria, arranged by the Section of Comparative Medicine of the Royal Society of Medicine. He began by regarding "the epithelium of Bowman's capsule as a filter – a sort of living muslin – with meshes of very fine calibre," and passed on to the investigations of Bayliss, Kerridge, and Russell, which showed that the limiting molecular weight of the substances passing the filter was in the neighbourhood of 70,000, at about which critical level stood, according to Adair's findings, the molecular weight of haemoglobin. He then brought into the story the researches of Geiger, Brinkman, R. Hill, Theorell, and Winton, and concluded by saying that haemoglobinuria was not a disease of the excretory mechanism but occurred whenever haemoglobin, from the disintegration of red blood corpuscles or from muscle, got into the plasma. "As the spectra of the two forms of haemoglobin have different properties there should be no difficulty in distinguishing between them if, in urine, they retain their native properties."

The next items concern J. B.'s appointment to three committees, and his personal health. Towards the end of January he went onto the Committee of the Medical Advisory Board for the Gas Light and Coke Company, and at the beginning of February he was asked also to join that Company's Medical Consultative Committee, the immediate business being the limitation of the vitiation, caused by gas fires, of the air of flats. The third Committee, in an entirely different category, was that in re the relation of alcohol to road accidents. His personal "vetting" in the matter of health was effected by Dr. Cole and by Dr. A. E. Barclay, the radiologist in charge of the course in that subject at Cambridge, and a reassuring negative report was the outcome.

Towards the end of February, to resume the more scientific story, he received from the Registrar of Trinity College, Dublin, an invitation to deliver the annual Purser Lectures in the University of that city; the Lectureship had been endowed in June 1930 by Miss

S. H. Purser in memory of her brother, the late Dr. John Mallet Purser (1839–1929), who had been Regius Professor of Physic from 1917 to 1925. J. B. replied accepting the invitation.

On 29 March there died one of the great figures of British physiology, who was in addition an old friend of J. B. This was Sir Edward Sharpey-Schafer, who had been born on 2 June 1850 and was, therefore, in his eighty-fifth year. He was the sole survivor of the "nineteen persons interested in physiology" who on 31 March 1876 had resolved to found the Physiological Society. His contributions to the science are too well-known to need repetition here, but he had also the rather unique distinction, when he retired in 1933, of having been a professor for fifty years, sixteen at University College, London, and thereafter thirty-four in Edinburgh. [1] Not long after the news of Sharpey-Schafer's death came word that the great Russian physiologist, Ivan Petrovich Pavlov, then in his eighty-sixth year, was seriously ill with pneumonia. However, he was to recover and preside actively over the fifteenth International Congress of Physiologists a few months later.

On 2 April J. B. returned to ordinary duties (Plate 49) after his sabbatical term, and M. A. B. wrote that "it has been a refreshment to him, and he has much enjoyed freedom for the researches on his sheep, and seems to have advanced in discovering the movements which take place in the 'Babies'! before they are born. He has now only two more left out of fifty." Near the end of the month came the joyous news that Henry had been appointed to the Dunville Chair of Physiology in Queen's University, Belfast, in succession to T. H. Milroy, who was soon to retire. It will be remembered that Milroy had been appointed in 1902 when J. B., with the support of Angelo Mosso, had also been a candidate for the post. On 6 May Cambridge was en fête for the Jubilee of Their Majesties King George V and Queen Mary, and on 8 May J. B. learned that he was to give the first address at one of the plenary

[1] William Harvey's teacher, Hieronymus Fabricius of Aquapendente, taught at Padua for fifty years and was Professor for all except the first two of them. Gerard Baldwin Brown (1849–1932) was Watson-Gordon Professor of Fine Art in the University of Edinburgh from 1886 to 1930, a record only twice equalled in that University's history. But the outstanding case must surely be that of D'Arcy Wentworth Thompson (1860–1948), who was Professor at University College, Dundee, from 1884 to 1917 and at St. Andrews from 1917 until his death, a total of sixty-four years. "He was always proud of this record – which is obviously unbeatable, as retirement at seventy is now compulsory under the new regulations." (Dobell, 1949).

sessions of the International Congress of Physiologists, to be held in Leningrad and Moscow early in August. He was naturally very pleased, but said to M. A. B., "Am I having a St. Luke's Little Summer, being asked to do this, combined with the Croonian and Purser Lectures?" A week later he received a letter from Professor Cathcart asking him if he would consider accepting the Regius Professorship of Physiology at Aberdeen as from October 1935, the retiring age being seventy. J. B. refused.

A week later still, on Thursday, 23 May, at 4.30 p.m., he delivered the Croonian Lecture of the Royal Society, his subject being "Foetal respiration." He began by saying that the lecture was "an attempt to state the principal facts known about foetal respiration in the mammalia. The word 'respiration' is used in a very broad sense: the transport of gases involves the circulatory system even more in the foetus than in the free organism, and therefore the principal factors in the foetal circulation must come under review." It is not possible to give a précis of the whole lecture – that would take too much space – but one should note certain features. Of these, one of the more important is the advance in J. B.'s appreciation of the subject as a whole – obviously, the enormous amount of experimental work done in the Lent term had greatly increased his insight as well as his practical acquaintance with the foetus. Further, though his main extra cardiovascular data were largely limited to determinations of the foetal blood pressure increase with age, he had been able, through determinations of oxygen usage and the like, to reach many interesting temporary conclusions about the circulation of the blood, both in the mother and in the foetus. A number of these were to be decided more directly within the next few years, but one must admire the extent to which he had already specified many of the problems, and the ingenious ways, both theoretical and practical, in which he had begun his attempts at their solution. Very definitely, it seems, this lecture established him as the modern leader in foetal physiology studies, and forecast his main preoccupation for the next few years. He had already discovered the growing inhibition, effected by the higher centres of the nervous system, of the reflexes elicitable in earlier stages of intra-uterine life; he appreciated the differential distribution of the better oxygenated and the more poorly oxygenated blood flows coming from the foetal heart, and he was getting interested in a particular

49—Joseph Barcroft lecturing, 1935

50—THE BARCROFTS WITH THEIR YOUNGER SON, ROBBIE, AND HIS WIFE, BETTY, ON THE PORCH OF NO. 13 GRANGE ROAD, CAMBRIDGE, 1935

Facing page 225

foetal by-pass, namely, the ductus arteriosus, which was destined to be one of his special objects of study in the future. He realized already the relative inactivity, during foetal life, of the alimentary canal, the kidneys, and the muscles of the hind limbs and of the more distal part of the trunk. Finally, we may note, as an important point, the fact that Dr. Donald H. Barron, who was to be his close associate in foetal work until the second world war interrupted their co-operation, was already busy and had discovered the onset of muscular tone in the late foetus when its surface was cooled [1]. But this was an experimental imitation of the change that occurs at birth, and the birth changes, though already beginning to feature prominently in J. B.'s researches, were not included in the scope of this Croonian lecture. All told, it was a very remarkable one – epoch-making, indeed, would not be an over-assessment of its importance.

A week or so after its delivery, Sir John Boyd Orr came to Cambridge to press J. B. to accept the Regius Professorship of Physiology at Aberdeen, but the latter's mind had been quite made up, and a talk with Professor Sir Frederick Hopkins merely strengthened him in his decision to decline the offer.

The next note in M. A. B.'s diary concerns something much more thrilling, namely, the announcement in the Birthday Honours List that J. B. was to be knighted. The Barcrofts read the news in the paper. Robbie (Plate 50) went and told the maids, and Barbara, the cook, came up and made "a charming speech on behalf of the kitchen, ending up, 'We are all very proud of you.' Then Robbie told Buttress the gardener, and he shed tears of happiness, and said that he did not feel like work." Telegrams of congratulation began to arrive three at a time, telephone and personal calls – the latter including one from ninety-two year old Lady Allbutt who had not been out for months – were innumerable, and the first post on the Monday morning brought sixty letters from friends expressing their delight at the well-deserved honour.

J. B., however, had shortly to go off to Dublin to examine, and to give the sixth and seventh Purser Lectures on 25 and 26 June respectively. The first was on "The mammal before and after

[1] In 1935–6 J. B. received a Medical Research Council grant for assistance by Dr. and Mrs. Barron in studies of the process by which the ductus arteriosus becomes closed after birth.

birth", and in it J. B. gave his audience, in so far as he could, some consecutive idea of the respiratory and vascular changes which occur during birth. As a preliminary, however, he had to say something of the life led by the foetus, and he noted that the information which he had been able to procure, mostly from experiments on sheep, had been elicited from Caesarean sections. He then dealt in succession with the foetal blood volume and blood pressure, the first respiration, slowing of the heart, cardiac outflow, the course of the blood stream, the ductus arteriosus, and respiration before and after birth. The first respiration after birth he showed to be due not to carbon dioxide excess, nor to increased blood pressure in the brain, but to oxygen lack. The slowing of the heart at birth could, he thought, be regarded as a protective mechanism, provided the lower rate was consistent with maintenance of the blood pressure. For it ensured that the circulation continued longer after the placental supplies had been removed, when the postnatal mechanisms had to be brought into action somewhat against time. In the section on the course of the blood stream he stressed the fact that the foetal liver has first access to the blood returning from the placenta with foodstuffs and oxygen derived from the mother. In the section on the ductus arteriosus, he showed that it must be wide open in the foetus and occluded after birth, and noted that its muscular structure put it into an entirely different category from the elastic pulmonary trunk and the aorta; he added, however, that for the time being the mechanism of closure of the ductus had to be left over as an as yet unsolved problem. In the final section he stated that the change-over in the sheep from the foetal to the post-natal type of haemoglobin appeared to occur almost exactly at birth. The whole lecture, apart from its content, was a fine example of J. B.'s graphic and arresting way of imparting a story that was in the course of being told through original research, and it is worthy of being re-read to-day. The second lecture can be regarded in general as a varialectio of the corresponding part of *Features in the architecture of physiological function*, and need not, therefore, be described in any detail here.

On 9 July J. B. went up to London for the night in order to be in readiness for his investiture at Buckingham Palace the next morning. His account of that morning, given in a letter to M. A. B., was as follows:-

"I thought you might like me to put down the 'happenings'

7.30 Tea.

7.45 I resolved to take your advice and not get up too soon so I breakfasted at

8.45 By the time I had paid a visit to the hairdresser and got tidied up it was

9.50 Off I started in the Underground and reached Green Park Station at 10.5 – but the glass had come off my watch. Watch in hand I strolled across the Park to the Palace where at

10.20 I deposited my hat and watch with a flunkey in exchange for a blue ticket.

10.30 We were paraded in a hall that I had been in before looking out into the garden and drilled. As soon as the man in front of you goes away, you make a bow to the King, walk up, put your right knee on a stool, the King dubs you, then you stand. H. M. shakes you by the hand, you step back, bow, turn, go.

10.45 We were all lined up in order – just behind me was Seymour Hicks.

11.00 A bell rang and the first man went in. I, being high up the alphabet, was third – so I was out by a quarter past eleven and that was that. While I knelt, my name was read to the King, who said in a deep guttural, "What is it?" It was then repeated. The King hit me on the left shoulder with a sword and said 'Sir', then on the right shoulder and said 'Joseph'."

On 2 August J. B. and M. A. B. embarked on a Russian boat, *Smolney*, at Hays Wharf, London Bridge, en route to the International Congress of Physiologists in Leningrad and Moscow; the other passengers included the A. V. Hills, and the quarters, the food, and the spotless cleanliness aboard evoked immediate favourable comment from M. A. B. At 5 a.m. on 4 August the ship entered the Kiel Canal and about eight hours later emerged into the calm waters of the Baltic – the weather, too, was perfect, in contrast to that which had obtained on the previous day. Monday, 5 August, the Barcrofts' wedding anniversary, found M. A. B. suffering from digestive upset due, Dr. O'Brien thought, to the food; as the day wore on, numerous others were reported to be similarly affected. The Captain gave a fine, if partial, lecture on the U.S.S.R. but had some difficulty at question time in explaining how the crew was paid. It was partly, he said, in foreign currency, partly in Russian currency, and partly in concerts and theatres; they also owned the army and navy, which was another part of their wages. And so on! In the evening the crew in question gave a concert; the Barcrofts did not attend, but learned later that their stewardess had been the prima donna of the evening, and had sung extremely well.

On 6 August some of the victims of enteric trouble were recovering but new cases had occurred. On opposite sides of the ship Esthonia and Finland were sighted and then Cronstad came into view. Dr. Rosenthal came out with the Customs officers and asked the Barcrofts, the A. V. Hills, and Professor Adrian to remain on board until the other passengers had gone ashore. Then these special ones followed one by one while a band played and cinematograph operators shot the scene; reporters also came up and recorded the impressions of J. B., A. V. Hill, and Adrian. Finally, J. B. and M. A. B. were driven off at a terrific pace in a taxi to the Astoria, where they were installed in the best suite, which they found most comfortable.

The next morning the Barcrofts and the Hills had a sightseeing drive, lasting two or three hours, round Leningrad. M. A. B. wrote, "We will always remember, when thinking of that drive, how much we were struck by the colours of the buildings – red, bright yellow, tawny brown and cream facades, with here and there a great burst of colour indicating a palace – all these shades being especially welcome as the cheering brightness of shop windows was entirely absent except in a few recognized places." Dinner at the hotel in the evening provided some difficulties, as the waiters were all old men (waiting being considered a low form of work unsuitable for young men) and in addition the guests could not explain that they did not desire *two* helpings of caviare (which they did not want at all) or *two* different kinds of soup, and so forth. Finally, they gave up the unequal struggle and sat among piled plates of food for an hour and a quarter. After their protracted meal they went off to the first event of the Congress, namely, an informal reception of members by the Physiological Society of the U.S.S.R. This was scheduled to take place at 8 p.m. in the Marble Hall of the Ethnographical Museum, but was delayed for two hours, during which the guests circulated through the museum, with its exhibits illustrating the folk customs of the 189 peoples comprising the Union. At 10 p.m. the doors of the hall were thrown open and the vast room, with its pink marble columns and green bronze dado, was revealed in all its magnificence. In this setting were arranged about 80 to 100 long buffet tables spread with a lavish profusion of Russian delicacies and wines; a large orchestra played at one end of a balcony, and countless waiters kept members' plates and glasses replenished for two hours on end. The Barcrofts, however, having already dined, merely partook of a little of the mineral water "marzan" which was their mainstay, and departed so soon as they could graciously so do.

The next morning the opening plenary session of the Congress took place in the Uritsky Palace, formerly the meeting place of the Duma and of the Provisional Government of 1917, and now of the Leningrad Soviet. Members passed, through a succession of four doors with armed guards, into the great auditorium, which was decorated for the occasion with palms and flowers, and M. A. B. and J. B. went to their seats on the platform. Each seat in the auditorium was equipped with a head-phone, and by placing the plug in the appropriate socket one could listen to the proceedings in either Russian, or English, or French, or German.

Academician Pavlov, the President of the Congress, who was on the platform with A. V. Hill and Louis Lapicque (as representatives of the International Committee) on either side of him, called the meeting to order at 11 a.m., and delivered a spirited address in Russian, entirely unperturbed either by the weight of his 86 years or by the flood-lights of the cinematographers who were busy filming him. He first welcomed the members of the Congress, and then paid a tribute to Sechenov (1829–1915), who was the first Russian physiologist to lecture, not from texts, but from his own experimental observations. Passing thence to the international aspect of science, Pavlov made a stirring plea for peace. When he said that he could understand the greatness of a war for liberty but that, at the same time, war was essentially a bestial method of solving difficulties, and one unworthy of the human mind with its immeasurable resources, the whole audience roared its applause.

Pavlov thereafter asked the meeting to rise in respect to the memories of Sharpey Schafer and of Macleod, who had died in the previous year, and as members stood up a large orchestra began to play Chopin's funeral march.

After Pavlov had finished, members were welcomed by I. A. Akulov (President of the Government Congress Committee) on behalf of the Government, by the aged Professor Karpinsky (President) on behalf of the Academy of Sciences, and by I. F. Kadatzky (Chairman) on behalf of the Leningrad Soviet. The Government speakers stressed the importance of physiology for the well-being of man and beast, and emphasized the educational and scientific efforts of the U.S.S.R.

Thereafter followed the pièce de résistance of the session, namely, W. B. Cannon's address – "bold, forceful, beautifully written and delivered" (Fulton). Before passing to his subject-matter proper ("Some implications of the evidence for chemical transmission of nerve impulses"), the speaker paid a tribute to the President of the Congress, and discussed in some detail and with considerable frankness the effects of national and international politics upon science and scientists. Quotations from a speech of such importance are liable to give only a very partial idea of its contents, and readers are therefore referred to the original. It is, however, only courteous to the country in which the Fifteenth Congress was held to repeat one passage. "In the Soviet Union, where the social importance of science seems to be especially appreciated, it is reported that the funds made available for the development and prosecution of scientific studies are relatively greater than in any other country of the world. These highly commendable acts of good judgment and sagacity offer examples to other governments. The law of the survival of the fit is still operative." From the idea of international co-operation between scientists, it was an easy transition to the mode of action of autonomic nerves on their effector organs, for at least a dozen nations had contributed to the more recent advances made in that particular field.

The ordinary scientific sessions began in the afternoon and went on during the morning of Saturday, 10 August. On the Sunday there were no sessions, and M. A. B. and Mrs. Cannon left at 10 a.m. with a party that was to be shown the Scythian gold collection in the Hermitage Museum. Their conductor was Pavlov's son, who recalled the visit which his father and he had paid to 13 Grange Road some years before, and how much his father had enjoyed the beauty of the garden. When they got to the Museum, Professor Pavlov himself came round and gave M. A. B. "such a warm handshake." The party were then shown the fabulous collection of gold ornaments belonging to Scythian kings – apparently even

Professor Pavlov was seeing it for the first time. The earliest specimens dated from about 2000 B. C., and it had been the custom, when a Scythian king died, for his horses to be buried with him. "An occasional wife was also included, and some slaves, so that he should not enter the next world unattended. The wife's gold ornaments, and the trappings of the horses, were very beautiful . . . The earliest ornaments were embossed with a conventional design of a deer being killed by a lion and a leopard, and that design in one form or another goes on right down the centuries in Scythian work, typifying the conflict between good and evil." J. B. was not in the party, but saw the exhibits later and in part furnished the above account of an incomparable collection. Much else was also seen in the Hermitage, but at that the guests were only able to sample its attractions.

At 6 p.m. or a little later a fleet of motor vehicles, in a line four miles long, took the thousand and a half members to Peterhof, the former summer park of the Tsar, about thirty miles from Leningrad. Crowds had collected all along the route to cheer and wave to the visitors, who reached their destination in about three quarters of an hour. It was a wonderful sight with its three palaces, lovely walks, and countless fountains. Those from the principal palace looking down to the sea were illuminated about 10.30 p.m., and there was also a firework display. But the time to go arrived, so back the procession started. M. A. B. and J. B. got to their hotel about 11.30 and then had supper with Dr. O'Brien, so it was very late before they got to bed.

On Monday, 12 August, J. B. had to attend scientific sessions, but after tea he and M. A. B. went off by car to visit the "Park of Culture and Rest" and found it all very interesting and enjoyable. Unfortunately, on the way back M. A. B. was again attacked by the trouble she had had on the *Smolney*, and had to retire to bed for two days. On the following day J. B. was reclining in his chair after luncheon when M. Hill came in and said, "Everyone is off to hear your paper" (an address, on "The velocity of some physiological processes", which was to open the second plenary session). To J. B.'s horror, the time had been changed, unknown to him, from 6 to 3 p.m., and he found that he had only five minutes in which to get to the Uritsky Palace, where he was due to speak. However, the Chairman's introductory remarks helped to cover his entry, and the address itself, given in a crowded auditorium, was much appreciated. M. A. B., during the day or two that followed, overcame her trouble, but in order to keep her company J. B. forewent the visit to Detskoye Selo (formerly Tzarskoye Selo) on the afternoon of 15 August, and the gargantuan feast (see Franklin, 1938) prepared there for members in what had been the Tsar's principal residence.

The second part of the Congress was scheduled to take place in Moscow, and to get there and back was to necessitate two long train journeys; further, the social programme was to include more strenuous sight-seeing, and a third huge-scale banquet. This seemed to the Barcrofts more than they could manage, so they made plans to leave Leningrad for Finland on Friday, 16 August. Dr. Higgins, an old American friend who had been attending M. A. B., came and pronounced her "free of toxin, and quite bright." Then there were packing, goodbyes, and handshakes galore, and at the station a farewell gift from Dr. and Mrs. Rosenthal of a colossal bouquet of mixed roses and red stocks. M. A. B.'s concluding note reads, "We were most kindly treated in every possible way, and owe much gratitude to the Soviet State for its great generosity, from start to finish, to two of its invited guests.

Despite that tribute, however, M. A. B.'s next entry reads as follows. "It seems to be the invariable experience of all those who, like ourselves, have crossed the border from Russia into Finland, to be seized with a quite extraordinary elation when this takes place. We felt it acutely, and lay back in our curious railway compartment with deep satisfaction – a feeling of 'freedom' predominating." Late that evening they reached Vipuri, and the next morning they went sightseeing in a "very-early-Victorian-Victoria, with charioteer to match," finishing up at the picturesque twelfth-century fortress. "Our first glimpse of the water and its Islands was most enchanting, and when kissed by the sun (it was cloudy to-day) we can imagine every longing for quiet beauty must be satisfied." In the afternoon they went on to Imatra, where for the sum of seven shillings a night they had a suite in the tower of the State Hotel, with the charming sitting room looking out onto the Rapids. "Living in Finland is extraordinarily cheap, and the cleanliness simply screams at one! The Rapids thunder below us and, a little farther away, the Falls are dashing up their spray, and despatching great trees down their powerful current. It is thrilling to watch them being whirled here and there, like spillikins."

Two days later, on 19 August, they went on to Helsinki, where they stayed three days. "Joe much enjoys the vapour baths," says the note for 21 August, "and had his second this afternoon, and was beaten with birch twigs in true Finn fashion." The next day they went on by train to Haemmelena, and drove thence to Aulanka-Karlberg, where they found Professor and Mrs. Robert Gesell, of the University of Michigan, and their daughter, who was being nursed back to health after a severe attack of the "Russian microbe". They enjoyed very greatly the quiet beauty of the place and stayed there until the end of the month, when they went to Aboe and embarked on the steamer for Stockholm. Unfortunately, M. A. B. had a relapse and had to go to bed for the last two days. The sunset, as they sailed away from Aboe, was completely lovely behind the never-ending islands, and made them say "Goodbye, dear Finland!" with very genuine feeling. Stockholm recalled happy memories of the 1926 Congress, but they decided to press on to Copenhagen, and even in that delightful city their stay was not over-long. They sailed in the *England* from Esbjerg and reached Liverpool Street on 5 September.

In giving the above account of the Barcrofts' time abroad, the writer refrained from presenting details of J. B.'s address to the Congress, and of his and Barron's communication, given on the morning of 15 August, on "The initiation of respiration at birth." For to do so would have interrupted too greatly the sequence of the general story. Now, however, the omission must be rectified, and there is a contemporary abstract of the address available in the *Lancet* – fortunately, because such a contemporary note is in some ways better than a précis made nearly two decades after the event. It states that "Sir Joseph Barcroft spoke of the velocities of some physiological processes and discussed the possibility that the rate at which chemical processes occur may be a limiting factor of importance in the body. In the ordinary loading and unloading of oxygen, the chemical events take place so much more rapidly than the physical ones that the rate of the chemical phase of the reaction may be regarded as negligible. Though the rate of combination of haemoglobin with oxygen may not be important in man, there are forms of life in which it is otherwise. In mice for instance, if the heart muscle contained ordinary haemoglobin, it would not be possible to say that the time of oxidation of the haemoglobin was quite inconsiderable as compared with the time of the diastole of the heart beat. The pigment in cardiac muscle is myoglobin not haemoglobin, and the chemical reactions of myoglobin take only about one-sixth of the time taken by those of haemoglobin; in the heart of the mouse and canary the pigment, actually, is not myoglobin but cytochrome, whose reactions are even faster. The rate of reaction of oxygenase and catalase and of carbonic anhydrase, which accelerates the conversion of carbonic acid into CO_2 and water, were also considered."

The communication by J. B. and Barron was, in its published form, a short one and can therefore be presented in full. "The experiments", wrote the authors, "have been carried out on the embryos of sheep, which while remaining attached to the mother by the umbilical cord, are exposed in a bath of saline solution. The period of gestation in the sheep is about 147 days. No movements have been seen in the embryo before the 36th day. Then two things may be seen (1) a spontaneous rhythmic wriggling movement (2) a reflex movement of the head when the nose is touched. On the 39th day the wriggling movement has disappeared but in its place there is a spontaneous rhythm at times, a marked feature of which is the drawing down of the diaphragm, so that the rhythm has a definitely respiratory aspect. By the 68th day this spontaneous gasping spreads to involve the opening of the mouth. By the 80th day the gasping rhythm ceases to be spontaneous but can be induced by pinching the umbilical cord, and even more markedly on releasing the cord. The onset is immediate. As pregnancy proceeds, it becomes more difficult to elicit the respiratory rhythm. A longer time elapses between the pinching of the umbilical cord and the onset of respiration. The maximum time is about the 120th day.

At 101 days the time is 10 sec.
,, 120 ,, ,, ,, ,, 63 ,,
,, 138 ,, ,, ,, ,, 42 ,,

At term there is a pause of perhaps ten seconds between the first breath and the second. The cause of the first breath is oxygen want. Ways of producing it other than pinching the cord are such as turn the haemoglobin into methaemoglobin, e.g. injection of hydroxylamine into the umbilical vessels. The respiration can be abolished by subsequent injection of blood from the mother and brought back by another injection of hydroxylamine. In character the respiration so produced is a gasp, similar to the dying gasp in cyanide poisoning, but the circumstance that the dying gasp of the foetus draws air into its lungs, initiates the free life of the lamb."

We can complete the 1935 story with two notes. The first is that, apart from his other publications of the year, J. B. was responsible for a passage on techniques for studying the changes in the size of the spleen; it appeared in Emil Abderhalden's *Handbuch der biologischen Arbeitsmethoden*. The second is the 17 December entry in M. A. B.'s diary, which reads, "J. B. continues to experiment on his sheep two or three times a week, and is much pleased with what can be attained with the aid of a local anaesthetic and a cinema film."

With the New Year he began his second sabbatical term, near its outset he published a *Physiological Review* on "Fetal circulation and respiration", and on 25 January he, Barron, and Matthews gave a communication to the Physiological Society on "The genesis of respiratory movements in the sheep." In the main, as J. B. stated, the review put before the reader such few facts as were then known about the foetal circulation and respiration in the sheep and the goat, with comparative notes about other genera. It was, therefore, a working résumé of the literature, plus some indications of the direction in which J. B.'s thoughts and experiments were tending. The communication to the Physiological Society was in effect a description of a cine-film that the authors had made, and it can conveniently be regarded as a whetting of the appetite for a longer, later publication of the same year.

Here, however, we must slip back for a few days and recall more public matters. On 20 January, at five minutes before midnight, H. M. King George V died at Sandringham, and the next day Edward VIII was proclaimed King. On 1 February Colonel Charles A. Lindbergh, who had come to England with his wife and three-year old son to rest from prying eyes and the Press, called on the Barcrofts and it seemed possible that he would come and do research in Cambridge; M. A. B. and J. B. both thought him a most charming man. A few days later J. B. had word with Professor George E. Gask, the surgeon, who was just back from Belgium, and who said that the Belgians considered outbreak of war with Germany likely during the current year. Those three items, culled from

M. A. B.'s diary, will serve to recall some of the non-scientific happenings of early 1936, and the increasing international tension which was not thereafter to abate.

In contrast to the above is an extract from a letter written by Professor Margaria of Parma, saying that he had dedicated his new book on physiology to, inter alios, J. B.; he also expressed his sincerest feelings of affectionate devotion to J. B., and his best thanks for all that the latter had done for him, and had taught him, while he had been working in the Cambridge laboratory. The next event was the delivery by J. B. of the annual Huxley Lecture in the University of Birmingham. The subject was "The effect of extreme changes of environment upon the mental condition." It did not add significantly to his previous developments of the same theme, and need not be detailed here; all we need note is that he was keeping in touch with the bearings upon that theme of high-speed motoring, record-making air flights, proposals for ascents into the stratosphere and so forth.

On 27 February, two days after the lecture, came the news of the death of Academician Pavlov (Plate 53), and J. B. was asked to produce an obituary of that great physiologist and Foreign Member of the Royal Society for publication in *Nature*. It appeared about four weeks later, the script ending with the sentence, "No better example then Pavlov could be quoted to illustrate the kinship between simplicity and greatness."

March began with a three days' visit by August Krogh to 13 Grange Road. A day or two later German armed forces entered the Rhineland, and the next morning, presumably on Government instructions, J. B. and M. A. B. went to the laboratory and packed up J. B.'s official documents for dispatch to safer keeping in London. Three Germans who were working with J. B. "celebrated" the occupation of the Rhineland at tea-time in the lab.; meanwhile, the same meal at No. 13 was marked by a social call by Dr. and Mrs. W. F. Windle and their family – Windle had come from the Department of Anatomy of Northwestern University Medical School, Chicago, to work with J. B. on foetal physiology, and he will figure from time to time in the subsequent story. On 11 March J. B. lectured in Glasgow, two days later he attended a Chemical Defence dinner, and on the Saturday he was present at the meeting of the Physiological Society.

51—JOSEPH BARCROFT AND HENRY HALLETT DALE IN THE GARDEN OF NO. 13 GRANGE ROAD, CAMBRIDGE, IN MAY 1934

52—JOSEPH BARCROFT AND A. V. HILL IN AN AFTER-LUNCHEON GROUP OUTSIDE THE INSTITUTE OF MOTHER AND CHILD, LENINGRAD, 1935

53—Ivan Petrovich Pavlov (1849–1936)

54—John Scott Haldane (1860–1936)

It was just as the evening of that day was changing into Sunday morning that the death occurred, in Oxford, of his old friend, John Scott Haldane (Plate 54), world-renowned for his contributions to pure and applied physiology and for much besides. Twelve years older than J. B., he had not long before returned from Persia and Iraq, where he had been studying sunstroke cases among oil workers, and he had then seemed in excellent health. A chill, however, had developed into bronchial pneumonia, and on 10 March he had been reported to be sinking. His son, J. B. S. Haldane, had suggested, and had himself provided the blood for, a transfusion; there had been a good response to this treatment, but unfortunately the improvement had not been maintained.

We have seen, at intervals in J. B.'s story, how it was related to that of Haldane, and obviously the older and the younger British leaders in the field of respiratory physiology had many common interests, even if on one particular point they continued to hold divergent views. In the first war, each had taken considerable personal risks in the effort to protect our forces against gas warfare, and each had also taken risks in peace-time research for equally altruistic ends. Both, too, had ventured beyond the routine limits of their specialty into its more philosophical aspects, though Haldane to a greater extent than J. B. Finally, both were examples of the fineness of character that is typical of the great scientist. At the memorial service for Haldane in New College Chapel on 29 April, Mr. H. W. B. Joseph said that "in him the intellectual love of truth was . . . united with complete sincerity; and it was impossible not to feel this in his company. It made him tolerant of others, and very slow to speak harshly of them. It gave or preserved to him the confidence and affection of those from whose opinions he dissented even in matters that tend to excite prejudice and passion. It set at ease with him children and uneducated men. It made his frequent absorbed detachment from what was going on around him a wholly friendly thing. If he spoke on any question where good and evil were involved, it lent to what he said a singular impressiveness."

Mr. Joseph finished by quoting from Haldane's book, *Materialism*, a few sentences which had already been quoted at the funeral service on 17 March. "The death of an individual is no disappearance of spiritual reality, but something in which God's manifestation is still present . . ." "I am an old man, to whom death will soon come; but in proportion as I realise that God lives eternally, and that what is alone real in me is God's manifestation, I cease to fear the end of what is merely individual, and therefore, as such, unreal in my life, or to feel that their deaths have truly separated me from those I have loved, or whose memories I honour . . ." "In our recognition of divine values we recognise the personality of God, and at the same time recognise that since God is present in us our mere individual existence is no real existence, and our individual extinction no real extinction. Religion removes the sting of death and individual disaster. In our oneness with God we find immortality and at the same time freedom – the freedom of eternally creative personality."

Towards the end of March, with his second sabbatical Lent Term over, J. B. went off with M. A. B. for a fortnight's holiday at Burford, Broadway, and elsewhere in the Cotswolds. Thereafter, there is a dearth of relevant notes until 10 May, on which day Sir Thomas Inskip told Kathleen Ball, M. A. B.'s sister-in-law, that in those days of very dark international situations J. B.'s splendid gas-defence work was the one bright spot on which to dwell.

We come next to three publications. The first, by Adair, J. B., and seven other workers, was a communication to the Physiological Society, at its Cambridge meeting on 16 May, on "The oxygen content of blood in the carotid and umbilical arteries of the foetal sheep." In late goat foetuses Huggett (1927) had found average contents of respectively 2.84 and 5.9 volumes per cent., and these figures supported the hypothesis that the streams of blood from the placenta and great veins crossed to some extent in the heart. Later findings, however, by Kellogg (1930) on dog foetuses suggested that the streams underwent complete mixture. The new determinations in the Cambridge laboratory supported Huggett's contention.

The second publication, by J. B., Barron and Windle, appeared in the *Journal of Physiology* on 10 June and was entitled, "Some observations on genesis of somatic movements in sheep embryos." Though a number of studies of the development of early foetal movements had previously been made by Windle and others, complete agreement had not been reached, and it had been hoped that observations on the larger embryos of the sheep might clarify the way in which behaviour becomes established during intrauterine life. The authors reported that (1) embryonic skeletal muscle contractions were elicited by faradic stimulation before the central nervous system functioned reflexly; (2) active reflex movements appeared in 23.5–25 mm. embryos, and were localized responses to mechanical and electrical stimulation; (3) integration of embryonic movements followed their appearance as separate phenomena. The writers concluded their discussion of the nature of the early active movements by saying that, in so far as they involved more than one neurone, they could apparently be classified roughly into three stages: the first, in which the movements of individual parts of the body were quite isolated; the second, in which two or three such movements were associated into a group; and the third, in which such groups were integrated into a general mass movement.

The third publication, by J. B. and R. H. E. Elliott, was styled, "Some observations on the denervated spleen." To make more certain of the completeness of the denervation, which had not been perfect in some of the earlier experiments carried out between 1924 and 1932, the splenic artery and vein had been cut across and reunified by the aid of Lim's couplers. The results were (1) that in resting dogs the alterations in size of the denervated spleen during the week after exteriorization are considerably more rapid and extensive than in the innervated organ; (2) that a spleen deprived of its nerve supply and with its venous return cut off may hold as much as one-third of the original blood volume of the animal; (3) that the denervated spleen may respond by contraction to the emotional stimulus of a sudden loud noise, but the contraction is considerably less than in the innervated organ; (4) that exposure of dogs to high temperatures results in a contraction of the innervated spleen, and in a slight enlargement of the denervated organ; (5) that exposure of dogs to low temperatures brings about a contraction in both the innervated and denervated spleen. The authors suggested that the response is largely humoral in nature, and probably caused by increased output of adrenaline.

Between the appearances of the first two publications, J. B. acted as the first examiner in the first try-out of the new Tripos which he had been instrumental in creating. Between the appearances of the second and third publications, an event of more personal importance was the birth, on 1 July, of John Barcroft, first child of Henry and Biddy, and first grandchild of J. B. and M. A. B. At the end of July J. B.'s duties took him off to Porton for three days; thereafter, early in August, he and M. A. B. went off on holiday, first to Gatehouse of Fleet, Kircudbrightshire, and then a fortnight later to Buncrana, on Lough Swilly, County Donegal. On 28 August they went on by bus to Dungannon where, having two hours to spare, they decided to take a taxi and have a look at Stangmore Lodge which (see Chapter II) had been inherited in 1926 by J. B. but of which he had, somewhat regretfully, had to dispose. It was an exquisite day and J. B. and M. A. B. much enjoyed walking round the estate. With its many improvements the property looked very attractive, "and Joe felt wistful about it." From Stangmore Lodge they went on to Portadown, where Mollie Barcroft and Muriel Richardson met them and M. A. B. and J. B. parted, the former to go with her in-laws to The Glen, Newry, and the latter to proceed to Belfast.

There he went on board the S.S. *Montcalm* of the Canadian Pacific Steamships Ltd., his immediate object being attendance at the Harvard Tercentenary Celebrations, and his secondary ones the giving of a series of lectures in the United States, and a visit to the Bests in Toronto. With him on the boat, and like him bound for Harvard, were his friends Sir Frederick and Lady Gowland Hopkins of Cambridge, and Professor and Mrs. August Krogh of Copenhagen. Also on board were several returning Olympic athletes, "magnificent looking youths and girls." Professor Krogh appears to have attended dinner on Friday, 4 September, but in general did not do so, either because of a general aversion to music or because of an aversion to the band on that particular ship – "certainly it is not at all good", was J. B.'s comment. His menu card for 4 September was autographed by the Hopkins' and the Kroghs, and decorated by a sketch which he did of Marie Krogh. At 7 a.m. on Thursday, 3 September, they were just abreast of Belle Isle, "a great massive island, several miles long, precipitous cliffs, flattish tops. The sun was shining on it, and it looked very beautiful." Early on Saturday, 5 September, they reached Quebec, and at 7.15 a.m. Professor L. J. Henderson (Plate 55), with Drs. Bock and Terry, came on board to take J. B. by car to L. J.'s camp, about half-way between Quebec and Cambridge, Mass. They reached it about 4 p.m., and left next morning about 10 a.m. for Harvard, where they arrived at 7 p.m., and "were at once thrown into a welcoming party at the [E. J.] Cohns' house – one of those carefully thought-out pseudo-picnics."

55—JOSEPH BARCROFT, LAWRENCE J. HENDERSON, AND FREDERICK GOWLAND HOPKINS, photographed on a golf course near Lake Memphremagog, Canada, on 5 September 1936, with the Green Mountains in the background

56—JOSEPH BARCROFT AND YANDELL HENDERSON AT YALE UNIVERSITY, 1936

From Monday, 7 September, to Saturday, 12 September, followed the unique Congress planned as a prelude to the actual Tercentenary celebrations. Some sixty or seventy men of high distinction from the whole field of learning and representing many countries communicated the results of their researches, and problems of interest to a variety of disciplines were made the objects of concerted attacks. The enterprise was most successful thanks to the careful selection of speakers who not only had 'the goods' to deliver, but also the faculty for expressing themselves intelligibly to those whose fields of learning were other than their own. J. B.'s own contribution came early in the list, and was illustrated by a film produced by his technician, John Freeman; one imagines that the subject was the genesis of respiratory movements in the sheep foetus. The audience numbered about eight hundred, but the projection arrangements for the 16 mm. film seem to have been most satisfactory.

On the 12th J. B. lunched with the President of the University, Dr. Conant, and thereafter went off to Wood's Hole to stay with the A. C. Redfields until the 15th, when the final celebrations began. These culminated in a three hours' ceremony in the "Yard" on the 18th with the President of the United States and about 15,000 other people present. After the opening prayer and a broadcast of the chimes from Southwark Cathedral, in which John Harvard was baptized in the seventeenth century, John Masefield, the Poet Laureate of Engeland, delivered a tribute in verse, and then came the conferment of honorary degrees – J. B., described as "an investigator of many phases of the respiration of higher animals, a beloved guide to younger men on both sides of the Atlantic", was one of those who was made an honorary Doctor of Science. Following the degree ceremony, President Conant gave his oration, "the courage and eloquence of which cannot be conveyed in a few words. Starting with" his "conception of the proper ordering of a University", it "developed into a plea for citizenship based upon the search for truth in all departments of intellectual activity. To the man of science [1] it was interesting to observe that to President Conant the health of a university depends upon the maintenance of a correct balance between four components: student life, the teaching of abstract subjects, professional training, and the search for

[1] The author of the anonymous account in *Nature*, 1936, *138*, 667–670, from which these quotations are made, was J. B.

new knowledge. Typical of the latter part of the speech was the demand for 'absolute freedom of discussion, absolutely unmolested enquiry.' This note of freedom was struck also by the President of the United States (Franklin D. Roosevelt) in his speech to the alumni of Harvard the same afternoon. 'In this day of modern witch-burning, when freedom of thought has been exiled from many lands which were once its home, it is the part of Harvard and America to stand for the freedom of the human mind and to carry the torch of truth'."

On the following day, J. B. was back at Wood's Hole with the Redfields for a welcome rest. On the 24th, however, he was in Cleveland, Ohio, where he was the guest of Dr. C. J. Wiggers, and where after dinner he lectured to an audience of about three hundred; the subject was, apparently, the same as at Harvard as the film is mentioned. "One man called Pierce who is in practice about fifty miles away", J. B. wrote to M. A. B., "said he had come specially to tell me what perhaps I did not realize (I certainly did not), that the outlook and development of their School and University is largely the result of Haldane's and my work."

On the 25th J. B. visited Parke-Davis' works in Detroit, and thereafter he was in Chicago until the 30th, when he went on to the University of Michigan in Ann Arbor, and was the guest of Dr. Robert Gesell. On 1 October, after an afternoon lecture, he went by plane to Detroit, and thence in another to Buffalo – to reporters he said on arrival, "That big bird is a bit marvelous." After staying overnight in the Statler Hotel, he proceeded on the 2nd to Ithaca, N.Y., where under the auspices of Dr. Asdell he lectured in Cornell University. The next evening he was with Professor C. H. Best in Toronto and dined with the Medical Club. Sunday, 4 October, he spent with the Bests – "certainly they are a lovable couple, and such nice children." He also visited "The Farm" where antitoxins were made, and took the opportunity of a ride on horseback with his host.

From Toronto he went to New York, and thence on 5 October reached New Haven as guest of Professor Yandell Henderson (Plate 56). In Yale University he gave three Terry lectures, dined with a group which included Dr. Harvey Cushing and Dr. Ross Harrison on the 5th, lunched with the President and dined with Professor and Mrs. John F. Fulton on the 6th, and lunched with Professor Walter Miles on the 7th. Then he went on to New York to deliver the first Miller Lecture and to dine afterwards, in a party of about fifty, at the University Club. On the 9th he arrived in Boston at 6 a.m. and breakfasted with Professor W. B. Cannon at 8 a.m.; at 12.30 p.m. Professors Cannon and L. J. Henderson saw him off for Montreal, where he arrived at 8.45 p.m. and stayed overnight at the Windsor Hotel. At 9 a.m. the next day he was seen off by Professor Meakins, and later boarded the S.S. *Empress of Britain* for his return home, arriving in Cambridge on the 16th.

Little need be added to the account above given of a strenuous few weeks except to give the gist of two lectures which J. B., apparently, gave in a number of places during his tour. One of them, to which reference has already been made, was on pre-natal development studies performed by J. B. in conjunction with Dr. Donald H. Barron and Dr. Frank Snyder. It was summarized by J. B. himself, when he was interviewed by a reporter at Buffalo, in the following words. "One has found out that a great many of the movements of life, supposed to appear after birth, really can be seen and estimated long before. Just as a steamer's engines are tried out before she sails, so vital movements, such as respiration, are practised long before birth. That really sums it up."

The other lecture dealt with the mental effects produced by severe cold and excess of carbon dioxide respectively or, as *Time* of 19 October 1936 more arrestingly put it, with "Freezing and Stifling". With regard to the former, J. B. had twice lain down naked in a freezing room, and had carried on until an assistant had seen that unconsciousness was imminent, and had come to the rescue with warm blankets and hot drinks. In each experiment J. B. had at first lain shivering, with his limbs flexed in a sort of effort to huddle up, and he had been very conscious of the cold. During this stage his nervous system, in an effort to fight the adverse circumstances and to preserve the body's heat, had been constricting the blood vessels of his skin and keeping the blood in the internal parts; he had also had to suppress, by an effort of will, his instinct to be up and about. Suddenly thereafter his nervous system had given up the struggle, he had stretched out his legs, and the sense of coldness had been succeeded by a beautiful feeling of warmth as his skin vessels relaxed – he had lain "basking" in the cold. At this point his initiative had gone and he was completely acquiescent while his body temperature, no longer kept up by cutaneous vasoconstriction, was falling. His natural modesty, also, had changed to "well, I don't know what", and he had no longer worried about what some person alien to the experiment would have thought if that person had come in and found him stark naked. "Clearly one should be very cautious about taking these liberties with one's mind, and that is the point; the higher parts of the central nervous system were the first things to suffer."

With regard to the effects of carbon dioxide excess, J. B. said that the highest concentration which he had known to be breathed experimentally was 11 per cent.; this had been inhaled for a short time by Mr. J. B. S. Haldane. Dr. R. Margaria and J. B. himself had breathed 10 per cent. of the gas for about five minutes, but 7 to 8 per cent. was probably as much as could be withstood for any extended period, and Dr. Margaria and he had been glad to emerge after 20 minutes in 7.2 per cent. Their symptoms had been similar in being connected with the highest parts of the central nervous system, but otherwise they had differed. Dr. Margaria, like Mr. Haldane, had suffered from headache for the rest of the day; J. B. had had mental fatigue for about two days. He added that the gas, while he was in the chamber, had reduced his ordinary niceness of manipulation of taps and so forth with the result that he had made two errors in taking gas samples. More important still, he would have been prepared to go into a court of law and to swear that one at least of those two samplings had been correctly carried out. On the occasion when the percentage had been 10, he had come out retaining his grip of things only with an effort. "Margaria and I agreed," he concluded, "on two things, firstly that we did not want to repeat this experiment unless there was some good reason for doing so, and secondly, that our reluctance was due to our unwillingness to expose the higher parts of our brain to the influence of so much carbonic acid."

There are three more publications of 1936 to be considered. The first of these, by J. B. and Barron, was on "The genesis of respiratory movements in the foetus of the sheep," and appeared in the *Journal of Physiology* on 10 October. The authors had found that the rhythmic trunk movements associated with ordinary respiration are developed between the 38th and 49th days of intrauterine life, are derived from a general mass movement of extensor type by the dropping out of the movements of the head and limbs, and cannot be elicited at this stage by asphyxial conditions of the blood. Toward the 49th day their frequency increases and they become more powerful; after the 50th day the rhythmic movements disappear as a spontaneous phenomenon, but can be elicited by stoppage of the blood flow in the umbilical cord.

The second paper, by Roughton and seven other authors of whom J. B. was one, described studies of the effect of temperature on the oxyhaemoglobin dissociation curve, mainly at pH 6.8 in *M*/15 phosphate buffer. Its summary should be read in the original, for it cannot conveniently be reproduced here.

The third publication was a communication to the Physiological Society at its meeting on 12 December. It was by J. B. and Barron, and was entitled, "The development of the 'righting' movements in the foetal sheep." They noted that between the 47th and 50th days of intrauterine life the spontaneous and induced activity of the foetus resembled an attempt to right itself and to stand up, and they detailed the build-up of such movements from the 38th day, and their partial suppression on the 52nd day. By the 64th day the movements, when unmasked by compression of the umbilical cord, were no longer to be described as "righting" or "standing". The various points were illustrated by projection of a cine-film which the authors had made.

From M. A. B.'s diary we may cull a few last notes for 1936. On 11 December came the dramatic abdication of King Edward VIII, followed by the accession of his brother, who took on the style of King George VI. Then the entry for 15 December takes us sharply away from the national to the individual news – J. B. broadcast in the "Scientists at work" programme, on "Caring for the nation's food." Many nice things were said about his address, and each of its twenty minutes' duration earned him a guinea! The next day was saddened for him and for M. A. B. by the death, at the age of 96, of Lady Arlbutt, a close friend for more than forty years. The last entry is that on 20 December J. B. was very pleased at being asked to become a member of the Advisory Committee of the London, Midland and Scottish Railway Company.

With the advent of 1937, J. B.'s remaining tenure of his Chair was reduced to nine months. Just after the year had begun, he received two heartening letters. The first was from Sir Charles Sherrington, by that time living in retirement at Broomside, Valley

Road, Ipswich. J. B. had obviously written to Sir Charles about the damping down of the skeletal muscle movements which he had noted in the sheep foetus from about the 50th day of intrauterine life. Sherrington's reply read:- "Dear Barcroft, how delightful! both the New Year greeting, and the experiment! A great experiment, which only yourself could have carried out – a *great* physiologist. What is your inference? That inhibition from 'overhead' is keeping the spinal reflex paths at very high threshold to keep things quiet in utero? Just as – or much as – in the case I suppose of the respiratory 'centre' and reflexes? You seem to be replacing the Coghill conception of generalized uncanalized foetal conduction by something much more understandable. I hope you are looking at the spinal cord for what stage of myelinization it may show." The second letter, from Y. Nisimaru in Tokyo, contained the cheering sentence, "I am always happy and encouraged whenever I see, hear, and read of you."

In mid-January J. B. attended, and much enjoyed, his first meeting of the L. M. S. Advisory Committee and the nice luncheon in the Euston Hotel which preceded it. A day or two later, on 20 January, Adrian came and asked him if he would consent, in view of his approaching retirement, either to have his portrait painted or to have a bust made of him. J. B. was naturally much touched by the kind thought, and of the alternatives chose the painting of his portrait. He was also asked if he would demonstrate an experiment, so that a cine-record of him at work in his laboratory could be preserved in that laboratory for future generations. More or less about this time, also, he became Chairman of the Committee of Management of the Cambridge Low Temperature Research Station. As a background to all this, he was very busy with further experiments on sheep foetuses, and was getting considerable satisfaction from his film-records of them. In February he and Barron published a short paper on "The establishment of certain reflex arcs in foetal sheep". They noted that certain localized movements could be elicited in 33–35 day embryos by mechanical and electrical stimuli, but showed that true reflexes did not exist before 44 days for the fore-limb and 47 days for the hind-limb. The implication was "that behaviour does not appear first in the form of isolated reflexes which are later collected and organized into reaction patterns."

The choice of J. B.'s successor in the Chair was made on 5 March, when Adrian was appointed as from 1 October 1937. Meanwhile,

J. B. was planning outlets for his still abundant energy in further government duties, and in his advisory work for the L. M. S. Railway Company.

On 13 March he and Barron projected before the Physiological Society, with a running commentary, a film which they had made on the subject of "Experimental 'chronic' lesions in the central nervous system of the sheep's foetus." By a comparison between normal foetuses and others in which the central nervous system had been transected at certain levels seven to ten days before study, they had investigated the damping down, to which reference has already been made, of the "respiratory" and somatic movements, and had demonstrated release phenomena in the transected, but otherwise healthy, foetuses. At this time J. B. and Barron were also engaged in a study of the closure of the ductus arteriosus, but were hindered through lack of a really suitable technique. It was, therefore, by a lucky chance that a short, cineradiographic film, made by Janker and Franklin, of the flow of blood plus contrast medium through a dog's heart was allowed as an extra demonstration, and followed immediately after the film by Barcroft and Barron. For this accidental juxtaposition of the two projections suggested to Barron that cineradiography was the technique of choice for the solution of the ductus problem, and J. B. agreed and wrote to Franklin, then Assistant Director of the Nuffield Institute for Medical Research, Oxford, asking if he and Dr. A. E. Barclay, the Honorary Radiologist to the Institute, would co-operate. Franklin and Barclay very readily agreed, but the beginning of the work had naturally to be postponed until a fresh season's pregnant ewes were available.

Towards the end of March, with his third sabbatical "leave of absence" over, J. B. went off with M. A. B. for a fortnight's holiday in Somerset, a particularly delightful county in which to be in spring-time, even if naturally-born lambs could recall work done on lambs delivered by Caesarean section! The return to Cambridge took place on 12 April, less than four weeks before J. B. was to officiate for the last time, as Professor, at a Cambridge meeting of the Physiological Society. At that meeting, on 8 May, he and T. Gotsev [1] spoke on the "Acquisition of blood by the foetus from the

[1] In 1951 I was told, by another of J. B.'s research colleagues, that soon after arrival in Cambridge Gotsev, in a particular experiment, found an unexpected rise of blood pressure and commented, "It is not so in Bulgaria!" – K.J.F.

placenta at birth," he, Kurt Kramer, and G. A. Millikan on "The attainment of saturation by the arterial blood at birth", Kramer and Millikan "On the effect of external temperature on the new-born lamb", J. B., Barron, Kramer, and Millikan on "The effect of urethane on the onset of respiration at birth", and Barron and Irene F. A. Thomson on "The cervical extension of the solitary tract".

The gist of the first communication was the suggestion that during normal birth a considerable amount of foetal blood (of the order of 25 or 30 ml./kg.) passes from the placenta and cord into the lamb. In the second one it was stated that, with oxygen as the inspired gas, the foetal blood was 96 per cent. saturated within 4 minutes from the tying of the cord; with ordinary air as the source of oxygen, the saturation fluctuated between 35 and 60 per cent. The authors concluded (1) that in the latter case the relative anoxaemia was due to the low diffusion coefficient of the new-born lung, which contained a good deal of fluid; (2) that within 4 minutes of cord ligation all the carotid blood was coming from the left side of the heart; and (3) that carbon dioxide administered with the oxygen could scarcely improve the percentage saturation. In the fourth paper the authors showed that urethane anaesthesia of the ewe, by extension to the foetus, delayed the onset of respiration in the latter; if the ewe was given instead a spinal anaesthetic, the onset of respiration in the foetus could occur, presumably through the mechanical stimuli evoked by handling it, even before the cord had been tied.

To have been concerned in five communications, etc., as well as being in general charge of a large and popular meeting of the Society must have been somewhat of a strain on J. B., but more was to come. For a number of well-deserved tributes were paid to him after dinner and, when called upon for a speech in reply, he was for once at a loss and said that any speech would have to be a short one, as he was feeling the occasion too deeply.

Four days after the meeting came the Coronation of King George VI and J. B. was the recipient, through his connection with the Department of Scientific and Industrial Research, of a Coronation Medal. On 14 May he agreed to accept the chairmanship of the Food Investigation Board of that Department, and also to be nominated as a member of the Royal Commission appointed to consider the future of veterinary education in this country. The entries for May end with the retirement of Mr. Baldwin and his succession, as Prime Minister, by Mr. Neville Chamberlain.

Early in June J. B. received a message from the Physiological Society conveying the good wishes of the members and expressing their hope that he would long continue to take an active interest in the Society's proceedings. Two days later *The Cambridge Review* published a tribute to him, mentioning inter alia "his unique gift of inspiring the co-operation and affection of younger men, many of whom owe much of their subsequent eminence to their early contact, through him, with the breath and spirit of research." Towards the end of the month he went to Bruxelles to lecture on the spleen, ? in French, and was presented informally to H. M. The King of the Belgians. On 1 July he was in Dublin to receive the honorary degree of Sc. D. from Trinity College.

From somewhat before the middle of the same month he was abroad for a fortnight on the Continent, studying matters of veterinary interest in Germany, Switzerland, and France; in Paris he also went into certain railway problems in connection with his L. M. S. advisory post. After reaching home, he had to go off for a brief visit to Porton. Sometime in August, in conjunction with J. P. Quigley [1], Adair and E. N. Goodman, he published a paper on "The difference in potential across gastric membranes and certain factors modifying the potential." The results found by these workers in unanaesthetized animals were not in agreement in some important respects with those of Sarre (1934) in anaesthetized cats, but this is scarcely the place to go into details. "Gastric potential production," to quote the last of the conclusions, "is dependent on an undetermined type of vital activity, apparently of the gastric mucosa. When altered by contact of the mucosa with effective substances, the influence may be transmitted to gastric tissue not in contact with the excitant."

About 10 August J. B. and M. A. B. left Cambridge for a well-earned holiday, going first to Greenore, then on to Carlingford with its memories of an earlier visit, and finally to the nearby seaside resort, Newcastle. In mid-September J. B. returned to Cambridge, and on 30 September he wrote to M. A. B. as follows. "This morn-

[1] Then on research leave from C. J. Wiggers' Department of Physiology, Western Reserve University Medical School, Cleveland, Ohio; at present he is Head of the Department of Physiology, University of Tennessee College of Medicine, Memphis, Tennessee.

ing I said my official goodbyes. I handed over the master-keys to Adrian, and we had a very affecting time – I don't think the tears were far away on either side. Secker refused to say goodbye. He said he would be in and out always, and was there if I wanted him at any time. I gave him a fountain pen which I think he greatly appreciated. Now I feel just a little . . .! Well, it could hardly be otherwise. As you once said, if I gave it up without a qualm it would be rather a criticism of the degree to which one's heart was on the job."

Though his official connection with the laboratory which he had adorned for so long ended thus at the end of the academic year 1936–7, J. B. was not, as we shall see, to desert it or Cambridge. Nor was his Fellowship at King's College co-terminous with his Professorship; instead, it was to continue for the rest of his life. Finally, as the remainder of this book will reveal, his energy on retirement from the Chair of Physiology remained unabated, and was to carry on his remarkable scientific productivity for yet another decade. His last day as Professor is, however, very obviously the right point at which to end this Chapter.

CHAPTER IX

1937–1941

In 1949 Adrian said of J. B., "When he retired from the Chair of Physiology in 1937 he was sixty-five but still at the height of his powers as an investigator. It was quite unthinkable that he should not go on in the laboratory as before, but as you know it is not always an easy matter for an Emeritus and an acting Professor to work together in complete harmony, and I should like to put it on record that his presence here, besides being an immense asset to our research strength, was never anything but a great comfort and encouragement to his successor. Of course, I never thought it would have been otherwise. Barcroft was a very wise and kindly man as well as a great physiologist."

Soon after his retirement, J. B. went to visit Glasgow and Edinburgh in connection with veterinary work. Then, on 8 October, he delivered the address at the opening of the winter session of the Welsh National School of Medicine, and part of it was published in the *Lancet* a week later under the title, "Physical unfitness in relation to density of population" – it is to be noted that the paper was by him in his capacity as Chairman of the Food Investigation Board of the Department of Scientific and Industrial Research. He contrasted the occurrence of unfitness among slum-dwellers with the fitness of agricultural workers, and described how a batch of unfit Army recruits, put on a special course and with extra feeding, had mostly become fit. The unfit, he thought, were not necessarily born so, and according to the available evidence the deterioration set in between the ages of 14 and 18, i.e., this was the critical period at which the physique of the country's youth needed most care. "So it boils down to this," he went on, "that if you are to turn a C 3 population into a fit population you must give them exercise and diet in both cases of the right kind and sufficient in amount. The accomplishment of this in densely crowded towns is not an easy matter . . . The doctor's business as a doctor is . . . to see that if a section of the community is C 3 for the sake of milk or exercise or anything else the matter comes to the public eye and is made the concern of those who can see that the want is made good."

A month later he opened a discussion, at the Medical Society of London, on national physical training (see *Anon.*, 1937), but said at once that, as a physiologist, he had little practical knowledge of the subject. Fitness, he thought, depended on two things, the most advantageous development of the inherited bodily powers, and the development of the greatest degree of resistance to disease; about the former, but not about the latter, he might reasonably say a little. He then re-quoted the experience with Army recruits which he had spoken about in Wales, but now had some doubt about the absolute value of the criteria on which the assessment of improvement in their physique was based, and thought that so short a course could not perhaps have done all that was claimed for it. Real preservation and increase of natural fitness would need to be effected over years.

Early in December J. B. had luncheon with Mr. R. G. Eves, who had been commissioned to paint his portrait, at the latter's house in Adelaide Road, Hampstead; the first sitting was arranged for 22 December. The only other notes for 1937 are concerned with J. B.'s work on the foetus. In 1935–6 and 1936–7 the Medical Research Council had given grants to named research assistants. For 1937–8 it gave a more general grant (which was to be repeated in 1938–9) to assist researches by J. B. and other workers in Cambridge. Two of the resulting publications, by J. B. and Barron, appeared in 1937. Of these, "Movements in midfoetal life in the sheep embryo" was among the papers in the 14 December number of the *Journal of Physiology,* while "The fundamental nature of the respiratory rhythm" was printed bilingually in the *Journal of Physiology of the U.S.S.R.*, though on exactly what date the present writer has not been able to determine; however, the two articles can conveniently be considered together.

In the *Journal of Physiology* paper the authors summarized results which they interpreted as follows. The fundamental movements of the foetus are "jerky" in type, but about the 50th day become controlled by influences arising in the region of the red nucleus. The "sustained" type of movement that is then substituted for the jerky one is subject, in older foetuses, to inhibition from above. In both cases, by appropriate intervention (production of "asphyxia"/

57—SUBSCRIPTION PORTRAIT OF SIR JOSEPH BARCROFT, painted by R. G. Eves, Esq., R.A., and deposited in the Physiology Laboratory, Cambridge

section of the brain stem) the influence of the higher centres can be eliminated, with consequent reversion to the more primitive state. With regard to the special case of respiratory movement, this individuates out of (or perhaps more correctly is the relic of) a generalized mass rhythmic movement, and at this stage it cannot be induced by asphyxia (the combination of oxygen lack and carbon dioxide excess caused by occlusion of the cord). At about 50 days respiratory movements are almost continuous, being evidently consequent on even quite trivial muscular ones. About 10 days later they are difficult to elicit, but can be induced by asphyxia, which causes the foetus to revert to the 50–day stage. In the foetus of 60 days or over in which the central nervous system has been cut between the mid-brain and pons (inclusive) there is almost constant respiratory rhythm of a "jerky" type. If the section is above the mid-brain, respiratory movements are also frequent but are of the tonic type. As the foetus ages, somatic movement and respiratory rhythm become increasingly independent but the linkage, which appears to be in the general region of the red nucleus, can be restored by asphyxia.

The paper in the Russian journal began with the arresting sentences:- "The essential nature of the respiratory rhythm presents a problem which cannot but be of outstanding interest to biologists. The words inspiration and expiration have come to connote the highest life and the ultimate dissolution of man." The authors then went on to say that there were three principal concepts, (1) that each phase of respiration initiates a message to the brain, checking that particular phase and initiating its opposite; (2) that there is in the central nervous system a continual urge to inspire, but that the very act of inspiration sets up afferent impulses which check the effort; and (3) "that respiration is due to rhythmic activity of the central nervous system. The modern apologist for this view was Graham Brown, and it was strengthened by the observation of Adrian and Buytendijk (1931) that there existed in the central nervous system of the goldfish an inherent rhythm which had the same frequency as that of the gill movements." Barcroft and Barron's observations on the early movements in the sheep embryo supported the third view. On the 36th day an external stimulus evoked a spasmodic extensor movement, about the 40th day an extensor rhythm, which could be spontaneous, was observed . . . By about the 49th day the foetus was so lively that it was difficult to manipulate it at all without consequent slight movements taking place, each followed by a rhythm. The result was that rhythmic movement scarcely ceased, and the foetus presented the general appearance of an ordinary animal breathing naturally; but when energetic movement took place as the result of a considerable stimulus, as with a rod, the rhythm quickened and deepened, giving the appearance of an animal out of breath as a result of the effort it had made. In general, then, during the stages described a mass movement was built up from localized movements and when built up became resolvable into reflex or other movements of definite functional significance. There we must end this abstract, noting however that it is necessarily incomplete and that those interested should read the full paper.

The year 1938 seems to have been a busy one for J. B. even by his standards; it was certainly more crowded than most men would wish just after retirement. To simplify the account of it, we can begin by dealing with a number of publications, which relate to the past rather than to the year in question. Volume *21* of the *Journal of Physiology of the U.S.S.R.*, which was the one concerned with the 1935 Congress, was for technical reasons delayed in its appearance until 1938; it contained J. B.'s address on "The velocities of some physiological processes", plus a photograph of him delivering it; it also included his and Barron's communication on "The initiation of respiration at birth", and the titles of their film-projection ("The origin of respiratory movements of the foetus") and demonstration ("The initiation of respiration at birth"). During the year the Cambridge University Press issued a second printing of *Features in the architecture of physiological function*, and a new book by J. B. was published by the Yale University Press in New Haven and by the Oxford University Press in London. If, however, the book was new, it was substantially the Terry Lectures given in New Haven in 1936 and thereafter, on the suggestion of the Yale University Press, given a much more consequent motif. For the title of the book, *The brain and its environment*, J. B. expressed indebtedness to Professor Yandell Henderson.

The work was a short one, divided into three Chapters, and its content was summarized as follows by J. B. in the Preface, dated 12 July 1937. "In the first chapter . . . I will say something about the very origins of behaviour in the embryo and the influence on these primitive happenings of some crude alterations in the foetal environment. In the second, I treat of the transition from the foetal to the postnatal condition. How does the alteration in the environment affect the organism? And so to my point of view with regard to the environmental conditions under which the mind has reached its present development. In the composition of a drama, besides the main plot there is not infrequently some subsidiary one. Besides the doings of the hero and the heroine, there will be a romance of some kind in the kitchen. And so here, throughout these chapters, there is something cropping up from time to time, which for want of a better term I shall allude to as 'anticipation'. By that, I mean the organization of some mechanism apparently in advance of the time when that mechanism is used and against some contingency which has not yet arisen. Our ancestors would have regarded the phenomenon as evidence of design, spelled by different persons with the 'd' differing in size. Most of us here will take the view, I imagine, that if we wish to build the truths of science and philosophy into the structure of a broadened and purified religion, it behooves us not to neglect this phenomenon when we come across it and to explain it, when we can, by natural causes."

With the above-mentioned publications out of the way, we can pass to 12 January 1938, when Dr. Loveday, Vice-Chancellor of Bristol University, came to 13 Grange Road for a couple of days, and Sir Louis Kershaw came to dinner; both were members of the Royal Commission on Veterinary Education, and matters veterinary were discussed. The next day, however, J. B.'s mind was abruptly switched to more personal matters by the news of the death, at the age of 62, of his only brother, David Malcolmson Barcroft. Two days later – presumably in J. B.'s absence – a communication was made to the Physiological Society on "The relation of the vagus nerve to the ductus arteriosus in the guinea-pig." The authors were J. B., J. A. Kennedy, and M. F. Mason, and the evidence produced by them showed that stimulation of the peripheral end of the left vagus nerve caused occlusion of the ductus, especially of that part nearer the aorta; similar stimulation of the right vagus nerve produced an uncertain effect, and stimulation of its central end, with the left nerve intact, was ineffective. In some cases the left vagal effects upon the ductus were separable from the slowing of the heart. The authors appended two caveats, (1) that the possibility of an additional *local* mechanism was not excluded, and (2) that pending further experiments the statement made applied only to guinea-pigs.

On the last day but one of January, J. B.'s address of the previous summer at the Journées Médicales de Bruxelles was published in *Bruxelles-Médical* under the title, "Signification physiologique de la rate." At the outset he said that splenic functioning was perhaps the most delicate (the colloquial epithet "tricky" might be a better translation of "délicat") subject in physiology. The published résumé stated that the spleen plays an important rôle in the embryo, the new-born animal, during post-natal life, and at death. In the embryo it is haemopoetic, at birth its contraction contributes to vascular tonus, during post-natal life it helps to regulate the quantity and quality of circulating blood, and at death its contraction is part of the final effort. With regard to the birth change, he pointed out that section of the umbilical cord is accompanied by contraction of the spleen, and the latter is of significance not because of the effect which the expulsion of its small content of corpuscles could have on the arterial blood pressure (the contribution from the placenta and cord vessels is infinitely larger), but because it is evidence of a tonic effect of the sympathetic nerves upon the blood vessels, just as the reduction of the heart rate indicates vagal tone.

Towards the end of February Mr. Eden resigned, on grounds of principle, from the Foreign Secretaryship and was succeeded by Lord Halifax. So far as J. B. was concerned, the last part of the month saw his portrait by Mr. R. G. Eves, A.R.A., finished thereafter, he visited Utrecht in connection wih his veterinary; interests; later still, he and Barron went to Oxford to carry out cineradiographic studies, in collaboration with Franklin and Barclay, at the Nuffield Institute for Medical Research. With regard to the portrait, the one mentioned went to the Academy exhibition, and it was, apparently, a smaller one which finally reached Cambridge. This latter, as we shall read, evoked criticism and, as that criticism will be mentioned, it seems only fair to quote also a contemporary appreciation by Adrian Bury of the powers of the artist in question. Bury (1938) wrote that, "Were I seeking a portrait of myself, to appear as I hope the intelligent spectator sees me, I should consult Reginald Eves. I have always regarded this painter as a master of character, especially in regard to men. There is a welcome, hail-fellow-well-met in Mr. Eves's style. He does not flatter or make you look handsome if you are not, but he will extract every ounce of interest out of your features, and leave you with the comforting feeling that you are *somebody* in the world and know a great deal about life. The old phrase 'a speaking likeness' can be applied to his portraits; indeed they give me the sensation that I am in the presence of the living person rather than the illusion in paint. And Mr. Eves, furthermore, is a lightning worker. He can achieve a fine study in two or three sittings, whereas some artists require many more."

With regard to the cineradiographic studies, a few words are demanded. The ductus arteriosus, with the time of closure of which J. B. and Barron were particularly concerned, had never been identified in radiographs and in the lateral position of the foetus, which for technical reasons had to be adopted, the ductus shadow was but one constituent in a composite picture formed by the shadows of the heart and neighbouring vessels. Further, J. B. and Barron stayed only for the precise duration of a particular experiment and returned to Cambridge immediately it was over. In this first season's work, therefore, their knowledge of the foetus was never adequately shared with Barclay and Franklin, nor was the latter's knowledge of cineradiography adequately communicated to the Cambridge visitors. The outcome was that, although some useful preliminary records of other features were secured, the identification of the ductus arteriosus in the shadow complex was wrongly made, and it was not until autumn, after communications had been presented to the International Congress of Physiologists in Zürich and a paper published in the *British Journal of Radiology*, that the conclusions about the ductus became suspect. The true story, elucidated by further experimental work, was to become available in 1939 and to cover considerably more than the time of closure of one foetal by-pass.

Sometime during February 1938 J. B. published a paper in *Scientia* on "The development of respiration in the mammal." In essentials, and even to some extent in the actual phraseology, it was very akin to "The fundamental nature of the respiratory rhythm" of the previous year, but the two journals catered for very different sets of readers, so the more or less duplicate publication was reasonable. On the other hand, any detailed analysis can be waived. By contrast, we should mention at slightly greater length an interesting extension of the studies by Windle and J. B., who in March published a paper on "Some factors governing the initiation of respiration in the chick", an animal which could be observed in its normal developmental environment without the use of depressing surgical procedure and anaesthesia. The first paragraph of the writers' summary read as follows. "The chick fetus begins to breathe air about 24 hours before it hatches on the twenty-first day. Rhythmic respiratory movements made their appearance normally at about 18 days of incubation. Spontaneous contractions of muscles involved in respiration occur at a much earlier time and in fact the very earliest spontaneous movements of the neck and trunk muscles in five and six-day old chicks continue throughout incubation and seem to be incorporated in the respiratory pattern."

Two other items in the March story are not particularly congruous, but both need mention. The Anschluss, on the one hand, became a fait accompli; on the other hand, J. B. was medically examined and his heart and lungs were found to be in excellent condition.

Early in April, he and M. A. B. had a holiday near Salcombe, and incidentally saw there the sailing ship, *Herzogin Cecilie.* In mid-April he was kept very busy with documents about veterinary matters, etc., on 12 May he gave a lecture on "Milk" at Papworth, and on 14 May he attended the Cambridge meeting of the Physiological Society. About two hundred and fifty persons had gathered together in the Lecture theatre to hear communications when Adrian announced that the proceedings would be interrupted for a pleasant ceremony, and called upon Sir Henry Dale to present J. B.'s portrait by Eves (Plate 57) to the laboratory on behalf of the subscribers. Dale said, "I feel privileged in being asked to perform this pleasant duty to-day. I am in the happy position of having known Sir Joseph longer than anyone else in this room. We were at school together and, though the first contact with him was not of a wholly sympathetic character as he executed his authority of Prefect upon me, this period was followed by seven years with many endearing memories as we finished school and entered the University together." Sir Henry then described "the wigwam in a passage behind green curtains" which served as J. B.'s laboratory for many years, and touched upon many episodes both grave and gay in his life. He spoke with feeling of the many who had benefited from J. B.'s generous assistance in their difficulties, and how he was always surrounded by a crowd of enthusiastic pupils to whom his willing help was ever forthcoming. In conclusion Dale touched upon J. B.'s many activities outside physiology, and said that inter alia he was spoken of at the War Office "with positive reverence".

Adrian stated that the portrait, if somewhat austere, portrayed the twinkle in the eye which, if he might say so, had lubricated the wheels of many stiff committee meetings from time to time. He also said that there was hardly a person present who did not owe something to J. B.'s generosity. Then, in his charming manner, he added, "He is a great professor, a great physiologist, a great friend."

Among the scientific communications to the meeting were three of which J. B. was part-author. With Mason and J. A. Kennedy, he described a new technique, free from the degree of surgical interference involved in methods previously used by himself and by others, for the direct determination of foetal oxygen consumption; it also gave the amount of the blood flow through the umbilical cord, and the lower limit of the maternal blood flow through the cotyledons (the subject was *Ovis aries*). The second communication, in collaboration with Mason, dealt with the oxygen saturation in the umbilical vessels, about which earlier findings, by J. B. and his colleagues and by others, had been extremely divergent. With much greater experimental precautions, a reinvestigation had produced figures indicating an atmosphere of much higher saturation than had usually been regarded as existing. The third communication, by J. B. and Barron, described an experiment in which the spinal cord of a sheep foetus had been transected at the level of C 4 and the subject had survived to be delivered by Caesarean section at 140 days. During the transection the right forelimb had been accidentally amputated at the elbow, and the authors detailed the consequent disparity in the right scapula, humerus, dorsal and ventral nerve roots, and gray and white matter of the spinal cord.

At the Society's dinner in the evening, the silent film which Dr. F. R. Winton and John Freeman had made of J. B. at work was projected in the Old Combination Room of Trinity College. Dr. L. E. Shore, in introducing it, told the members that, if he were to begin a recount of J. B.'s kindnesses, twenty-four hours on end would not be sufficient time.

A number of members who were unable to be present in person associated themselves in spirit with the tributes to J. B., and among them was the doyen of British physiologists, Sir Charles Sherrington, who had written as follows from Edinburgh. "I cannot – to my great regret – 'assist', as our French friends say, at the portrait ceremony on Saturday. I am tied in the north until next week. But I cannot allow the occasion, and its tribute to yourself, to pass without sending you this line of whole-hearted congratulation – and admiration. What physiology and Cambridge owe to your devotion is not easily said. It must be a great source of pleasure to you to think about – and many others *are* thinking about it now – not least, believe me, Yours ever, C. S. Sherrington."

On 23 May J. B. learned that he had been elected a Foreign Honorary Member of the American Academy of Arts and Sciences, Boston, Mass. Towards the end of the month he was very busy, hoping in a few more visits to conclude his work in connection with the Commission on Veterinary Education. On 2 June he went to Aberdeen for the Physiological Society meeting, and eight days later he and M. A. B. visited the Royal Academy Exhibition to see Mr. Eves' portrait of him. This was, apparently, a larger one than that which had been presented at Cambridge on 14 May. It was "regarded from every angle and disapproved of strongly by M.A.B.!" Four days thereafter Adrian presided at a dinner given by Cambridge physiologists to J. B. He, naturally, was on Adrian's right, and the remaining hosts in order of seating were Rushton, Millikan, Tunnicliffe, Matthews, Roughton, Verney, Willmer, Winton, and Shore (on Adrian's left).

Three days *post*, but presumably not *propter*, this dinner J. B. developed a pain in his right side and on 3 July he entered Nuffield House, Guy's Hospital, for diagnosis and treatment. The radiograph revealed a large-ish renal calculus and the main treatment decided upon was medical rather than surgical. News of J. B.'s indisposition got round, and during the first five days callers totalled twenty! On 29 July he went from Guy's to the Sun Clinic on Hayling Island, but it was not until 26 August that the calculus was passed, and not until 4 September that he was home again.

In consequence of all this he was unable to attend the Sixteenth

(Jubilee) International Congress of Physiologists, which took place in Zürich from 14 to 19 August, and at which he was to have introduced Discussion Thema No. 8 with a paper on "Problems of foetal respiration." This paper is available in published form; it was a useful summary, but added no important fresh findings, so we need not analyse it here.

One item of interest which antedated the Congress needs mentioning. It was the receipt of a letter from Mr. W. S. Morrison, of the Ministry of Agriculture and Fisheries, expressing his own and Colonel Colville's thanks for the work which J. B. had carried out as a member of the Commission on Veterinary Education in Great Britain. In late August he received another letter, this time from Lord Stamp, asking him to serve for another two years on the L. M. S. Advisory Committee on Scientific Research.

The month of September 1938, as all remember, was one of severe international tension, with Mr. Chamberlain's visits to München courageous perhaps, but more assuredly illusory, attempts to restore a situation which was beyond such means of restoration. Let us for a moment see it through one person's eyes, in other words, quote from M. A. B.'s diary. On 16 September is the note "Chamberlain flying back from Munich", on 27 "The sad plot thickens. Cambridge is becoming air-minded. Throngs queuing up for gas-masks," on 28 "Everyone full of anxieties. I have been mildly laying in stores – jams, sugar, soap and Christmas chocolates, etc. Chamberlain, Mussolini, Daladier, and Hitler to meet to-morrow at Munich," on 29 "10,000 children to arrive in Cambridge to-morrow, evacuated from London", and on 30 "Stop press. Children not coming. [Some, however, did.]" It was on 29 September that the so-called Munich agreement was signed. Mr. Chamberlain returned to England on 1 October, and five days later was given a vote of confidence in the House by 366 votes to 144. His speech included the sentence, "When a man gets to my age and fills my position he tends to feel that criticism and even abuse matter little to him if his own conscience approves of his action."

If we have to recall such matters in order to get the general background for J. B.'s biography, it is nevertheless pleasant to revert to his personal story, and an appropriate note of transition is provided by Peters (1949), who wrote that "As far as capacity for committee work was concerned I can remember him a year before

World War II coming into my laboratory. At that time he was trying to get people to say they would be reserved for work in World War II. He told me incidentally that he was devoting much of his time to getting shells and fuses put together, because apparently things had got behind. This direct attention to the main point, whatever this might be, was a well marked characteristic of his mental activity." About mid-October J. B. attended the autumn dinner of the British Association for Refrigeration in his capacity as Chairman of the Food Investigation Board, and in his speech said that he would like to see a refrigerator regarded as a necessity in every house. With the turn of the month he went up to Aberdeen for the opening, on 4 November, of the new Reid Library in the Rowett Research Institute. Two days later he went off to Denmark, which country was already experiencing Nazi pressure, and on 9 November he lectured in Copenhagen to a large and very appreciative audience. The next day he had dinner with the Niels Bohrs in that city, and on the following one paid a visit to Elsinore.

Back in England, and later in the month, to be precise on Saturday 26 November, a letter from him to Robbie read as follows:- "My life still goes on concerning itself with things about which I know nothing. Monday, it was the elimination of dud pilots from the Air Force, before they killed either themselves or anyone else. Tuesday, advertizing dressing-gowns at a sale for 'SASMA' of which I had only once previously heard. Wednesday, research in fattening pigs. Thursday, selection of a man to work at the curing of bacon. Friday, the effects of wrapping babies in blankets. Saturday, a little normal life. To-morrow. Back to the elimination of dud pilots."

Had he been gifted with prescience, he could have added that two days later still he would become a grandfather for the second time. For on 29 November Michael Joseph was born to Biddy and Henry Barcroft.

On 14 January 1939 J. B., Kramer, and Millikan published a paper on "The oxygen in the carotid blood at birth". The research had arisen "from a desire to obtain a record of the alteration of environment of the brain, in respect of oxygen, at birth", and the recording (by Kramer's method) had been continuous during the birth of lambs by Caesarean section. After ligation of the cord saturation had dropped to 10–20 per cent. for a minute or more, but had thereafter risen, within five minutes, to 75 per cent. in lambs breathing air and to 95 per cent. in lambs breathing oxygen. As change from air to oxygen at four minutes had raised the former value at once to the latter one, there could have been no great amount of circulation through the parts of the lung not accessible to gas; on the other hand, it was no proof that the whole lung had expanded. The high saturation when oxygen had been administered from the start was inconsistent with the short-circuiting of any significant amount of blood through the foramen ovale.

A few days later J. B. had a letter from Dr. P. Brandt Rehberg, of Copenhagen, about his lectures of the previous year and about plans for the visits of further British physiologists to Denmark. It included the following. "I have to thank you for the lectures too – they were a great success with the members I can tell you. Like a fairy tale, one of them told me. And I hope we have got something started – that your visit here was really the introduction to fruitful contact with English science for us. I cannot thank you enough for pointing out the possibility of help from London and for what you already have been doing." This was shortly followed by a letter from Dr. Orahovats, of the Physiological Laboratory in Sofia, saying that the University of Sofia, on the recommendation of the Medical Faculty, had accorded J. B. the title of Doctor of Medicine honoris causa. "The motives were not only your services to science in general but in particular the interest you have taken in the development of physiology in our country. It is a peculiar pleasure to me that the name of my teacher to whom I owe so much as regards my education as a worker in the field of science will remain among those honoured by my own University. The official papers will be forwarded to you by the Rector of the University."

In the middle of January J. B. and M. A. B. had received the pleasing news that Robbie had been made Assistant Military Adviser to the Central Provinces, and that he had secured this much-coveted Cavalry post at a lower age, apparently, than any of his predecessors. By the end of the month, with the rank of Captain, he was back on leave in England.

In February J. B. was concerned, as Chairman of the Food Investigation Board, with some – for him – unusual problems, namely, the gas storage of apples and pears, the chilling of beef, and the brine-freezing of fish. On 14 February he, J. A. Kennedy, and Mason published a paper on "The blood volume and kindred properties in pregnant sheep," and he and Kennedy one on "The distribution of blood between the foetus and placenta in sheep." With regard to the first paper, observations had been made on the blood volume, plasma volume, corpuscle volume, haematocrit reading, haemoglobin value per ml. blood, and the total haemoglobin in sheep during pregnancy; the method used had been the injection of Evans Blue (T. 1824), readings being made by the method of Kennedy and Millikan. In sheep which bore one lamb each, the blood volume curve rose to a summit about the end of the third trimester, dropped somewhat during the second, and rose considerably during the third, both rises being mainly in plasma volume. Appreciable rise in plasma volume and fall in corpuscular volume took place while the foetus was of negligible weight. The total haemoglobin remained fairly constant for about fifty days, then showed a sharp and considerable drop which was not reflected in the corpuscular volume, and subsequently rose gradually until at term it had more or less regained its initial value. In the second paper the authors reported that the absolute amount of blood in the placenta plus cord remained fairly constant for the last third of pregnancy, equalling that in the foetus at 100 days, and dropping to a quarter or a fifth of the total by term. The conditions of foetal blood pressure suggested that increasing quantities of blood could be driven per minute through the placenta as pregnancy proceeded. The ratio of cells to plasma rose from about 30 : 70 at half term to about 40 : 60 at full term, and the total haemoglobin in the foetus from 4 g. at 80 days to 80 g. at term. This increase in the foetus took place after 100 days, whereas the only large fall in the mother was at about a third of the way through pregnancy. The only other note for February is that J. B. was in Edinburgh on the 23rd, as the guest of Sir Thomas Holland, to lecture to the Edinburgh Medical Society.

The major events of March were those of the tail-end of what Winston Churchill (1948) styled "the Munich winter". At the beginning Great Britain recognized Franco's government and near the end the Spanish civil war closed. In between, at 6 a.m. on the 15th the occupation of Bohemia by German military forces began, and a few days later Memel was similarly taken.

On 14 March another paper by J. B., Kennedy, and Mason appeared in the *Journal of Physiology*, the subject this time being "The direct determination of the oxygen consumption of the foetal sheep." The method used was calculated to obviate objections attaching both to the original one of Cohnstein and Zuntz (1884) and to the fairly recent one of J. B., Flexner, and McClurkin (1934). The average value found for the foetal oxygen consumption was 0.0043 ml./g./minute. The calculated rates of blood flow through the umbilical cord varied with foetal age and size, the lowest value being 111 ml./min. in a foetus of 111 days and the highest 600 ml./min. in a foetus of 129 days. Calculated limiting rates of flow through the uterine structures ranged from 106 ml./min. in the case of the foetus of 111 days to 475 ml./min. in the case of one aged 137 days.

On 31 March J. B. and M. A. B. departed from Cambridge en route to Glenarm, County Antrim, but they had to leave early on 8 April for England as J. B. was "needed", and he did not get home until four days later. Presumably the "need" was that mentioned in the *Evening Standard* of 27 April, which stated that he had joined the group of scientists who were conducting Air Raid Precautions experiments on behalf of the government. "He is examining", the paper said, "the effect of blast pressure on air raid shelters, an aspect of the problem which was stressed in the recent Hailey report." On 19 April Mrs. Cubitt held a reception at the Rubens Hotel, London, in connection with the wedding (which had taken place on 17 March) of her daughter, Betty Hermione Durancé Cartwright, to Robert Ball Barcroft. Towards the end of the month J. B. was elected a Foreign Associate of the National Academy of Sciences, Washington, D. C.

Early in May he learned that Mr. Eves was depositing the portrait which had been in the Royal Academy Exhibition in 1938 as his diploma picture on becoming a Royal Academician. Later in the month Their Majesties embarked in *Empress of Australia* for Canada. Scientific items were two in number. The first was that J. B., Barron, A. T. Cowie, P. H. Forsham, and A. MacDonald gave a communication to the Physiological Society on 13 May on "The effect of asphyxia on inhibition of respiratory movement in the sheep's foetus." They had found that the oxygen level in anterior fontanelle blood at which release of inhibition took place was remarkably constant, dropping from about 25 per cent. at 100 days to about 15 per cent. at term. The carbon dioxide level was variable, and the hydrogen-ion level was not determined. In the absence of figures for the latter, it was not possible to say that the release was due to oxygen deficiency, but merely that the oxygen level was a surprisingly accurate indicator of the degree of asphyxia required. The second scientific item was concerned with J. B.'s own A. R. P. work, and it was to the effect that goats exposed to blast in Anderson shelters had emerged unscathed.

On 15 June Their Majesties embarked in *Empress of Britain* for their return to this country after their exacting but extremely successful tour through Canada – successful in that it strengthened the intangible bonds linking Canadians and the Throne, as was shortly to be demonstrated. The same month saw another publication by J. B. and Barron, this time on "The development of behavior in foetal sheep." The summary stated that "Observations on the prenatal development of the sheep indicate that the first responses to the stimulation of peripheral sensory nerves – whether they be exteroceptor or proprioceptor, and regardless of their area of distribution – are restricted in the amount of musculature they involve. As development proceeds the responses aroused by some nerves – mainly those distributed to what we have regarded physiologically as the head – become more and more extensive. Other nerves – notably those to the trunk – never attain the ability to arouse such extensive reactions. Inasmuch as the nerves to the head appear to develop most rapidly, the extensor responses appear early in behaviour. Just when the first local responses appear to be aroused from the trunk has not been definitely determined. However, of these two responses the extensive, when it occurs, appears dominant and the localized response secondary in the same sense that the head of an animal is its dominant part, the trunk the secondary."

This may be a suitable place to mention two other 1939 publications by the same authors, when the actual dates of publication are not known. One is "Further observations on the developement of respiratory movement in the foetal sheep" – it appeared in *Livro de Homenagem* aos Professores Alvaro e Miguel Ozorio de Almeida, was received early in April, and published in Rio de Janeiro. In the main it was an already told story, but it included some extra facts and some suggestions. The inhibition of respiratory movement in the later stages of intrauterine life was unaffected by decortication and seemed to depend upon a centre in the rostral part of the forebrain. By appropriate transverse sections of the brain and also – interestingly enough – by longitudinal midline section the respiratory movements could be released from inhibition. In fact, their occurrence or otherwise seemed to depend upon the balance between afferent nervous impulses and the inhibitory activity of the forebrain centre.

The second and more important paper, entitled, "Movement in the mammalian foetus," was a forty-five page summary of the whole subject which appeared in *Ergebnisse der Physiologie*. It cannot be described in detail here, but we should at least indicate its content. After a bibliography and introduction it passed on to reflex and spontaneous responses in the sheep embryo, and a comparison with histological findings. Then came types of movement – jerky, sustained, inhibition, rigidity – and analysis of types in relation to levels in the central nervous system. This was followed by evidence of levels from the plantar reflex, patterns of movement (respiration, righting and postural, progressive), myogenic patterns, spontaneous movements, the individuation-syntheses controversy, and conclusion.

The final paragraph of this last read as follows. "The nervous system commences to assert itself by the anticipation of motility by sensation. Having established the reflex, its next step is to dominate the more local reflexes by the reticulo-spinal system, connected at one end with sensation in the face, at the other with the body generally. Having so far consolidated its position, something higher is developed which on the one hand controls the general type of movement and on the other carries up with it the essence of what is purposeful, leaving behind what is, in essence, routine. The next step is, having established all these things, to dominate them still further by the process of inhibition so that movement only takes place as required; its dominance is so great as to apply even to the routine movement of respiration, but the more purposeful and elaborate the movement the more completely it is dominated, so that finally the highest part of the brain has a free field in which to play and the mechanism with which to do so. Such then is the development of that phenomenon on which Sherrington laid such stress, 'The Dominance of the Head over the Body'."

In July J. B. accepted an invitation to join the Advisory Council of the Department of Scientific and Industrial Research, a membership which he was destined to retain until 1944. Towards the end of the month he went to Aberdeen for the Annual Meeting of the British Medical Association. At it he opened a discussion in the Section of Medical Sociology (Nutrition) with a paper on "Food conservation in relation to national food supply", and one in the Section of Physiology and Biochemistry with a paper on "The intra-uterine development of respiratory effort." With the latter we need scarcely deal once again; the former, however, was a new and fascinating story from J. B.'s ready pen and can be commended to the reader for its interest and as an exercise in the technique of presentation. It dealt with the contribution which food investigation had made to the facilities for the supply of commodities to this country, especially in time of emergency. Foodstuffs were discussed under three main headings, according to the length of time they could be kept, and it was considered that the ultimate goal would be the manufacture and storage of the vitamins.

Back from the meeting, J. B. set off for a holiday in Killarney and Glengariff but it was ended, as so many were in that summer, by the deterioration in the international situation. Late on 23 August, Germany and Russia signed a non-aggression pact for ten years – it was, in fact, destined to last for twenty-two months before Germany disregarded it. The next day the Government's preparations and Mr. Chamberlain's own words gave warning, as indeed a B. B. C. broadcast at 9 p.m. on 22 August had virtually done, that war was imminent. M. A. B. and J. B. accordingly packed and returned to Cambridge, which they reached on 25 August. On 1 September, at dawn, the Germans attacked Poland and on 3 September Great Britain declared war, and Winston Churchill became a member of the War Cabinet and First Lord of the Admiralty. Shortly after the declaration, as readers will remember, the wailing of the sirens gave the first, though in that instance an erroneous, warning of an imminent air raid.

In between the wars J. B., like C. G. Douglas of Oxford, had been a member of the Chemical Defence Committee. This, until shortly before the outbreak of the second war, had been under the War Department but at some time in 1939 it was transferred to the Ministry of Supply and, presumably at about the same time, J. B. became a member of the Chemical Board of that Ministry. In peace-time the Physiological Laboratory of the Experimental

Station at Porton was largely staffed by Medical Officers seconded from the Navy, Army, and Air Force, but these were pretty certain to be taken away on the outbreak of war, and arrangements had been made to replace them. When war did break out, Professors Lovatt Evans and G. R. Cameron went at once to Porton, and J. B. and Douglas soon followed them. Though they were still on the Chemical Warfare Committee, it was thought best for them to be on the spot at Porton in case gas warfare began again, as everyone at that time expected it to do. In consequence, No. 13 Grange Road was let, and J. B. and M. A. B. went to live in Salisbury.

There, for a moment, we must leave the war story, and pick up the foetal research one with mention of a paper, which appeared in the September number of the *British Journal of Radiology*. It was by Barclay, J. B., Barron, and Franklin, and was entitled, "A radiographic demonstration of the circulation through the heart in the adult and in the foetus, and the identification of the ductus arteriosus." In the 1939 experiments the ductus had been identified beyond doubt in the cineradiographic records, both in planned ways and also through a fortunate accident in one particular case. More than this, however, some of the major features of the foetal circulation had been directly and objectively recorded for the first time, and a beginning made of studies of the functional post-natal closures of special foetal by-passes, in particular the ductus arteriosus and foramen ovale.

The summary included the following passage. "In the foetus, the whole of the superior caval blood is seen to pass into the right ventricle and out through the pulmonary valve into the pulmonary trunk; from this vessel it passes on the one hand into the pulmonary arteries and, on the other, *via* the ductus arteriosus, into the descending aorta. As the brachio-cephalic artery leaves the aorta proximal to the entry of the ductus arteriosus, the superior caval blood does not pass to the coronary system, the head and fore-limbs. The inferior caval blood has a double course through the heart. The main part goes through the foramen ovale to the left auricle and ventricle, and passes out into the aorta and coronary and brachiocephalic arteries. Hence, the heart and brain are given preferential treatment with respect to the supply of oxygenated blood coming from the placenta. On the other hand, a minor part of the inferior caval blood passes with the superior caval flow into the right ventricle and out into the pulmonary arteries and, *via* the ductus arteriosus, into the descending aorta."

While we are on the subject of foetal physiology, it seems right to note that the war dissolved one of the most productive partnerships in this field, namely, that between J. B. and Barron. There will be some further mention of the latter, for publications of results lag some time behind the conclusions of researches. But he, in company with many other Americans, had little choice save to return to his own country when ours, in which he had been doing such fine work, went to war. So in person, if not in spirit, he ceased to be directly associated for the future with J. B.'s investigations.

J. B. himself, and M. A. B., were back where they had left off at the end of the first war, but it must have been very much more trying for them, with J. B. now sixty-seven and M. A. B. not much younger, to be uprooted from their pleasant home, with its beloved garden, for an indefinite period. There was, however, no doubt in their minds as to where their duty lay, and they wasted no time in vain regrets or – in M. A. B.'s case – in putting such on record in her diary. One great difference in 1939, apart from the material changes at Porton, was that, whereas in the first war J. B.'s attention had in no small measure been directed towards the victims of gassing, in the second war he and others were chiefly concerned with measures to be taken if gas was used, and it never was. While no one can regret that fact, it meant, and meant increasingly as time went on, a rather humdrum existence for all in the Physiological Laboratory at Porton. Work did not cease, but it became of a rather routine character, concerned with improvements in protective devices, continued study of pathology and treatment, and investigation of the properties etc. of any new compounds which might possibly have application to chemical warfare. There was nothing spectacular in all this, but it nevertheless involved long hours of activity for both the Committees and the Research Departments. J. B. was particularly affected in the former aspect, for he was Chairman of the Physiological and Medical Sub-committee, and also of a Factories Medical Sub-committee which was set up to keep an eye on the health of those engaged in chemical warfare work.

The only other notes for 1939 are more domestic in character. Early in December M. A. B. returned to Cambridge to take over No. 13 from the initial tenants and to re-let it to a Miss Fox. Late in the month she called at the house "and made the acquaintance of the charming Prince Alexander of Yugoslavia. The Queen (his Aunt) called yesterday."

At the beginning of 1940, apart from his work at Porton, J. B. was continuing weekly visits to London in connection with certain of his posts, and about this time another duty was added to his already long list, namely, membership of the Advisory Council for Scientific Research and Technical Development. In mid-January, by contrast to all this war-time activity, there appeared in the *Journal of Physiology* two papers that had been sent off to the Editorial Board a month before war was declared. The first, by J. B., Barron, Cowie and Forsham, was on "The oxygen supply of the foetal brain of the sheep and the effect of asphyxia on foetal respiratory movement." They had determined the oxygen content and saturation of the blood in the carotid artery and cerebral venous sinuses and seen at what level of asphyxia, produced by occlusion of the umbilical cord, respiratory movements were "released". Of interest were the findings that the carotid saturation up to the last week of gestation was of the general order found in the arteries of persons at very great altitudes, and that in the last week before birth there was a marked drop down from even this low level. The second paper, by J. B., Kennedy and Mason, was on the "Oxygen in the blood of the umbilical vessels of the sheep"; improved techniques had been used, but the summary of the findings and the discussion of them cannot be reduced to a sufficiently short form for inclusion here, and those interested must read the original account. No other publications by J. B. appeared in 1940, a fact which itself shows how fully his activity had been diverted by first the imminence, and then the outbreak, of war. He was, however, at some time during the year, elected Vice-President of the Marine Biological Association, and that must have recalled work done at Plymouth in between the wars.

A little before the two papers mentioned in the previous paragraph appeared, M. A. B. had gone off to Belfast for a fortnight's visit. On her return to this country, she called at No. 13 Grange Road and had a talk with Miss Fox about the interesting visitors who had been to the house; she also met Princess Paul of Yugoslavia and Countess Toerring-Yettenbach, who were in the house when she called. The earlier visitors had been H. M. Queen Marie of Yugoslavia and her younger sons, Princes Tomislav and Andrej, who had not stayed, and Princes Alexander and Nicholas, sons of the Prince Regent Paul of Yugoslavia, who had been house-guests. To complete the list, we can add that H. R. H. The Duchess of Kent had arrived on Saturday, 6 January, for the week-end to celebrate the Greek Christmas.

On 1 February J. B. was one of a number of members of the Royal Society Dining Club who entertained a delegation of French scientists; thereafter there is little to note until mid-March, when he and M. A. B. went off for a fortnight's holiday in Cornwall. In early April Germany invaded Denmark and Norway, and Major Quisling's surname went into general use as a synonym for a particularly distasteful kind of traitor. It is pleasant to revert from such memories to our story proper and we have, fortunately, the schedule of a typical day for J. B. about this time. He rose at 7.30 a.m. and at 9.10 left for Porton, returning at 5.15 p.m. for tea, after which followed an hour's lie-down and then an hour's walk with M. A. B. Through all his many perplexities he maintained his serene attitude of mind, and it would be impossible to say how many he helped by his counsel, wisdom, and kindliness, all so unostentatiously and naturally extended to those with whom he came into contact.

Early in May he was in London for three days with a full programme, including a visit to the House of Lords for the projection of films connected with his work. But the main notes for that month are of major events. On 1 May Winston Churchill was placed by the Prime Minister in a position in which he could greatly influence our conduct of the war. He was to preside, in the absence of Mr. Chamberlain, at meetings of the Military Co-ordination Committee, and to be responsible, on its behalf, for giving guidance and directions to the Chiefs of Staff Committee, which he was empowered to convene when necessary. Further, he was to have his own central staff under a Senior Staff Officer (Major-General Ismay) who was to be an additional member of the Chiefs of Staff Committee. From Churchill's point of view, this was largely a gift of immense responsibilities without effective power in his own hands to discharge them. But in the event the arrangement was purely temporary, for on 10 May, soon after the German invasion of Holland and Belgium, Mr. Chamberlain resigned and in the evening of that day H. M. the King commissioned Mr. Churchill to form a government. In the early hours of 28 May the major part of the Belgian Army surrendered, and that same day the evacuation from Dunkirk began; it was completed on 4 June, by which time a third of a million British and allied troops had been landed in England. Parliament assembled on that day to hear from the Prime Minister his account of what had been happening.

His speech ended with the soon famous passage:- "Even though large tracts of Europe and many old and famous States have fallen or may fall into the grip of the Gestapo and all the odious apparatus of Nazi rule, we shall not flag or fail. We shall go on to the end. We shall fight in France, we shall fight in the seas and oceans, we shall fight with growing confidence and growing strength in the air; we shall defend our Island, whatever the cost may be. We shall fight on the beaches, we shall fight on the landing-grounds, we shall fight in the fields and in the streets, we shall fight in the hills; we shall never surrender; and even if, which I do not for a moment believe, this Island or a large part of it were subjugated and starving, then our Empire beyond the seas, armed and guarded by the British Fleet, would carry on the struggle, until, in God's good time, the New World, with all its power and might, steps forth to the rescue and the liberation of the Old."

With the collapse of France on 16 June, and the consequent reduction in the sphere of the conflict, Mr. Churchill's words of 4 June became even more significant, but it is necessary now to leave the national story and to revert to that of J. B. On the evening of 18 June he had to go off to London, and that night there was an air raid on Southampton and Andover, both sufficiently near Salisbury, where M. A. B. was. A week later she was visited there by Miss Fox and Prince Alexander of Yugoslavia, and presumably got news of No. 13 Grange Road and of Cambridge; the sirens sounded again that evening. The next day J. B. went off for three days to Cambridge and London, and early in July he was again in town, with nine meetings to attend in the next three days. In mid-July Professor Cameron, who had recently left Salisbury and taken up his quarters in the Rectory at Winterslow, Wilts., wrote to M.A.B.: "You will be glad to hear that we manage to keep Sir Joseph in order at Porton, a rather difficult task, I'm sure you'll agree. However, one mustn't give up trying. My only regret about leaving Salisbury is that I do not have your company. I sincerely hope that we shall meet again in better times."

Towards the end of July a strenuous tour was planned for J. B. It was to last from 2 to 9 August, and to take him in succession to Cambridge, London, Liverpool, Sutton Oak, back to Liverpool, the I.C.I. works at Randle, near Runcorn in Cheshire, Edinburgh (c/o Professor Marrian), Aberdeen (visits to the Terry Research Station and to the Rowett Institute at Bucksburn), and back to London. He had, however, scarcely embarked on the tour when, on 3 August, he felt "a tightening pain in the chest." He was sent to the Evelyn Nursing Home for a week, and told to take care of himself and not get overtired before the winter. With such warnings, he and M. A. B. planned a well-earned holiday, which began on 13 August with a week in Bude, Cornwall, and concluded with another in Chagford, Devon, the while what later became named "The Battle of Britain" continued (it had begun on 10 July and it reached one of its two peaks, the raid on Tyneside, on 15 August). On 26 August they were back in Salisbury, but J. B. was nearly free of the "clutch" which he got most noticeably the first thing in the morning.

On 4 September he may have attended the funeral service of Sir Joseph (J. J.) Thomson, O.M., in Westminster Abbey, but the evidence on the point is not precise. Sir Charles Sherrington, who was definitely there, described the scene in the following words:- "The great rose-windows flooded us and the measured music flooded up over us in the old unhurried 'tempo', while the ashes – of the founder of subatomic physics – awaited disposal under a floorstone of the nave; the service as it happened went forward between two incursions of German barbarism, i.e., two indiscriminate bombings quite irrespective of military objectives!" Sir Charles' letter – to the present writer – was written from North London on 11 September, and London had been the special objective of "blitzes" on 6, 7, 8, and 9 September. Sir Charles, then aged eighty-two, mentioned the matter somewhat laconically in the brief sentence, "London is becoming the storm-centre, which is an added interest to being here." J. B. was in town on 10 and 11 September, staying overnight in the Athenaeum, so he must have seen much of the destruction that had been produced. He was also delayed in his return to Salisbury on the following day, for owing to the damage to the railway he had to go to Clapham via Waterloo. Other raids followed those mentioned, and M. A. B. had some interesting letters from her sister-in-law, who said that everyone got plenty of sleep despite the bombing, the proof being that no one seemed to require a "shut-eye" after lunch. She herself always remembered what J. B. had said in the first war, "The place where you are is so much smaller than the place where you are not." Her husband, William Valentine Ball, after a heavy raid had remarked to her, "It sounds a silly thing to say, but I wouldn't like to be out of it."

About this time, when travelling by rail was anything but restful, it was decided, much to M. A. B.'s relief and joy, that J. B. and Douglas should henceforth travel to and from London and elsewhere by car. As, by the end of the year, there had been several trips to London, and others to Sutton Oak, Manchester, and Lancashire respectively, the physical sparing to J. B. must have been considerable. On one occasion at least, however, he took to the train again and that was to go to Cambridge about mid-October and, while there, to take part in a luncheon at St. Catherine's College. Lord Woolton, the Minister of Food in the Coalition Cabinet, was present and one presumes, from the menu, that the meal was intended to show that a satisfactory calorie intake could be provided without ordinary butchers' meat and also at a low cost – under a shilling. J. B. said it was all excellent, so it may be of interest to note the menu. There was a choice of leaf protein soup or cream of yeast, then a choice of sauté of kidney and blood or whale casserole, with cabbage horsebeans and potatoes, and finally Scotch woodcock and coffee. Yeast bread was provided, and vegetable curry for sampling. Epicures who are not prepossessed by this list may note that Erbacher Marcobrunn 1921 and Volnay 1923 were also on the menu, though not included in the estimated cost of the meal!

Apart from the change to car-travel, two further arrangements which came into effect before the end of the year helped to lighten J. B.'s burden. The first was that on 28 November he and M. A. B. transferred from the Old George, Salisbury, to the Railway Hotel at Porton. This meant a shorter distance to go to work, and also a private sitting-room, fire, and good food. The second improvement was the engagement of Michael Christie-Miller, aged 17, to act as J. B.'s secretary. On 19 December M. A. B. noted that "his competence seems unlimited for what is required." On the same date she gave J. B.'s revised daily schedule as follows:- "Up at 7.15 sharp, breakfast at 8, off about 9, sometimes kindly driven to the Camp by Captain Richardson. He returns most days to lunch and then has a rest to 2.30. Then walks to the Camp and gets home about 5.15. 'Relaxation' or writing his book until dinner, and listening in at 6 and 9 to hear the history of the moment."

Over Christmas he was indisposed with "a chill or whatnot" and did not get back to work until 2 January. During the rest of that month, however, he paid three or four visits to London, and one each to Oxford, Crewe, and Cambridge. In February he and M. A. B. had a holiday in the Savernake Forest region, getting back to Porton on 24 February. The next day J. B. left, unaccompanied by M. A. B., for a five days' tour to Randle, Glasgow, and finally the University of Edinburgh, where on 28 February he delivered the Sharpey-Schafer Lecture to a crowded audience. The subject was "Four phases of birth", and the opening passages read as follows:-

"Until the last two or three years little has been added to the meagre knowledge of the physiology of birth possessed by our forefathers. This may seem strange, for each of us depends for our very existence on its successful negotiation. Millions have died who might conceivably have lived, given greater knowledge on the part of the responsible people. Yet there are reasons for the want of progress; at any particular birth the attention of those concerned is completely and rightly concentrated on the effort to get that individual child into the world as satisfactorily as possible and they have little opportunity for observation and less for experiment. What I shall say towards the more accurate description of birth falls under four headings:

"1. Birth might be described as a change in the atmosphere in which the foetus lives: the external atmosphere, that with which its skin is in contact, and the internal atmosphere, which for our purpose is essentially that to which its brain is subjected.

"2. At birth a considerable volume of blood seems to be transferred from the placenta to the foetus. I shall discuss the reasons which account for an excessive quantity of blood being in the foetal circulation just before birth, the extent of the plethora, why the redundant blood is transferred to the neonatal organism and its fate when it gets there.

"3. The change in conditions means that on birth the blood must acquire its oxygen from the air instead of from the placenta;

therefore, on birth, a great quantity of blood must be circulated through the lung. Up to birth, on the other hand, the pulmonary circulation is functionally redundant and is actually short-circuited.

"4. There is the all-important subject of the first breath."

The summary shows that in essence the lecture contained no significant fresh facts – that, indeed, could scarcely have been expected when J. B. had been off on war duties for so long. On the other hand, it was a useful summary of individual pieces of research already mentioned in this biography, and may, therefore, appropriately be reproduced here.

"During the latter half of the period of gestation in the sheep the quantity of foetal blood in the placenta remains relatively constant, while that in the foetus increases with the growth of the placenta as much as 6–8 times. The growing needs of the foetus are met, in the placenta, by an increased rapidity of blood-flow and by increasing quantities of haemoglobin in the blood.

"A considerable volume of the foetal blood circulating in the placenta is transferred to the foetus at birth. The excess of corpuscles is broken down and the iron is stored.

"Evidence is given of the functional closing of the foramen ovale and the ductus arteriosus within a few minutes of birth.

"Evidence is also given showing that the essential neuromuscular mechanism for drawing the first breath is laid down between the 34th and the 50th day of gestation, and that asphyxia, far from stimulating the early spasmodic rhythms of the respiratory type, actually depresses them. At this stage exposure or asphyxia excite no activity in the embryo.

"By the 60th day of gestation higher levels of the brain have developed sufficiently to inhibit the lower centres; so that the 60-day foetus appears much more inert than the active 50-day foetus. Asphyxia depresses the higher centres and liberates the lower centres, thus converting the inert 60-day foetus functionally to the active 50-day foetus. Exposure has the same effect.

"At birth the lamb experiences both partial asphyxia – because of suspension of the placental circulation – and exposure. It responds with the respiratory movement which it developed some 100 days before. Sensory impulses from the skin heighten the tendency towards respiration."

The most important outside event of the following month was

the passing of the Lend-Lease Bill, to which President Roosevelt gave his assent on 11 March. In J. B.'s personal story we have to record that No. 13 Grange Road was now serving as a convent with a Mother Superior in charge, and that on 16 March J. B. was laid up for some days with a quite unusual type of chest cold and a trying cough, in consequence of which it was nearly a fortnight before he was back to duty, and even then not fully recovered. Another publication by him appeared on 15 March in *Schweizerische Medizinische Wochenschrift*, the subject being "The oxygen capacity of foetal and neo-natal blood." Professor E. Rothlin, of Basel, had in September 1940, through the present writer, invited contributions from a number of British physiologists in honour of Professor W. R. Hess, of Zürich, who was to be sixty years old on 17 March 1941, and J. B. was one of the few who had managed to produce a paper – most said they were too busy with their war-time duties. In his conclusions J. B. wrote that "Arguments have been given to show why and perhaps how the foetus at term contains more haemoglobin than is necessary immediately after birth. About 15 per cent. of the haemoglobin in circulation at birth seems to be broken down at birth and the bile salts excreted (in exaggerated cases icterus neonatorum). Whilst the organism can afford the haemoglobin as such, it cannot afford the iron which is stored as against future formation of pigment."

Early in April M. A. B. wrote that J. B. was now well but was a little pulled down by his cough, that in addition "the clutch" had reappeared a day or two earlier but had abated again. The cough had quite gone by 8 April, when he went off by car to Slough, Crewe, and London. Ten days later he was off again to London, and then on to Cambridge for two nights. This was very shortly after the extremely severe air-raid on London in which Lord and Lady Stamp and their eldest son had been killed. Lord Stamp, apart from having been Chairman of the L. M. S. when J. B. was attending its Committee meetings, had been Chairman of the Governors of the Leys School since 1936. Sir Henry Dale, Vice-Chairman of the Governors, writing to J. B. on 21 April, said:- "You are quite right in supposing that the tragic death of the Stamps comes as a sad blow. All kinds of national and international interests will suffer through his loss. He was a remarkable combination of great ability, quickness of grasp and terrific energy, with a high power of passing, day after day, from one great responsibility to another without any sign of fatigue or confusion; and with it all he had a simple goodness and modesty which must be very rare in combination with such dynamic efficiency."

A little while after J. B.'s return from Cambridge, he went for a six mile walk with M. A. B. without getting overtired, but doubts obviously persisted, and on 24 April he went to be examined by Dr. J. A. Ryle at Guy's Hospital, and to ascertain if possible the cause of the "clutches" which he got in his heart from time to time on going up hill. At the end of his examination, Dr. Ryle said to J. B.:- "Diagnostically, your coronary arteries are a little too rigid. At your age it is not a matter for concern and your arteries generally are splendid and you look very well. My advice is (1) Walk a little more slowly than you want to; (2) Don't carry heavy bags; (3) Don't walk too much after meals. Sit for half an hour when possible; (4) Rest for your week-ends if you can." When J. B. asked him why he was better than he had been, as he did not think that arteries got unstuck, Dr. Ryle asked, "Do you mean over a long or over a short period?" J. B. said, "As compared with a month ago", and Dr. Ryle indicated that a collateral circulation might have developed; as regards shorter terms people often suffered more in cold than in hot weather.

Four days later, acknowledging a cheque which J. B. had sent for Guy's, Dr. Ryle wrote:- "It would probably be a good thing if I were to give you an overhaul every now and then both for my own satisfaction and to keep you advised and Lady Barcroft reassured. Cold, fatigue and hurry (especially after meals or in cold weather) are the chief things to avoid. Walking more slowly than you want to is the habit to aim at. One lazy day a week with breakfast in bed is a justifiable indulgence. Moderate exercise at a moderate pace in warm weather is not contra-indicated." He added that he had not mentioned medicines on the day of examination, but a nitroglycerin tablet dissolved under the tongue was the specific if discomfort or oppression should give place to pain – a development which need not ever occur.

During the following month, J. B. continued with his work at Porton and his trips away from it, including in the latter a visit to London during which, on 20 May, he gave a special afternoon lecture at the Royal Institution on "The development of function in the mammalian organism." It was in effect a description of a film illustrating his and Barron's work. Its documentation and its setting in relation to the researches of other observers were given by Barron (1941) in his article, "The functional development of some mammalian neuromuscular mechanisms," and were therefore omitted by J. B. The audience numbered about forty, and he received pleasant comments afterwards from Sir William Bragg, who had invited him to give the lecture, and others. Dr. Daniel P. O'Brien, of the Rockefeller Foundation, wrote on the next day, "Your talk . . . was most stimulating and I ought to send my congratulations on a magnificent piece of work. Your audience was thrilled, I could see."

Between this time and his sixty-ninth birthday on 26 July, J. B. had a number of trips away from Porton to London, Cambridge, and various places in the north, and obviously had a busy programme which in the conditions of the time could have daunted even a much younger man. With an occasional time off for rest, however, he got through it without overstrain and also, as usual, found many opportunities to help both young and old who were in difficulties and needed advice.

More specifically, in July he was one of eleven signatories who issued an invitation to scientists who might be interested in forming a Nutrition Society; the first mooting of such an idea had been made about a couple of years earlier, but plans had been abandoned on the outbreak of war. The signatories to the 1941 document were the heads of various well-known bodies and institutes engaged on nutritional research in this country, namely, J. B. himself (Chairman, Food Investigation Board), Dr. H. Chick (Head of Division of Nutrition, Lister Institute), Professor J. C. Drummond (Professor of Biochemistry, University College, London; Scientific Adviser to the Ministry of Food), Dr. J. Hammond (Physiologist, Animal Research Institute, Cambridge), Dr. L. J. Harris (Director, Dunn Nutritional Laboratory, Cambridge), Sir Frederick Gowland Hopkins (Professor of Biochemistry, Cambridge), Professor H. D. Kay (Director, National Institute for Research in Dairying), Sir Charles J. Martin (late Director, Lister Institute), Sir Edward Mellanby (Secretary, Medical Research Council), Sir John Boyd Orr (Director, Rowett Research Institute) and Professor R. A. Peters (Professor of Biochemistry, Oxford). It was thought that meetings of researchers would serve a useful purpose, especially in enabling those studying different aspects of the same problem in agricultural and medical institutions to meet and help each other with information and constructive criticism, and the need for such a Nutrition Society had obviously only been emphasized by the contingencies of war.

It is little wonder, therefore, that the proposal was ratified when those interested held a meeting, convened by Sir John Orr, at the Royal Institution in London on 23 July. Membership of the new Society was to be limited to those actively engaged in research relating to nutrition, including such varied fields of it as the physiological, biochemical, agricultural, medical, sociological, economic and public health aspects. The main function of the Society under the circumstances then obtaining would be to hold conferences to discuss special themes, particularly those of importance during the war. The meeting agreed that it would be useful for the same period to have a separate Scottish group of the Society, and a Provisional Committee was elected with authority to act in accordance with the foregoing principles, and to function in the first place for one year. It consisted of Mr. A. L. Bacharach, Dr. H. Chick, Dr. E. M. Cruickshank, Dr. H. H. Green, Dr. J. Hammond, Dr. L. J. Harris, Professor H. P. Himsworth, Professor A. St. G. Huggett, Dr. F. Kidd, Dr. S. K. Kon, Sir John Orr, Dr. B. S. Platt, and Dr. H. M. Sinclair.

About a week after this important meeting, J. B. and M. A. B. were thrilled by the former's receipt of an invitation to form a nucleus of a School of Veterinary Physiology in connection with the Agricultural Research Council. The duties were to begin in October and to take J. B. back to Cambridge, and he accepted with pleasure, though that word is perhaps an inadequate expression of his and M. A. B.'s happiness. The appointment was to be for three to five years and carried a good salary, and M. A. B. wrote that "it is unusual for a man entering upon his seventieth year to have such good fortune." The immediate problem was to be connected with the speeding-up of war-time food production in Great Britain.

Acceptance of the new post meant that J. B. would retire, as from 4 September, from his Gas Warfare activities, now reaching the long span of a generation. But he felt that his possible work in that sphere had been completed, even if he would always look back with pleasure to the many contacts which he had made during the period. M. A. B. rejoiced at the prospect of his having a more leisured life after his own heart and of his being freed, with winter and early black-out time again approaching, from about two or three days' railway travel each week. Though *he* never complained, M. A. B. had a nightmare feeling of the tax on him that it all meant, and was inordinately relieved by the knowledge that such strain was now over.

J. B. himself wrote about the post to Robbie in India. "Things have changed a bit for me", he said, "as I am taking up a new job, and therefore leaving here, to return to Cambridge! It is not a Ministry of Supply job, but one under the Agricultural Research Council, concerned with the physiology of ruminants and ultimately how, if possible, to raise them on poorer foods than at present. There is less glamour about the new job, and it takes me away from the Services [1], which I deplore. On the other hand, 'Food' is a much more immediate problem than the gas, and most of what I can do for this war here, has been done . . . Moreover, to do the job here to my satisfaction, I would have to be knocking about these ranges in all weathers, and that in winter is a bit beyond me. So, as someone has said, 'One door closes, and another opens'."

With the future for the next few years thus determined, J. B. and M. A. B. enjoyed a very happy thirty-eighth wedding anniversary on 5 August, and two days later they were in Cambridge, presumably to make preliminary arrangements for the return. M. A. B. had a brain-wave, and went along to No. 13 Grange Road to ask the Mother Superior if they could have rooms there as paying guests in October. Unfortunately, the Mother Superior was away and her reply, when it came, was exclusive – "No gentlemen permitted."

On 10 August Colonel and Mrs. Miles came to tea with the Barcrofts at the Railway Hotel, Porton, and there were mutual regrets over the coming parting. A week later, M. A. B.'s last Sunday there, she and J. B. had a very pleasant tea at the Commandant's house at the Camp, and the next day she had a letter from Surgeon-Commander A. Fairley, R. N., saying that Professor Cameron and he and others wished to give the Barcrofts a parting

[1] Apart from the direct connections via Porton, J. B. was a member, according to *Who's Who*, of the Army Medical Directorate Consultative Committee and of the R.A.F. Medical Advisory Board, though the duration of these memberships was not stated.

present. "We called," he wrote, "on behalf of all Sir Joseph's colleagues in the Physiological Department. His departure will leave us all with rather sore hearts as we will miss not only his inspiring leadership, but also a great friend." M. A. B. slipped off that week to Nantwich for a rest, but was back on 27 August to supervise the large amount of packing – a lorry was expected to call that day for the numerous boxes and cases and to take them to London, whence another one would carry them on to Cambridge. In her diary she wrote, "How often we will think of these two years away, and of all the kind friends, and lovely walks in lovely country, and, as always, many blessings, for which we are truly thankful. Joe to-day wound up his Porton work of twenty-five years, and quietly slipped away after lunch there."

The official thanks came, if we may anticipate, about a month later in a letter written on 22 September by J. Davidson Pratt, of the Ministry of Supply, The Adelphi, London, W.C. 2. "My dear J. B.," he said, "I have been away on a few days' leave, otherwise I should have written sooner to convey to you my great personal regret and that of the Department that circumstances have made it necessary for you to sever your connection with Chemical Defence after such a long association, namely, twenty-four years in all. You have already heard at the Chemical Board and at the Physiological Sub-Committee the appreciation which all your colleagues feel for the admirable work which you have carried out over all these years and for the stimulating and genial atmosphere which you have always brought to the discussions. We shall miss you very much indeed but we hope that we shall be able to see you at least from time to time."

On 2 September, to revert to the chronological order, J. B. and M. A. B. learned, to their great joy and relief, that a pied-à-terre had been found for them in Cambridge – a friend had engaged rooms for them at Mrs. Watson's, 1 Cranmer Road. Two days later they went on board *The Duke of York* and had a smooth crossing to Belfast, whence they went on to Shandon Guest House, Ballymore, County Donegal, where Henry and Biddy, plus their two children and an Austrian nannie, were already installed. Nearly a month full of much joy, laughter, and happiness followed, and we may perhaps extract two particular items from M. A. B.'s diary. There was no black-out and Micky, the younger grandson, who had never seen windows with curtains undrawn after sundown, called out on one of the first evenings, "Mummy, come and see the dark colour outside." The second note is that on 21 September, a lovely day, the four adults went up the Hill after breakfast and J. B. gave a preliminary reading to the other three of his forthcoming Belfast lecture, "A gas attack. What to do, and when to do it."

Henry left for Cambridge on 25 September, and four days later his parents said goodbye to Biddy and their grandchildren and left for The Glen, Newry, where they stayed for three days. On 2 October they went on with Mollie Barcroft and Muriel Richardson to Belfast, where Dr. Edholm joined the party at tea. Then they proceeded to the Whitla Medical Institute, where J. B. gave his lecture to the largest audience of doctors that the hall had, apparently, ever held. It seemed to give much satisfaction. After it, J. B. and M. A. B. went on to Dr. Hilton Stewart's house, where they stayed awhile before embarking for England.

Soon they were installed in No. 1 Cranmer Road, Cambridge, "in two charming attic rooms." They rejoiced to see King's College Chapel again and were pleased with the "welcome back" that they received from so many friends. J. B. was also delighted with his new prospects, and M. A. B. acted as his voluntary Secretary, "always awaiting instant dismissal", as she wrote, "for my many mistakes, but his patience is inexhaustible!" At any rate, they much enjoyed their work together in the laboratory, and on 18 October it was the venue for the inaugural meeting of the English group of the Nutrition Society, and for its first scientific meeting, which was also the first English meeting. At the inaugural meeting Sir Frederick Gowland Hopkins, who had first lectured on nutrition at Guy's Hospital a half-century earlier, gave a brief retrospect of the subject, and the Hon. Secretary read messages of goodwill from seven American workers, and from the Biochemical Society, the Physiological Society, and the Royal Society of Medicine. At the afternoon session of the scientific meeting "Clinical signs of dietary deficiency" in man and animals were discussed, and J. B., as Chairman, summed up. He "referred to the present status of laboratory methods in the diagnosis of deficiency disease and recalled a similar position which arose after the introduction of such diagnostic aids as the electrocardiograph by Mackenzie and Lewis. Clinicians were at first sceptical as to their usefulness, but this was mainly because the apparatus was costly and the technique specialized. He felt that laboratory methods in the study of malnutrition would soon reach a state of recognition and applicability comparable with that subsequently enjoyed by the technical methods used in cardiology. As far as the question of the separate study of the various nutritive factors was concerned, he felt no apprehension that this would detract from a proper study of malnutrition as a whole. He looked forward to the time when enough was known about nutrition to construct a completely synthetic diet."

On 22 October Sir Charles Sherrington, looking somewhat frail at eighty-three, looked in on the Barcrofts at the laboratory. At the end of the month they received from their friends at Porton, with best wishes for their continued happiness, the gift of an antique English tea-pot of the Chinese Chippendale period (1783). The friends in question were Professor Cameron, Squadron-Leader Watt, R.A.F.V.R., Dr. Phillips, Surgeon-Commander Fairley, R. N., Major Sadd, Group-Captain McClurkin, R.A.F., Professor Gaddum, K. Harrison, Dr. Fildes, Lieut. Colonel Walker, R.A.M.C., Dr. Boyland, Surgeon-Commander Vey, R. N., Lieut. Colonel Bamford, R.A.V.C., H. L. Green, Captain Short, R.A.M.C., H. Garnett, Captain Blount, R.A.V.C., Professor Lovatt Evans, Major R. Rabinowitch, Dr. Courtice, Surgeon-Commander McIntyre, R. N., Lieutenant Somerville, R.A.M.C., Professor Sugden, A. F. Childs, Surgeon-Lieut. Commander Foss, R.N.V.R., Captain Steadman, Dr. Douglas, Surgeon-Lieut. Commander Guild, R. N., Captain Curwen, R.A.M.C., W. D. Seaton, and Mrs. Humphrys. On 8 November J. B. and M. A. B. attended service in King's College on the occasion of the visit of H. M. King George of the Hellenes to receive an honorary degree from the University. Lydia Lopokova, wife of J. M. Keynes, Fellow and Bursar of King's, was present in national costume, and many were touched by the anthem, "Blow out you bugles, over the rich Dead!", the words of which had been written in the first world war by Rupert Brooke, Scholar and later Fellow of the College.

On 15 November the *American Journal of Anatomy* published a paper by Barclay, J. B., Barron, Franklin and Prichard, which was entitled, "Studies of the foetal circulation and of certain changes that take place after birth", and which can be regarded as in some respects an extension of the paper published by Barclay, J. B.,

Barron and Franklin in 1939. It had been drafted by Barron, and somewhat amended by Barclay, Franklin and Prichard, who had done more work, in the absence of J. B. and Barron, in the 1940 and 1941 seasons. Presumably it served some particular purpose of Barron rather than of J. B. and the Oxford team, so there is no need to analyse it here.

On the same day M. A. B. wrote that "Work in the labs has its strenuous moments when letters and interruptions seem to pour in, but Joe seems to think it all very light work when compared with his Porton days." A week later she stated that "The room in the labs is now nearly quite settled," and three days later again that "Our life together in the labs is very pleasant and each day I become more accustomed to typing, and help Joe more effectively." During the month J. B. was re-examined by Professor Ryle, who gave his reassuring verdict, "I find it difficult to find anything the matter."

Early in December Japan, which had been our enemy since late July, attacked the United States with a corresponding reaction on the part of the latter. A few days later Dr. O'Brien, of the Rockefeller Foundation, came into the labs. He had just returned from the States and, whereas before depressed by the fact that America had been neutral, was now all smiles because she had taken her place beside Great Britain and the Dominions and other co-belligerents.

About this time the Barcrofts had news that Robbie's first book had been accepted for publication; apart from being an efficient horseman and cavalry officer, he had discovered a flair for writing; for long he had been known as somewhat of an artist, and he was in the future to illustrate, as well as write, a number of books. About this time, also, but on the graver side, visits were received from Mrs. Hunt (widow of J. B.'s first-war colleague, Dr. G. H. Hunt) and her younger daughter Jill, who were very anxious about the elder daughter, Margery, and her husband and baby in Hongkong. With the Christmas Day news of the surrender of that city, the anxiety reached an even higher pitch, and it was to be months before definite information became available.

No abrupt change in J. B.'s manner of life marked the end of the year 1941, but that seems a fitting point at which to close another Chapter of this biography, for by that time he had given very great and strenuous service – almost too great for his age and physical condition – to this country in its war effort, and had thereafter settled down in Cambridge to a new form of work which, while exercising fully his unimpaired mental ability, had lessened to a manageable degree the strain upon his physical powers. It remained for him and M. A. B. to become re-established in their own home at No. 13 Grange Road, but that was not to be for some time yet, and for the moment we must leave them living rather courageously, for people of their age, in two attic rooms in someone else's house – apart from that, co-operating finely and happily in J. B.'s room in the Physiology Laboratory.

CHAPTER X

1942–1944

Among the good wishes which J. B. received for the New Year were those of Professor W. W. C. Topley, Secretary of the Agricultural Research Council, who also wrote:- "Everything that matters has to be done by people who know far more than I do about the problems concerned, and the A. R. C. will succeed only if it can obtain the help and interest of people like Keilin, Harington and yourself. I'm feeling very comfortable about animal physiology, and a few other things look like going well. . . . One of the things that are still bothering me a little is the way we work our standing scientific committees. I'm sure we've been too bureaucratic and civil-servicey about it all. The sort of thing that really works is your informal ruminant digestion conference, not a lot of little sub-A. R. C.'s with agenda and minutes, and the right to examine and criticize programmes and grants. However, that's a personal view and one must watch one's step in a world of vested interests."

In view of the above, it is of interest that J. B.'s Animal Physiology Unit held a symposium in the labs on 5 January, that fifteen persons attended, that Sir Charles Martin took the chair in the afternoon, and that all went very well. Later in the month, through the mediation of Professor A. V. Hill, J. B. had an interview with Mr. Robert Hudson, the Minister of Agriculture, and found that the latter shared his views about the drying of meat and milk, especially the latter. Early in February the Minister wrote to J. B., commenting on the excellence of his tinned products.

At the Hampstead meeting of the Physiological Society on 14 February J. B.'s first publication of the year was in evidence. It was a communication, by himself and Barron, on the "Circulation in the placenta of the sheep." The weight of the cotyledons was greatest about the twelfth week of gestation, and the cause had been found to be the formation of great masses of foetal tissue histologically similar to the Wharton's jelly of the cord. These masses tended to disappear from about the fourteenth week onwards, leaving their vascular coverings. Towards term, owing to rearrangement of the foetal and maternal vascular elements, conditions for the exchange of materials between mother and foetus became less favourable than they had been somewhat after the beginning of the last third of gestation.

On the last day of February the second scientific meeting of the Nutrition Society took place in the London School of Hygiene and Tropical Medicine. The topic was "Food production and distribution in relation to nutritional needs", and J. B. summed up at the end of the afternoon session. Inter alia he said, "The dominant note of the meeting has been an urge to action, a desire to do something useful. The machinery of the Society ought to be elaborated to crystallize the views of each meeting and place them at the disposal of the appropriate authorities. This is desirable because Government Committees are made up of *selected* people but, in a democratic assembly such as The Nutrition Society, it is open to anyone, be he farmer, vitamin expert, or any other kind of specialist, to state his views. Each member of the Society has some specialized corner of experience or knowledge and, for that reason, machinery should be set up for getting their views into a form accessible to those responsible for policy."

On 19 March he attended the memorial service for Sir William Bragg, which began at 12 noon in Westminster Abbey, and ten days later M. A. B. wrote in her diary:- "Our lives seem to move faster and faster in many ways. J. B. very busy, here, there, and everywhere. He is spending a week-end at Hammersmith for the study of how the infant first breathes, and this work is what he likes extremely, and is to be the subject for his Linacre Lecture on May the 6th."

April saw the publication of his Belfast lecture of 1941 under the title, "Gas attacks: what to do and when to do it", and late in the month came the pleasant news that Robbie was now a temporary Lieutenant-Colonel. J. B. himself continued to be very busy with his further studies of the foetus, and with preparations for the Linacre Lecture, which was in the gift of St. John's College, Cambridge. He had thought that the audience might be a small one, but long before the lecture began people began to pour in and by 5 p.m., the hour of commencement, the room was packed. The Master of St. John's gave a gracious welcome to J. B., who replied suitably and then lectured for an hour, after which he projected a film in illustration of his talk. The subject of the latter had been "The onset of respiration at birth" and it did not contain much new material, to judge from the abstract published later in the *Lancet*. We can therefore content ourselves here with reproducing the opening passage and the closing sentences. In the former J. B. said that "The inspiratory effort is an event so dramatic as to have stamped itself on the imagination of the idealist as the earnest of a new vital principle; to the realist the first breath is the necessary initiation of life in a new environment. To quote the words of Dr. D. H. Barron: 'When an animal is born and begins its struggle towards an independent existence, its first efforts are those of breathing. Breathing is living; the onset of respiration is the beginning of life.' If I may figure the first breath as a chord struck on an instrument, I may divide a consideration of the subject into some description of the instrument itself, and some investigation of the impact upon it." The closing sentences of the lecture were: "Such then is the picture that I draw of the onset of respiration at birth. Perhaps it is too much to claim even that it is a picture; rather I regard it as a blocking out of one, for a lifetime might be spent in filling in the details."

On the last day of May the Nutrition Society held its fifth Scientific meeting, again this time at the London School of Hygiene and Tropical Medicine. The topic was "Problems of collective feeding in war time", and Lord Woolton, the Minister of Food, was the first speaker. J. B. summed up after the afternoon session, and said, "Lord Woolton expects the Nutrition Society to help him. He certainly can rely on us doing this in every way possible. Today's discussions have shown how it can be achieved."

Three weeks later he went north to Edinburgh, Aberdeen and Ayr in connection with his duties for the Agricultural Research Council and the Food Investigation Board. In Aberdeen he gave a demonstration on the dehydrated foods with the preparation of which the Low Temperature Research Station at Cambridge had been occupied, and it was in every way most successful. From Scotland he went south to Penrith, where M. A. B. joined him on 27 June. They went on to Cockermouth, and on the Sunday morning attended the Friends' Meeting and found it restful and helpful. After three weeks' holiday in Lakeland, during part of which they were joined by Henry and John Barcroft, they were back in Cambridge on 18 July, and a week later J. B. read a paper on "The utilization of desiccated foods" to the Nutrition Society at its sixth scientific meeting. This meeting was in fact a joint one, the other party to it being the Food Group of the Society of Chemical Industry. The venue was the British Medical Association House in Tavistock Square, and the general topic "Dehydration of foods and the effect on their nutritional value." At luncheon between the morning and afternoon sessions members sampled some of the dehydrated foods which they had been discussing.

Sir Edward Appleton, Secretary of the Department of Scientific and Industrial Research, opened the meeting and said that the papers to be read and discussed would deal with work carried out as part of the programme of the Food Investigation Board of his Department; the experimental part had been conducted at the Low Temperature Research Station, Cambridge, at the Torry Research Station, Aberdeen, and also at the Dunn Nutritional Laboratory, Cambridge. He further noted that, when the Food (Defence Plans) Department had been formed in 1937, it had at once sought the assistance of his Department in solving a number of problems. Also, on the outbreak of war, the Food Investigation Board, under J. B.'s chairmanship, had generously decided to subordinate its own programme on the wider aspects of food processing to matters connected with our food supply in time of war.

The next day was J. B.'s seventieth birthday and in the evening, at No. 1 Cranmer Road, Dr. Wynne, aged eighty-one, made a touching speech, after which he and the other residents drank J. B.'s health in port. On the four following nights Cambridge suffered from air-raids, but J. B. and M. A. B. had agreed that it was wisest to remain in bed on such occasions, thus avoiding the wear and tear of getting up and sitting downstairs without sleep for two to three hours. There were more raids early in August, and on one night J. B. and M. A. B. broke their rule, and watched from the latter's window while a German plane was caught in three searchlight beams and nearly hit by an anti-aircraft shell. The noise all around was terrific and the whole place was brightly illuminated by flares dropped by the enemy.

On 19 August J. B. left London for Aberdeen, where he arrived the next day, visited the Macaulay Institute, and stayed overnight with Sir John Orr at the Rowett Institute. For dinner he drove about fifteen miles to the house of Major Keith, a member of the Agricultural Research Council; also present were Sir Robert and Lady Gregg, the former likewise a member of the Council, and in addition a Director of the London, Midland and Scottish Railway Company – he said that the Company was beginning to be interested in nutrition problems. On 21 August J. B. went on to Inverness and on the next day to Dingwall, whence he drove over some of the most beautiful parts of the Highlands to see cases of cobalt deficiency in sheep. He visited five farms belonging to collar-and-tie farmers farming some thousands of acres each. "I feel an awful humbug," he wrote, "going about talking to these people, but the cobalt treatment has done a lot for their pockets and evidently it is a great thing for a real live member of the Agricultural Research Council to visit them. To-day [23 August] I bought six lambs on one of the farms – four sick with cobalt deficiency and two not." They were to go to Cambridge with cobalt-deficient food enough to keep them while Dr. H. K. F. Blaschko studied them. From his Highland run-around J. B. returned to Dingwall, whence on 25 August he moved on to Gleneagles Hotel, Auchterarder. The next day that hotel was the locale of the seventh scientific meeting (third Scottish meeting) of the Nutrition Society, the topic being, "Food supplies in relation to human needs. Part 3. Signs and symptoms of deficiency diseases." About two days later J. B. was back in Cambridge.

During the same month a short note from him, from Barron (now at the University of Missouri), and from Forsham (now at Harvard Medical School) was published in *Science*. It was entitled, "The blood pressure in the umbilical vein of the foetal sheep," and stated that pressures measured by them just before the war all lay between 10 and 18 mm. Hg., and that, in foetuses of approximately equal age, the lower venous pressure was always concomitant with the higher pressure in the umbilical artery, suggesting that the variation was due either to the degree of resistance presented by the placental vessels or to the distance from the foetus of the point at which the pressure was measured.

The next item of interest is that on 15 September H. M. King Haakon of Norway and H.R.H Crown Prince Olaf visited the Low Temperature Research Station at Cambridge and afterwards lunched at King's College on dehydrated foods cooked by the College chef, who was afterwards presented to the King. The crême brulée made of dried milk was described as a dream! Others present were Sir Edward Appleton, Secretary of the Department of Scientific and Industrial Research, Mr. E. Barnard, its Director of Food Investigation, Mr. A. Fjeldstad, Norwegian Minister without Portfolio, Colonel Nordlie, A. D. C. to the King, Captain R. Dormer, His Majesty's host, Dr. L. J. Harris, Director of the Dunn Nutritional Laboratory of the Medical Research Council, Dr. H. Hunter, Director of the Plant Breeding Station, National Institute of Agricultural Botany, Lieut. Colonel Ostgaard, A. D. C. to the Crown Prince, Mr. J. A. McGillivray, of the Ministry of Agriculture, Lieut.-Commander Smith, English Attaché, Mr. Ystgaard, Norwegian Minister of Agriculture, F. L. Engledow, Professor of Agriculture, Cambridge, J. B., Professor J. H. Clapham, Vice-Provost of King's, and finally a member of the party who was unaccounted for and whom J. B. named *S. H. Addow* on the supposition that he must be the King's private detective!

A week after this J. B. and M. A. B. received the happy news of the birth of a third grandchild, Sarah Agnes Barcroft. From that we pass on to 15 October, when a paper by J. B. and Barron appeared in the *Journal of Comparative Neurology*, describing their "Observations on the functional development of the foetal brain." It extended previous ones on the behaviour of normal foetuses and foetuses with brain lesions, and localized more precisely the brain regions essential for the specific aspects of the foetal activity. The features studied had been the development of respiratory movements and the development of the righting and postural reflexes in sheep foetuses, and the results demonstrated that with respect to these the brain developed functionally from behind forward. On 16 October J. B. lectured on "Ventilation" at "The Arts School", and the next day he took part in the eighth scientific meeting (fifth English meeting) of the Nutrition Society in the London School of Hygiene and Tropical Medicine. The general subject was "Trace elements in relation to health", and J. B. opened the discussion with a plea for a more precise definition, if temporarily only an experimental one, of the term "Trace element". His first suggestion was that a trace element should usually be a metallic one, fluorine and iodine being exceptions; his second suggestion was that it must be something which actually operates in the organism. Thirdly, he said, the element must be present in the right amount, mischief arising in some cases through excess, in others through deficiency. Fourthly, it must be present as a trace and tentatively he defined that as not more than one part in twenty thousand in the organism. Fifthly and lastly, the action of a trace element should be essentially that of an enzyme.

On 3 November he and M. A. B. crossed overnight from Heysham to Belfast; M. A. B. was to stay in Northern Ireland for a fortnight, but J. B. went on to Dublin, where on 5 November he lunched at Trinity College, and at 4.30 p.m. lectured on "Dried foods" to the Royal Dublin Society, and explained the reduction in cargo space made possible by dehydration of foodstuffs. Showing his audience small circular tablets, he demonstrated how they could be transformed into a substantial meal of stew, cabbages, and carrots. A small white tablet which he said had been assembled five months ago in Australia and which had travelled through the tropics without refrigeration became in a short time a jugful of milk which looked and tasted perfectly fresh. These foods, he insisted, were not substitutes but were every bit as good as the commodity which was processed. The cubic space occupied was reduced in the case of meat to one sixth, of fish to about one ninth, of vegetables to one tenth, of eggs to one tenth, and of milk to one eighth (with a keeping time of ten months). Potatoes, however, were difficult to process bacause of certain chemical substances which they contained.

That evening he dined and slept at Trinity College. The next day he went on to Newry, and on the following one left Belfast en route for Castle Douglas. On Monday, 9 November, he visited areas in Kircudbrightshire, and went on thence to the Hannah Dairy Institute (c/o Norman Wright), and to Glasgow, where he was the guest of Professor Geoffrey Fleming. On the Wednesday at 4 p.m. he gave the Finlayson Memorial Lecture, on "Phases of foetal life", at the Royal Faculty of Physicians and Surgeons, and a day or two later was home again. The phases which he described in the lecture were those of the trigeminal, pontine, mid-brain, and just pre-natal foetus, and in addition to the main story he included a new section on the development of vascular reflexes, noting that the cardio-inhibitory centre was active before birth in the lamb, though not until after birth in the rabbit.

There are two more publications of 1942 which need to be mentioned. One, which was by Barclay, J. B., Barron, Franklin and Prichard, appeared in the November number of the *Journal of Physiology* and was on the "Pulmonary circulation times before and after functional closure of the ductus arteriosus." It gave the results of an analysis by the Nuffield Institute team of records obtained during the seasons in which it had been associated with J. B. and Barron, and the subsequent ones in which it had carried on alone. The results were that in mature sheep foetuses the average pulmonary circulation time was 2.7 seconds, and that after functional closure of the ductus arteriosus this time was reduced to 1.4 seconds.

The other publication appeared in the Michaelmas Term number of the *Cambridge University Medical Society Magazine*, and was entitled, "Respiratory patterns at birth". It described the different ways in which babies commence pulmonary respiration at birth, and was based on J. B.'s short experience at the British Postgraduate Medical School at Hammersmith earlier in the year. Three obvious patterns had appeared, namely, the rhythm, the single prolonged inspiration, and the gasp, and J. B. noted that cyanosis was associated with the second, and markedly so with the third type. With his more detailed knowledge of the developments in the sheep foetus, he was able to explain the rhythm and the gasp, but there was no parallel for the second pattern. "Speaking generally", he concluded, "we may say that the type of respiration pattern is contingent upon the sensitivity of the nervous system at birth, that this sensitivity is affected either by anaesthetics or by asphyxia, the higher parts being more readily affected than the lower ones; and that the more normal the condition of the brain, the earlier respiration will appear, and the more normal will be the respiratory pattern; while the greater the degree of asphyxia, the greater the abolition of function in the higher parts of the brain, and the greater the approximation to gasping in the respiratory pattern."

On 25 November J. B. was invited to join the B. B. C. Brains Trust on 7 December, but he declined as he felt that his mind was not sufficiently 'slick' to do it justice. Early in December M. A. B. listed in her diary his various activities, and readers may be interested in the result. He was Head of the Unit of Animal Physiology of the Agricultural Research Council; a member of the Council itself; a member of the Council of the Department of Scientific and

Industrial Research; Chairman of the Food Investigation Board of that Department; Chairman of the Sub-Committee for the study of lactation; Chairman of the Publications and Programmes Committee of the Nutrition Society; Chairman of the Managing Committee of the Low Temperature Research Station; and member of the Church Patronage Committee and of the Estates Committee of King's College. For a septuagenarian that was no mean list!

On 9 December *The Times* published a letter from him on the international aspect of freedom from want, and the need for a world survey. On Christmas Eve he and M. A. B. attended the service in Kings's College Chapel, and on Christmas Day itself, after a visit to the laboratory, they met Mrs. Hunt and her younger daughter and drove out with them to their house at Great Shelford, where they had a very happy time, and whence they returned on foot to Cambridge. At the Christmas dinner at No. 1 Cranmer Road in the evening the others present were Dr. Wynne, Colonel and Mrs. Phillips, Colonel and Miss O'Brien, and Mrs. Woodley, and the dinner and the friendly atmosphere were much appreciated by M. A. B. and J. B. Living in someone else's house, however, was no adequate substitute for living in their own home, and they were already thinking of returning before long to No. 13 Grange Road. They realized, on the other hand, that they would have to live on the ground floor and to let the upstairs part and, indeed, were awaiting the architect's plans for the conversion. On the very last day of the year J. B. received a telegram of New Year's greetings, sent by Professor Propper-Graschenkov on behalf of the Institute of Experimental Medicine, Moscow; it wished him the "best of health and active work for the welfare of civilised mankind."

On 12 January 1943 Dr. Franklin Kidd, Superintendent of the Low Temperature Research Station, wrote to J. B.:- "Your letter of the 28th December, 1942, which I have circulated for the staff to read, was an extremely inspiring one, to me personally, and to all of us. I should like you to know that we feel that we owe a great deal to you for the unfailing confidence you have had in us, and for your skill in 'putting over' our results. As you know well we have had our moments of frustration, and at these times I personally have found great comfort and support in your confident courage."

Outside such matters of work, J. B. and M. A. B. continued to discuss returning to No. 13 Grange Road, and on 21 January they wrote to the Mother Superior saying they must regain possession on 17 March. Mention of the house is a reminder of how greatly they prized the garden behind it, and it is not out of place to note that Buttress, who had worked in it so faithfully for so many years, retired about this time and was succeeded by Moore.

The sixth English meeting of the Nutrition Society took place in the London School of Hygiene and Tropical Medicine on 6 February, with "Nutrition in pregnancy" as its topic. J. B. spoke on "Nutritional functions of the placenta", and his talk was so attractive that one would like to give it in full. He began as follows. "The title assigned to me does not offer an easy problem. Taken strictly it may be questioned whether the placenta has any functions in the active sense, or whether as Needham (1942) thinks it is merely an ultra-filter. If it is merely an ultra-filter, then the fundamental processes on which the nutrition of the embryo is based must reside in the mother or in the foetus or in both. The only role which the placenta could play would be the blocking of this or that material which might be injurious to the development of the foetus, for it is obvious that everything necessary for the development gets through. In spite of much that is said about the efficiency of the placenta in this or that mammalian species, the fact remains that, judged by the resulting foetus, they all seem equally efficient. The sheep, for instance, compared with man, produces a foetus at a higher stage of development, equally large and in a shorter time. The horse yields to no animal in the efficiency of its offspring at birth; it is alleged that a foal which Dr. Hammond desired to weigh at birth, promptly ran away, and was only caught with great difficulty. If, therefore, we find that the efficiency of the placenta in species A appears on one count, such as, for instance, the reduction in the layers which form the placental barrier, to be greater than that of species B, it behoves us to examine whether, in species B, there is not some other factor which enhances the efficiency in that species.

"There are three questions to which I should like to be able to give answers:

1. What role a placenta plays with regard to each important material which passes across it.
2. How these roles can be and are upset.
3. What troubles would supervene in the case of such impairments.

Frankly I cannot do this. While a great deal is known about the placenta, very little is known about the meaning of all this information. Thus, the placenta is known to harbour a vast population of chemical substances the functions of which, if indeed they have any, are a matter of sheer conjecture. Let me commence by saying something about the formidableness of the placental barrier." And so on!

His final sentences were as follows. "It will have been evident from what has been said, that oxygen is the element to which the placenta seems to present the most formidable barrier and, as a further proof that the possibilities for the foetus of getting oxygen are almost exhausted at birth, there is the fact that, in the rabbit, the blood emerging from the uterine vein becomes increasingly reduced as pregnancy proceeds, till, at term, it is almost devoid of oxygen. The opinion to which I am being forced is, that the size of the foetus is limited largely by that of the placenta, more particularly by that of the placenta as a barrier to oxygen. What it is, however, which limits the size of the placenta is still a question."

A few days after this meeting M. A. B. was planning in greater detail the return to No. 13, and was hoping that Mrs. Giles, late of Emmanuel College, would be the tenant of that part which was to be leased. It was presumably in view of the forthcoming move that J. B. secured the services of a new secretary, Mrs. Cobblestone, who began work on 2 March. Possession of No. 13 was regained a fortnight later; the Mother Superior allowed Sister Clair to stay on and help M. A. B. settle in; J. B. was away during the process, and he and M. A. B. in any case were to wait a while before actually taking up residence. In the meantime, the joy of the garden beginning to undergo its spring transformation was a continuous thrill to M.A.B.

Nature of 13 March contained a very interesting letter from J. B., Rachel McAnally and A. Phillipson on the physiological action of acetic acid in living tissues. Volatile acids had been found to be produced in large amounts in the sheep's rumen, and some at least of them, preponderantly acetic acid, had been present in considerably greater quantity in the blood coming from the rumen and large intestine than in that coming from the other parts of the alimentary canal. Acetate added to Ringer's solution perfused through the isolated heart of the rabbit had disappeared at about the same rate as glucose had originally disappeared from Ringer-Locke's solution, and the acetate had had some merit under the conditions obtaining in the authors' experiments as the heart had beaten for four to six hours on the acetate-containing solution compared with not more than two hours on the acetate-free one. Investigations were proceeding to see whether or not the acetic acid was oxidized but, whatever its fate might be, the fact that it did disappear opened wide fields for speculation.

On 22 March word was received that Robbie, with the rank of Captain, was off to more active war service than had hitherto been his lot; three days later J. B. attended a luncheon, given by the Duke of Norfolk at Claridge's to various people with farming and allied interests; then on 4 April, at long last, he and M. A. B. went back to full residence at their home, and the latter noted in her diary the rapture they experienced at seeing their belongings round them once again.

There are no other relevant items in respect of April, and in respect of May there are but three, delight at the news of the liberation of Tunis on the 8th, attendance by J. B. at the seventh English meeting (subject: Nutrition in infancy) of the Nutrition Society at the London School of Hygiene and Tropical Medicine on 22 May, and a journey by him to Edinburgh on the evening of that day. A month later, on 20 June, he left for a longer visit to Scotland, beginning with the Torry Research Station, the Department of Physiology of Marischal College, and the Macaulay Institute for Soil Research, Aberdeen, then spending a night with Major James Keith at Udny, Aberdeenshire, and finishing on 23 June at the Rowett Research Institute, Bucksburn, and once more the Torry Research Station. After travelling south overnight, he was kept busy in London another four days before returning to Cambridge.

On 1 July, under the rota arrangements in force, his services as a member of the Agricultural Research Council came to an end, and later in the month he received a letter of thanks from Sir John Anderson, Lord President of the Council. It read as follows. "I know well how deep an interest you have taken not only in problems of animal nutrition and physiology, but also in every aspect of veterinary science. May I say how fortunate we count ourselves in that you are continuing for the present to give to the Agricultural Research Council service, which I and my colleagues particularly value, as the first Director of the Unit of Animal Physiology which the Agricultural Research Council have established at Cambridge . . ."

At some time during July an article by J. B. on "The preservation of food" was published in *Nutrition Abstracts*; in the middle of the month he went off with M. A. B. to Blakeney for a fortnight's holiday; thence he travelled on to Bristol for a week in connection with his veterinary work. Soon after his return, M. A. B. was without domestic help, and she recorded in her diary the daily programme which she carried out at the age of sixty-eight! It began with "Rise about 7 a.m. Go down, open up the house. Finish dressing. Call J. B. at 7.30. Then prepare breakfast, usually about 8.5 or 8.10. Afterwards J. and I make his bed." Thereafter, except for an hour's rest after luncheon, she was busy until after dinner in the evening. Wives do not always get all the mention they should in biographies of their husbands, and it seems only right to mention that J. B.'s freedom to pursue his scientific work was due in no small measure to the domestic devotion of M. A. B., carrying without complaint the extra burdens imposed upon her by war-time conditions.

Shortly after the onset of September the outlook for the allies changed markedly for the better with the surrender of Italy, and the prospect of a successful outcome seemed measurably nearer; certainly, there was a very definite uplifting of spirit everywhere and a hope that the remainder of the struggle would not last too much longer.

On 7 October representatives of the Press visited the Low Temperature Research Station and were welcomed by J. B. in his capacity as Chairman of the Food Investigation Board of the Department of Scientific and Industrial Research. He explained that this Department and its sister bodies, the Agricultural Research Council and the Medical Research Council, all came under the Committees of the Privy Council, and that each was responsible for research on foodstuffs. The Agricultural Council was concerned with research on growing crops, on livestock, and on such livestock products as milk and butter; the Food Investigation Board dealt with such products after they had left the farm; and the Medical Research Council, in particular Dr. L. J. Harris of the Dunn Nutritional Laboratory, made drastic tests of the farm products after these had been treated by the Food Investigation Board. The work of the Board was carried out at three centres, fish being preserved at the Torry Research Station at Aberdeen, fruit at the Ditton Laboratory near Maidstone, and other articles at the Cambridge Low Temperature Research Station. During the last three years the work of these stations, in accordance with the special needs of war-time, had dealt almost entirely with refrigeration, and with that up to the point of producing really satisfactory articles on the scale of a few tons each. After that stage had been reached in each case, the problem of production on the "cargo scale" had passed to the Ministry of Food.

On the ground that the proof of the pudding was in the eating, the visitors were regaled with a luncheon of reconstituted desiccated products. It consisted of roller dried soup; shepherd's pie, potatoes, carrots and cabbage; stewed blackberries, plums, Allington pippins and custard; kippers on toast; and coffee. J. B. claimed that all the items were as wholesome and tasty as the original materials from which the dried products had been made, and the guests agreed his claim.

The following day was very definitely a red-letter one, for on it the B. B. C. announced the award to J. B. of the Copley Medal, the highest in the gift of the Royal Society. Sir Godfrey Copley, who had been elected a Fellow in 1691, had founded and endowed the annual award, but it was not until 1731 that the first recipient was chosen. J. B. was away from Cambridge on the day of the announcement, and returned to find a large collection of congratulatory letters and telegrams awaiting him.

The gold medal and silver replica were not to be presented to him until the last day of the month, and four days before that he had a difficult task to perform, namely, to lecture on "The preservation of foods by drying" at the Royal Institution, London. The difficulty lay not in the talk itself, but in the fact that it had to be illustrated by the making of a shepherd's pie from dehydrated meat, powdered mashed potatoes, and dried onions, all under the critical gaze of about a hundred members of the opposite sex. The lecture is available in print and there is also a contemporary account of the cooking which states that "Everyone's mouth watered. Sir Joseph looked at his pie with something amounting almost to affection. Women leaned forward. 'Now', he said heartily, looking at the clock and the cookers, 'we will put on the pie a layer of block potato.'

There was a shout, 'The pie – its gone!' 'Oh!', exclaimed Sir Joseph. The pie had been whisked away by an over-zealous attendant . . . There was the sound of running feet, and a panting attendant burst in, bearing aloft the missing pie. He had been overtaken in time. Cheers burst out. At the end of a fascinating lecture, most favoured to sample its flavour voted it the finest pie ever made. The women crowded round it. Sir Joseph stood modestly in the background. His pie had disappeared once before. Now it disappeared forever."

We pass from that lighter interlude to the serious business of 30 November. M. A. B. went up to London with J. B., but she lunched with Lady Dale and her party at Brown's Hotel, while J. B. lunched at the Royal Society, sitting at a table for ten with the President (Sir Henry Dale), General Smuts, Major Attlee, Sir John Anderson, Lord Woolton, the High Commissioners for New Zealand and for India, and the recipients of Royal Medals, namely, the Astronomer Royal and Professor Bayley.

After luncheon the ladies joined the gentlemen and proceeded to the Hall, the President arrived and the proceedings commenced with routine business. Then the President announced the award of the Copley Medal (applause) and gave a very pleasant résumé of J. B.'s scientific career. We cannot reproduce it in full here, but we can quote the beginning and the end, which read as follows. "The researches on the respiratory function of the blood, in respect of which this highest of the distinctions in the Society's gift is awarded this year, have occupied a central position in Barcroft's lifework. Their record is one of steady purpose and unbroken progress over a period of some forty-five years . . . In a preface to his book, Joseph Barcroft finds a connexion between what he learned in sailing boats and what he has done in research. We may think of him, perhaps, as one whose instinct and aptitude have led him to venture as an explorer beyond visible horizons, rather than to sound remoter depths of theory in seas already known. Such a thought would place him in a long tradition of this Society, in company with such great students of the respiratory function as Boyle, Hooke, Mayow and Lower among our earliest Fellows, and, of those who over the centuries have received this Copley Medal, with Stephen Hales and Joseph Priestley and, most intimately of all, with John Scott Haldane, who received it nine years ago. Barcroft's work, like Haldane's, of high scientific merit in itself, has extended its influence far beyond the laboratory over a wide range of the beneficent and creative activities of mankind at peace, and now again, for the last time let us hope, to those imposed by the dire compulsion of war. We rejoice to know that in him the hunger for knowledge is still unsatisfied, and that he is still sailing his craft towards new horizons."

When the President had finished, J. B. went up the steps onto the platform, and Sir Henry presented him with the Medal, a large envelope containing the announcement, and a small one containing £35 (loud applause). Returning, J. B. placed it all in M. A. B.'s lap, and she had just time to peep at the Medal before Sir Henry began about the next recipient of an award. Thereafter came the Presidential address, and then dinner for J. B. at the Royal Society while M. A. B. went off to stay with her sister-in-law, Gwen Ball.

Before leaving 1943 we have to notice one further publication, namely, a communication which J. B. and I. Maureen Young, of Bedford College, gave to the Physiological Society at its meeting on 27 November. It was on the "Oxygen in the blood emerging from the brains of post-mature foetal rabbits". The extension of gestation had been effected by administration of prolan and progesterone, and blood samples had been taken from the cerebral venous sinuses by intracranial puncture. The authors found that "During the period of post-maturity the oxygen saturation of the blood deteriorates progressively, the oxygen capacity rises up to the 34th day. The foetuses therefore pass through a period of moderate anoxaemia (which may well contribute to respiratory activity) to reach one of profound anoxaemia and ultimate death. The placental mechanism for the supply of oxygen appears unable to keep up with the foetal growth."

The first notes for 1944 are that J. B. went off to Hammersmith on 16 January to make further studies of newborn babies at the Postgraduate Medical School, and that on 22 January he, McAnally and Phillipson gave three communications to the Biochemical Society at its meeting at the same School. They had studied the formation of volatile acids from cellulose in the alimentary canals of the horse, rabbit, pig and sheep. There was no marked production of such acids in the stomach of the first two, but there was in that of the pig, and particularly in that of the sheep, where the rumen and reticulum were extra sites of fermentation processes – the acids disappeared before the glandular portion of the stomach, styled the abomasum, was reached. In the small intestines of all four species there was usually no significant formation of acids; in the caecum, however, there was a high production, with progressive fall thence along the rest of the large intestine. In the blood leaving the large intestine of all four species the concentration of volatile acids was higher than in the blood circulating elsewhere, and the same was true of the blood coming from the stomach of the pig and from the rumen, reticulum, and to a less extent the abomasum of the sheep. Proof of the possibility of direct absorption from the rumen of lambs was provided by insertion of the radiopaque medium, sodium ortho-iodo-hippurate, into a rumen from which all other exit paths had been surgically barred. The substance was found radiographically in considerable quantity in the bladder, and iodine was detected in the urine. The lining of the rumen, like the skin, was of stratified epithelium, but the corneous layer was thin, and the general mass was similar to the water-permeable Malpighian layer of the skin. The third communication elaborated the acetate heart-perfusion experiments already mentioned in the 1943 story, and summarized all three papers in the following words. "The communications just given amount to a complete metabolic scheme, starting with cellulose and perhaps other carbohydrates, carried out by organisms in the gut which engender volatile acids, principally acetic and propionic; these in turn are absorbed into the blood and disposed of in at least one organ, the beating heart. The proportion of carbohydrate metabolized in this way is in the herbivora important enough to make this scheme rank alongside other metabolic patterns." A contemporary view of its importance will be given later in this 1944 story.

The day before the Biochemical Society meeting J. B. had been much saddened by the news of the sudden death in office of Professor Topley, F. R. S., at the age of fifty-seven. He had been Professor of Bacteriology and Immunology at the London School of Hygiene and Tropical Medicine from 1927 to 1941, when he had been appointed Secretary of the Agricultural Research Council. An obituary notice appeared in *Lancet*, i, 198, and a letter from J. B. which was published in the same journal on 12 February added further appreciation of Topley's work from one who had been so closely associated with him.

In March it was announced that the Royal College of Obstetricians and Gynaecologists was to confer its honorary Fellowship on J. B., and Sir Charles Sherrington wrote from Gonville and Caius College, offering his congratulations on "an outstanding compliment. You have founded a new line of enquiry, and they recognize that . . ." On the day that Sir Charles penned his letter, 16 March, J. B. was in Belfast, where at 8 p.m. he gave a lecture-demonstration in Queen's University on "Foods of the future". The demonstration technique was similar to that which he had used in 1943, i.e., a cottage-pie was prepared from dehydrated foods, cooked, and at the end divided into samples for the audience to taste; this time, however, his daughter-in-law, Biddy, acted as his chief assistant. One of the enthusiastic audience wrote afterwards:- "It is a long time since I have listened to such a delightful, instructive and entertaining lecture. For one thing I heard every word which I seldom do in lectures . . . Sir Joseph spoke without notes, clearly, fluently, and with amusing little sallies of wit . . . The applause was loud and long." From Belfast J. B. went south to see his relatives, on the night of 19 March he stayed in The Woodhouse, Bessbrook, with his cousin, John Richardson, and on the evening of the next day he lectured in Newry Town Hall under the title, "A Newryman reports". The lecture was fortunately published in the local press and, as it gives J. B.'s own retrospect of his life to date, supplements in certain respects the account given in this biography, and is also most attractive reading, it is reproduced here in full.

"Tonight", he said, "I feel like a boy who had been too long away from home ('mitched', I think, is the word), and now on his return was met with the stern interrogation: 'What have you been doing with yourself all this time?' The justice of the question is obvious. A town is but a larger family, and it would be a sad day for a family or a town if the components of either ceased to regard themselves and their fellows as 'members one of another', and to be interested in one another's doing.

"The interest is mutual and, for my part, I would much rather spend an hour in hearing about Newry than in talking about myself, for in some ways Newry has changed very much within my memory, and in others it is much the same. A great many things have gone. There were three large and important flour mills. There were at least four important spinning concerns from which troops of mill-hands debouched at dinner-time. There were two large timber firms, and the quays by the canal were piled high with wood. There was the salt works, a clay-pipe factory, a foundry, which served for much of the southern portion of Ulster. There was the Newry Mineral Water Company and, I think, more than one firm of blenders who provided whiskey for the local mineral waters – though not on the same terms as business was conducted at a place at which I once found myself on the River Zambesi – there they made soda water out of the river water and sold it at fabulous prices for the necessary purpose of diluting the whiskey, which they gave away. I may say I did not sample the whiskey either before or after its dilution. But to return to Newry. There was a Member of Parliament for the Borough as well as for the County; indeed, at that time The Glen and everything south of the river was in County Armagh. There was the modest fleet of the Dundalk and Newry Steam Packet Company, and at some time a steamer of great antiquity, called the *Robert Burns*, which belonged to the Salt Works. The Albert Basin and the canal were full of shipping, Norwegian barques wintered in Newry and, lastly, there was a wealth of mud, even in Hill Street. Now many of these things are gone or reduced to a fraction of their former dimensions, and I would like to know what has taken their places, for Newry today, though possibly a little less populous, presents a much more thriving appearance.

"It has spread out in all directions: the mud has gone. No one walking up High Street to-day would know it for the slum of fifty years ago. Whence this apparent prosperity? It is true that the shipping turns round faster and, therefore, does not clutter up the quays. It is true that as I go about the world I get an occasional thrill from the sudden vision in some alien harbour of a little steamer with a red, white and blue funnel bearing the name of some tree on her bow, and I say the families of those men in that boat probably live in Bridge Street. Yet the mystery is not completely explained and, as I say, I should prefer listening to the explanation than talking of myself. But in other ways this flux of people and things has not changed Newry. On a winter's day, if you look across at Camlough Mountain from the old Belfast Road you will see two sunsets on the same afternoon; still when you cross the canal at Dublin Bridge your eyes will wander to Carlingford Mountain and, if you are so minded, you will say to yourself: 'I will lift up mine eyes unto the hills from whence cometh my strength', and your imagination will wander to the Lough. For my part, fate having taken me to many of the spectacular harbours of the world, I am glad to think that I learned to love Nature, clothed in her gentler garments, 'where the Mountains of Mourne sweep down to the sea.'

"But now to the task set me of giving an account of myself. You will not want a rehearsal of the trivialities of the routine life of a University Professor, though these together with similar occupations in the lower rungs of the academic ladder have filled up most of my time. More interesting will be such excursions as have added truer knowledge of the subject which I professed, namely, the function of the human body.

"This, too, in a sense, started in Carlingford Lough. Believe me, education is not the accumulation of facts and the assimilation of vocabularies; it is the cultivation of the qualities of mind which God has given us. One of these, in my case, was the urge to break out from that hill-girt stretch of water to navigate in my own little boat the tides and channels beyond Greenore, to find myself on the open sea and thence to cast my eyes on what was beyond the visible horizon. This was the natural urge of youth which my wise parents, perhaps remembered by some here, did nothing to discourage, knowing that it was the highest form of education.

"And all that urge in later life, by an easy and natural process, transformed itself from the material sphere of boats and mountains and waterways to the intellectual sphere, the pursuit of new knowledge of abstract matters – abstract, though often with an important practical bearing. Here, by way of parenthesis, let me say that throughout forty years of married life, my wife, herself the daughter of a famous astronomer, has supported my intellectual excursions with no less sympathy and understanding than did my parents in the matter of boats and sailing. The material basis of all the higher forms of organised life is combustion. Just as the fire produces its heat or the motor its power by the oxidation of fuel, so the body accomplishes all its manifold tasks from climbing stairs to solving mathematical equations on a basis of the oxidation of food. Begin thinking about almost anything and you very soon want to know on what scale it is taking place, and so it happened that I got caught up in the problem of food which had to be oxidised in order to produce a given result, in order to climb the stairs, in order to think out something difficult, in order to digest something tough, and so forth. At the very commencement it was how much oxidation was necessary to produce saliva. Truly a most singular topic, but even that brings back a conversation which always mildly amuses me. I will tell you. One way in which the world, or at least my world, seems to have changed, and, I think, changed for the better, is that religion seems now to be less a matter of 'don'ts' than it used to be. I never now meet anyone who tells me that God will size me up on a yardstick of whether I do or do not smoke, but in those days it was otherwise, and one good man took me to task for the use of tobacco. He told me that it was bad for me and, when I asked him to go into a little more detail, he told me the excretion of saliva occasioned by my coquetting with the pipe was a wholly unwarranted strain on my system. I did not argue the point with him, but I was able, for my own satisfaction, to calculate, and I suppose just then I was the only person in a position to calculate, what that strain was in terms of the amount of food which had to be oxidised to make good the loss. This I estimated as being the equivalent of a piece of ham considerably smaller than a waistcoat button. In those spacious days of unrationed food that did not seem to be anything so great as to convince me that my pipe should be put by – though actually it has been on other grounds. Well, I went round the various organs of the body in this way, or many of them, calculating how much oxygen they needed to do their job, and interesting enough it was to me, but I conceive that it would be very boring to you. I will say no more than that, having made these calculations, which meant about ten years' work, I commenced to ask myself what would happen if the various organs of the body could not get the oxygen they required. You know what happens if a motor can't get the oxygen requisite for the efficient combustion of the petrol; it ejects black, oily stuff and makes a most unpleasant smell as well as using more petrol, and it loses power. Well, what about the body?

"Actually the starting point of this particular interest was an invitation from a German Professor to go and study the matter on the Peak of Teneriffe, which is some 12,000 feet high. I should, perhaps, explain that to go up a high mountain or to make a balloon ascent is one of the ways to deprive yourself of oxygen for, as the atmosphere proves rarer, so you get less oxygen in each lungful of breath which you inhale. Well, to go back to my German friend, I very soon found that behind him there was a German of another type who was, in a sense, the business manager of the expedition. I was given a hint that I should consult the Foreign Office about going – this was some years before the war of 1914. The Foreign Office said: 'Oh yes; we would prefer you to go,' and some more besides. How well I remember setting out one dark and cold Sunday night at the time of year in a stopping train from London to Southampton. How well I remember sitting opposite the business man, who fixed me with his eyes and dangled German decorations and all sorts of things before me if the expedition was a success, and looked at me as much as to say, 'What mugs these English are!' I, on my side, felt sufficient of a humbug, for I naturally did not reveal that the Foreign Office had said they would prefer me to go – and other things. Well, from the point of view of the business manager, the expedition was not a success, because the friend who asked me to go was a very honest man and would not lend himself to any statement that the place to which we went on the mountain was highly desirable as a resort for the cure of consumption. It was highly successful from my point of view, because I found out a good deal about what happened to the blood of persons who were deprived of the amount of oxygen which they needed.

"Other expeditions followed to the Alps and to the Andes, at which I learned a great deal more. Speaking broadly, the upshot of all these expeditions was to add to an interest in the effect of oxygen-want on the body, a greater interest in the effect of want of oxygen on the mind.

"But let me say a word about the body first. One of the ways in which want of oxygen shows itself is that the blood in its passage through the lungs fails to acquire its natural bright-red colour, and this shows itself in the general colour of the more delicate parts of the body. My mind goes back to the journey which I once made from Lima, which is near the sea level, in a train up the Andes to an altitude of about 16,000 feet. This journey was accomplished between seven in the morning and one in the afternoon. You could see the altitude telling on those in the carriage by looking at the skin under their nails, which got bluer and bluer as the ascent continued. But the most striking example was when we came down. We lived in the Andes among a marvellous set of men – engineers operating very up-to-date copper mines up in the mountains. I grew very fond of these people, but life is very monotonous up there, and life is a strain, all of which leads in some cases to the same troubles as elsewhere. Well, there was one man in the mess who had an extremely purple face, for which reason we were most careful in our conversation to avoid the subject of alcoholic excess as being untactful, but we did the man a gross injustice. Unknown to us, he came down in the same train as ourselves, and when we saw him at Lima his face presented the beautiful pink coloration of a child. His trouble was merely the delicacy of his skin, through which the purple colour of the blood circulating underneath made itself unusually evident.

"And now about the mind. At that altitude on the world's surface people's minds play strange tricks. Sooner or later everyone's mind commences to deteriorate if they go high enough, but the form which that deterioration takes depends on the person, and on how fast they go up. Someone in America has accused me of saying that if you go up rapidly you present symptoms rather similar to those of alcoholic excess, and if you go up slowly you suffer from symptoms not unlike those of industrial fatigue. By rapidly I mean in minutes or hours, as you might in an aeroplane; by slowly, I mean in days or weeks as you might if ascending to some high mountainous region. I cannot remember having made this profound remark, but actually it is not very far from the truth. For experimental purposes, it is often easier, instead of actually making the ascent to the rare strata of the air, to put the person into a chamber from which the air can gradually be pumped. And I must say that, in experiments of this sort which I have seen, the victim has behaved in a curiously alcoholic manner. He often becomes garrulous and tends to repeat himself over and over again, loses his sense of responsibility and, finally, at a sufficiently high altitude, he has a 'black-out' and loses consciousness.

"All this has a very direct bearing on flying, for which reason, if the crew of the aeroplane are going beyond a certain height, they must breathe oxygen if they are to retain their faculties, and clearly in war the force which can give its pilots the best equipment in this respect is the one which will attain the highest altitudes, and be at a corresponding advantage. I said that a man penetrating to an ever-increasing altitude lost his sense of responsibility. In this connection it used to be the practice of the Air Force – I do not know whether it is now or not – to make any pilot who was going to a high altitude commence breathing oxygen at a quite low level. They did not allow him to put it off until he reached an altitude at which the oxygen was actually necessary for fear that by the time that consummation occurred the man would have so far lost his judgment as to be unaware of his need.

"And now to pass to slow ascents, such as the would-be climbers of Everest perform. If the ascent is slow enough a considerable degree of adaptation takes place. No one could suddenly be transported to anywhere near the height of Everest and remain conscious, but by going slowly, acclimatising each day a little, it is possible to climb to somewhere near the top of the highest peak on the globe; indeed, it would be possible to exist there if only the climber had not to face the extra strain of climbing.

"But this all tells on the mind, too. It takes different people in different ways. Like overworked individuals, they tend to become temperamental, not to say quarrelsome. When I look back to the days in which I was responsible for a party of workers in the Andes, one of my pleasant reflections is that I never heard any one of them say a hard word. I can give them no greater praise. Ultimately the want of oxygen in the rare air tells on the body, too, but it tells on the mind first. For instance, the mining colony in the Andes used to play lawn tennis. We commented on the fact that the tennis was of a very gentle character, what at college we would have called 'pat-ball', and we asked, 'Have they not got strength enough up here to hit the ball harder than that?' 'Oh yes', was the reply, 'but the difficulty is to control its direction.'

"And so with many other things. You can do them, but at an excessive cost of mental energy. I was told that the officials of the Copper Corporation where we were could write a difficult report as well more or less up there at 15,000 feet altitude as down at the sea level, but it meant a fortnight's holiday afterwards to get over the strain.

"Well, to go to other matters. When people are confronted with an entirely new situation, something outside the range of experience, they very often have to go for advice to those who have worked from first principles. So it happened that when the British Army was confronted with gas in the last war, their medical authorities scraped together the few persons who had a back-ground of work on the theory of respiration – myself among them. This started an interest which lasted until about a couple of years ago, when it seemed that research on food was of more immediate urgency than research on gas, but that period saw the whole evolution of the gas-mask, ending with the supply to a whole civilian population of respirators, in my opinion, of sufficient efficacy to make the use of gas by the enemy not worth while. And then there have been other activities in which not only I have taken a part, but also the neighbourhood of Newry. When first A. R. P. was set going, there arose the question of the efficiency of the Anderson shelter. I can see with my mind's eye a great stretch of flat land on the East Coast of England. In the centre was fixed a large bomb; all round it at varying distances were Anderson shelters, and in each was a goat. When all was set, and the bomb ready to detonate, we went away about half-a-mile and hid behind a wall waiting for the explosion. The crash came, and we returned to find the goats blinking away. After that experiment I think Sir John Anderson felt pretty easy about his shelters. But what has this to do with Newry? Well, in the East of England it is not so easy to pick up goats. So I told them to consult my son, who is a Professor in Queen's University, as to whether he could advise the Home Office where to get goats, and after the experiment was over, I saw the receipt for the animals, and was thrilled to see the name 'Rooney' on the heading.

"How well I remember that The Glen Fields, in my youth, had been let to Mr. Rooney, and I imagine that the goats came from his successors.

"In the ten years before the war my scientific interests drifted into, perhaps, a rather curious line. Going round nearly a whole circle, I told you that I started by measuring the amount of oxygen which the various organs of the body use, and now I was to measure the amount of oxygen used by the developing animal from the time of its conception till that of its birth. I very soon found that I was faced with the same old problems. If opportunities for getting oxygen placed at the disposal of the growing organism are strictly limited, it is, as you might say, rationed by its mother, but proportionately as it grows it is needing more and more oxygen and, therefore, like the man on ascending the mountain, it is getting to a point at which it must either get out into the air or be suffocated. Nature has brought matters to a very fine point, the creature gets out, but not before it has to do so. For the last two years I have been working at food. During the height of the submarine campaign particularly, it was necessary to develop methods by which the greatest possible amount of nourishment could be packed into the smallest possible space and be reduced to the least possible weight. In war-time many of us have had to undertake work which is far removed from our ordinary interests. In that sense I do not regard my interests in transporting nourishment as being a part of my scientific career, and, therefore, having said my lesson, I will now ask to 'get down'."

There are no items in respect of April 1944 until we come towards its end, when J. B. went up to London to be presented with the honorary Fellowship of the Royal College of Obstetricians and Gynaecologists; this is perhaps a suitable place, when one has not the exact commencing date, to note that he was Chairman of the College's Nutrition Committee from its inception to his death. The official visitors on 29 April were Sir Henry Dale, President of the Royal Society, Lord Moran, President of the Royal College of Physicians of London, and Sir Alfred Webb-Johnson, President of the Royal College of Surgeons of England. After a buffet luncheon at the College's house, 58 Queen Anne Street, the ceremony commenced at 2.15 p.m., and J. B. was allowed ten minutes in which to express his appreciation of the honour done him and to say a little about a phase of his work, previously selected by the President of the College, Dame Louise McIlroy; the one which she had chosen was the condition of the foetus in prolonged pregnancy.

During May, in collaboration with McAnally and Phillipson, he published in the *Journal of Experimental Biology* longer accounts of the absorption of volatile acids from the alimentary tracts of the sheep and other animals, and of the absorption of sodium ortho-iodo-hippurate from the rumen of lambs, and in the same number McAnally described the technique for the determination of total volatile acids in blood. As the accounts were merely fuller ones and did not add significantly to the essentials already given above, we can dispense with a précis here. On 20 May J. B. attended the eleventh meeting of the Nutrition Society in the London School of Hygiene and Tropical Medicine. The topic was "Budgetary and dietary surveys of families and individuals. Part 2", but J. B.'s only contribution was to interpose at one point with a practical suggestion anent a certain provision for research. Four days later he went off to Belfast again, this time on some government work for the Ministry of Agriculture; he was back in Cambridge within a few days.

June 6, Invasion Day, with all its significance, is one that must be mentioned even in a biography such as this, otherwise we shall be in danger of forgetting the national and international background against which the personal drama is set. With that due remembrance made, however, we can pass on to July and record two items. The first of these can be given in J. B.'s own words, contained in a letter to Henry, which read:- "I am embarking on a new venture as Chairman of a Committee of the A. R. C. to overhaul the whole field of animal nutrition, some field!" The second is that in relation to the work of the Royal Commission on Population, the Medical Research Council appointed a Committee under J. B.'s chairmanship to consider problems of the physiological aspects of human fertility. A co-ordinated programme of experimental research under its direction was, in the event, initiated during the remaining stages of the war.

On 10 August he and M. A. B. left for their summer holiday, which they enjoyed partly in Worlaby House, a King's College farm in Lincolnshire, and partly in the Shandon Hotel, Ballymore, Northern Ireland.

On 3 September J. B. went north to Edinburgh and on the evening of 5 September he assembled a party in the North British Hotel for what turned out to be a fascinating discussion on aspects of farming. The others present were a first-rate practical farmer, the A. R. C.'s own research people, and Professor Scott Watson, who had recently undertaken the educational activities of the Ministry of Agriculture. Writing to M. A. B. in the train to Aberdeen the next morning, J. B. said that the talk had probably repaid the country the whole expenses of the trip even if they never presented a report at all. He added, more personally, that he had lost all the tired feeling he had been troubled with during the previous week and was now very fresh and well. In Aberdeen he was to look round the Rowett Institute that afternoon, next morning to hold a meeting, and next afternoon to drive to Montrose, visiting a farm en route.

On 8 October, about which time Cambridge was again being troubled with nightly alerts, he set off for a round trip to London,

Weybridge, Shinfield, and Compton. About the middle of the month his five-year membership of the Advisory Council of the Department of Scientific and Industrial Research ended. Late in the month he went to Leeds to give the inaugural address at the beginning of the winter session of the Medical School. He then journeyed on to Edinburgh to give the same talk, on problems of foetal life, to the Royal Medical Society of that city, also to speak to the Royal Society of Edinburgh – of which he had recently been made an honorary Fellow – on "The microflora of the alimentary canal." In this paper he considered the microflora (1) as providing a basis of food for the individual, (2) in relation to vitamin synthesis, and (3) as agents for the digestion of carbohydrates. The utilization of volatile acids considered as food made a fourth section. In between the two Edinburgh engagements he paid a visit to Castle Douglas and inspected areas in which "pining" was present. On the last day of October he was at the Torry Research Station, the next morning at the Rowett Institute, and that evening on the night boat from Glasgow to Belfast. On 2 and 3 November he was at The Glen, Newry, and he also called at The Woodhouse, Bessbrook; then he had a few days with Henry in Belfast and returned home.

The next items are about two short publications which were dated 25 November. One of these was a communication to the Physiological Society by J. B. and G. Popják on "Lipids in maternal and foetal blood-plasma in sheep." The results, the speakers said, were not necessarily applicable to all mammals, but in the sheep the foetal blood curves ran, more or less parallel to the maternal, at a third to two-thirds of their level. The relationship suggested, without proving the point, that the lipids passed through the placenta and were disposed of in the foetus, either by storage or otherwise, at a considerable rate. The second publication was a letter to the Editor of *Nature* from J. B., J. F. Danielli, W. F. Harper, and P. D. Mitchell on "Wharton's jelly considered as a conducting path." It gave some initial findings, but finished with the statement that "Further research is required to ascertain how far this non-vascular pathway in the cord is of importance in the foetus."

There remain two more events of the year to which reference should be made, and the first is that on 5 December J. B. addressed the Student Christian Movement at Newnham College. The manuscript was found among the papers at his bedside after his death and was published in the *Lancet* of 22 December 1951 under the heading "Christianity and Medicine". Those who read it and who are unacquainted with J. B. except through the medium of his scientific communications will find another aspect of his personality revealed, or in part revealed, to them in the article in question.

The other event was that on 30 December he attended the twelfth English meeting of the Nutrition Society, which took place at the London School of Hygiene and Tropical Medicine, and had for its general topic, "The nutritional role of the microflora in the alimentary tract." J. B. himself gave a paper on "The utilization of volatile acids", and this and other contributions from his Unit inspired Dr. J. Stewart (of the Moredun Institute, Gilmerton, Midlothian), who was the first speaker in the subsequent discussion, to say that "In the papers we have just heard . . . findings important enough to change all textbook theories of ruminant digestion have been described." There is no need here to give the gist of that latest version of the new story, for we have already had the essentials of it in the early part of the 1944 narrative. It was, however, a considerable triumph for the comparatively recently established Unit of Animal Physiology to have elicited such praise for its research results, and it showed that in and around J. B. the faculty for noting the existence of a problem, together with the readiness and technique to tackle it, and the flair for bringing the investigations to a successful conclusion, remained unabated despite the fact that the leader of the team was now two past the psalmist's threescore years and ten.

The point seems an appropriate one at which to end another Chapter. We have seen J. B. in reminiscent, retrospective mood at Newry in the earlier part of 1944. We see now that he was then wrong in concluding that his main scientific life was past: in the next Chapter we shall see how he continued it vigorously up to the last.

CHAPTER XI

1945–1947

In January 1945, apart from posts already mentioned, J. B. held the Chairmanships of the Nutrition Survey Group of the Agricultural Research Council, of the Physiology Sectional Committee of the Royal Society, of the English Committee of the Nutrition Society and of its Survey and Educational Sub-committees; he was also a member of the Council of the Veterinary Trust and the representative of the Royal Society on the Council of the Royal Veterinary College. As if all that were insufficient, he was preparing five lectures on foetal life for delivery in the Cambridge Medical School, had fifty ewes under way to provide material for about five months' foetal studies, was envisaging making a film on foetal life for the British Council, was busy with a chapter for Marshall's book on *Reproduction*, was planning the filming of human foetuses at the West Middlesex Hospital, and observations on the human foetal pulse at the London Postgraduate Medical School. Finally, he was continuing the preparation of the book, begun while at Porton, which was eventually to appear as *Researches on Pre-Natal Life*.

His first publication of the year, a longer account of his work with Maureen Young on the "Internal oxygen environment of the brains of post-mature rabbit embryos," appeared in January, and was summarized as follows. "Litters of post-mature foetuses have been produced in rabbits by the injection into the mother of 100 i.u. of chorionic gonadotrophin and 5 mg. of progesterone on the 25th day of pregnancy, confirming the work of Snyder. The foetuses grew on the average from about 45 g. to about 80 g. between the 30th and 36th days. The largest foetus obtained was just over 100 g. The placentas underwent no commensurate alteration in weight. Indeed, it is doubtful whether there was or was not any growth of the foetal placenta after the 31st day. The oxygen saturation of the blood from the posterior fontanelle of the brain fell from the 25th day onwards, and by the 35th day blood from this situation was on the average only 17 % saturated. The brain therefore during the days of post-maturity was subject to an atmosphere which imposed an ever-increasing stringency in respect to oxygen. The active intra-uterine respiratory movements which occurred at this time could reasonably be attributed to the degree of anoxia obtaining though our experiments do not offer rigid proof that this was the case. It would be reasonable, also, to attribute the ultimate death of the foetuses to asphyxia."

On 24 February he attended the thirteenth English meeting of the Nutrition Society at the London School of Hygiene and Tropical Medicine, but did not make any significant contribution to the proceedings. The topic was "Factors affecting the nutritive value of bread as human food."

Thereafter there are no details of his activity until July, and in the interval a great change had come over the national and international picture. On 23 April the 'dim-out' which for some time past had replaced the 'black-out' followed its predecessor to an unregretted demise, and everyone's spirits lightened. Then, on 8 May, VE Day at last arrived; from 8.30 to 9 p.m. that evening salutes to H. M. The King occupied the B.B.C. programme, and then came His Majesty's own address to his peoples on the memorable occasion. The following day, 9 May, was the official date of the termination of the war in Europe.

Reverting from such happenings to more personal ones and passing forward a month or so, we have next to record two publications by J. B. The first of these was on "The microflora of the alimentary canal", and it appeared in the June number of the *Proceedings of the Royal Society of Edinburgh.* The second appeared in the July number of the *Journal of Endocrinology* and was entitled, "The preparation and biological effects of iodinated proteins. I. Introduction." J. B. had written it in 1944 as Chairman of the Agricultural Research Council's Conference on Lactation. The first experiments showing that the feeding of dried thyroid gland to cows produced an increase in milk secretion had been made in Canada in 1931, and in 1934 and 1935 it had been shown, at our own National Institute for Research in Dairying, that subcutaneous injections of thyroxine were also active. Unfortunately, neither technique was suitable for general use on the commercial farm, but later studies by other researchers had led to the suggestion that

58—Sir Joseph and Lady Barcroft in their 'office' in the Physiology Laboratory, Cambridge, September 1942

59—Informal group, photographed at the rooms of the British Council, 1946, of some of the members of the International Nutrition Conference

Facing page 319

iodinated proteins might prove satisfactory, and as from 1942 work had been carried out by Dr. A. S. Parkes and others. J. B.'s task at the Conference had been to introduce the team which had co-operated in the investigations; thereafter its members had detailed the results to date.

On 13 July he and M. A. B. set off on their summer holiday, going first for a short while to Worlaby, where they had been in 1944, and then via Belfast to Cushendun, County Antrim; Belfast was gaily decorated for the visit of Their Majesties and H. R. H. Princess Elizabeth. The holiday party at Cushendun included Henry and his family, and they were all together until 7 August, when J. B. and M. A. B. left for their thirty-hours' journey home.

While they had been away, the General Election had taken place, and with the victory of the Socialists Winston Churchill, the great architect of victory, had resigned from the office of Prime Minister. About the time of J. B. and M. A. B.'s arrival back in Cambridge, the first atomic bomb was dropped over Japan, and at midnight of 14–15 August that country surrendered. Officially, 14 August was the date of termination of the war in the Far East, while the next day was celebrated as VJ Day; the surrender terms were signed on 2 September.

On 15 September there occurred an event of much interest to J. B. in view of his family background as described in Chapter II of this biography. The event in question was the Bessbrook Centenary, which was commemorated by the visit of a distinguished company, and by the publication of a short, but interesting, volume about the origin and development of that social experiment in a village community. At 1.15 p.m. Their Excellencies The Governor of Northern Ireland and the Countess Granville arrived at the Town Hall, Bessbrook; at 4.45 p.m., with the official business over, they, the Prime Minister of Northern Ireland, and other distinguished guests had tea at The Woodhouse; at 5.30 p.m. they left. The Woodhouse, as readers will remember, was the home of J. B.'s cousin, John Richardson, one of the Managing Directors of the Bessbrook Spinning Company, Limited, and J. B. had visited him there in 1944.

Six days after this J. B. and M. A. B. partook of a dinner given by the Adrians in the New Guest Room of Trinity College. The occasion was a farewell party to Dr. and Mme. Cordier, who had fled from France some years earlier. On 27 September J. B. left to visit Dr. Tidcombe and thereafter to take part in the Physiological Society meeting at Oxford. He spoke on "The range of weights of foetal sheep at various ages." The foetuses which he had weighed had been the offspring of Welsh ewes and an unspecified ram, and the weights at term had ranged from 7.6 down to 1.8 kg. As that great diversity had appeared only after 130 days, and was not shown in the crown-to-rump length (i.e., in bone), J. B. suggested that "some foetuses falter in the growth rate of some at least of their soft parts."

In October there were visits to Cambridge by Professors Hoet of Louvain and Krogh of Copenhagen. On the last day but one of the month, M. A. B. was delighted to get a telephone call from Margery, elder daughter of Mrs. Hunt of Great Shelford; it will be remembered that this daughter of J. B.'s first-war colleague, Dr. G. H. Hunt, together with her husband and child, had been in Hongkong at the time of its surrender. On the last day of October J. B. went to Oxford to hand over to Blackwell Scientific Publications, Ltd., the script of his new book on pre-natal life. As we have already mentioned, its preparation had been a part-time occupation for J. B. for some years; he had recently been toiling hard to get it finished, frequently breakfasting at 7.45 a.m. in order to get a little extra writing-time into his heavy curriculum.

There are no notes for November, and those for the next month begin with the statement that on 10, 11, and 12 December J. B. delivered the Harben Lectures at the Royal Institute of Public Health and Hygiene, London. The overall title was "The respiratory function of the blood," the individual lectures were on "The usefulness of haemoglobin", "Man under conditions of stress", and "The transition from placental to pulmonary respiration", and the chairmen were respectively Sir Edward Mellanby, Dr. J. Browning Alexander, and the Right Hon. Colonel Walter Elliot, President of the Institute.

In the first lecture J. B. made three main points:-

"(1) Haemoglobin, by reason of its solubility and the great amount of oxygen with which it can unite, has made the warm-blooded creature possible."

(2) Haemoglobin, by reason of the nature of its union with

oxygen, has made respiration as we know it possible in warm-blooded animals.

(3) Haemoglobin, or rather the haemoglobins, by reason of the diversity in detail of their chemical compositions, spread their function far beyond those of pulmonary respiration and constitute a major factor in adaptation of living organisms to their environments."

In the second lecture he said that "The performance which man can 'put up' under conditions of extreme stress depends in some instances upon the capacity of his blood to absorb gases, notably oxygen, and appropriately to transfer them to their ultimate destination. I shall consider then life under conditions approaching the lowest barometric pressure at which man can function, which divides itself into –

(*a*) Performance under conditions of sudden oxygen want as in aeroplane ascents.

(*b*) Under conditions of chronic oxygen want as in the Andes where populations exist up to 16,000 feet or more and in the Himalayas where the limit of human existence appears approximately to be reached,

and I shall also enter into some comparisons between these conditions and others, such as exercise, poisoning with asphyxial gases, 'black-out', etc."

On 12 December he introduced his third subject as follows. "The present lecture deals with the transition from intra-uterine life to that of the free individual, in so far as that transition is concerned with the respiratory function of the blood. The problem which Nature has to face is the following: to establish an organism which can at once carry on an existence of rather limited activity within its mother's womb, and yet can at once – in a few seconds or minutes – become detached from all its former sources of nourishment and face the shocks of an existence in the outside world. To have solved this problem with so small a percentage of failures seems to me to be no mean achievement."

It would be pleasant, but it is scarcely possible, to enlarge here upon the above brief indications of the contents of the three lectures. We can, however, fittingly find space for the last passage of the third one, which read:- "Dr. James Young was kind enough on one occasion at the London University Unit at Hammersmith, to let me watch ten babies being born in order that I might endeavour to ascertain whether this picture, built up from Caesarean sections in the sheep, had any counterpart in human births. Out of the ten cases, one was an almost perfect example of the type of which I have just spoken. There was no cyanosis, hence the blood was well oxygenated, and as soon as the head was thrust upon the world, a rather shallow normal respiration established itself. At the other end of the scale were the most cyanotic foetuses – those in which the oxygen in the blood was most depressed. They did not breathe at once. 'In that most exciting 70 seconds of physiology', you held your breath to see whether they would breathe at all, whether they would live or die; in time the breath came and it was a typical gasp – the dying foetus in its last effort had opened the door to life and a free existence, to me always the most dramatic achievement of the Respiratory Function of the Blood."

In the same month, December 1945, J. B. and Barron published an article on "Blood pressure and pulse rate in the foetal sheep." The pressure had been measured by a new method, styled the needle method, which applied to the umbilical artery gave readings progressively lower, from about half-term onwards, than did the mercurial manometer method applied to the carotid artery. The authors gave reasons for preferring the needle method readings. With regard to the pulse rate, they had found that this increased up to 70–80 days, and thereafter decreased. After double vagotomy, however, there was progressive increase up to term. The pulse, therefore, in the normal foetus came more and more under vagus inhibition from 80–90 days onwards, and the authors gave details of their findings. The last two conclusions were that approaching term both the carotid sinus and cardiac depressor mechanisms were functional; and that lowering of the blood pressure as the result of stimulation of the central end of the vagus and with both vagi severed could be demonstrated late in gestation.

The last note for 1945 is also concerned with the functioning foetal cardiovascular system. Franklin listed lacunae still obtaining in the cineradiographic studies of the sheep foetus as follows:- (i) Recording of the placental blood-flow, if such was feasible; (ii) recording of the blood-flow through the cord, and timing of its cessation under various conditions; (iii) recording and timing of the cerebral circulation and of the blood-flow through the limbs. He discussed the possibilities with his colleague, Dr. A. E. Barclay,

Hon. Radiologist to the Nuffield Institute for Medical Research, and wrote to J. B. to see if the latter would collaborate in such further studies. On 19 December J. B. wrote agreeing not only the plan, but also the period – 25 April to 1 May, 1946 – during which it should be carried out. Unfortunately, in the event Barclay was ill in the spring of 1946, and J. B. died in the following one. So the further studies were not, in fact, made.

The first note about 1946 is that in January an article by J. B. on "The storage of food by refrigeration" appeared in *The Scottish Journal of Agriculture.* It was of considerable interest and practical importance, but we can confine ourselves to extracts from the last paragraph, which read as follows:- "For a previous number of this *Journal* I wrote an article on the preservation of food by drying; now I have written one on the preservation of food by cold. Looking into the future, the possibility may be foreseen of combining the two processes in that known as 'freeze drying.' . . Whether this process can ever develop into anything of value as a practical method only the future can tell; it may always prove too expensive, and perhaps impossible, to work on a commercial scale, for the products are very brittle. I concluded my article, however, with a mention of freeze drying because, whilst all methods of food preservation which add to the larder of the common man are interesting, those which hold a prospect of adding the purest and most nourishing commodities are most interesting of all."

On the last day of the month he gave a lecture, which was pronounced a great success, to the students at St. Mary's Hospital Medical School. In February a paper by Lorber, Lifson, Wood, and J. B. was published in the *American Journal of Physiology.* It was on "The metabolism of acetate by the completely isolated mammalian heart investigated with carboxyl-labeled acetate." J. B., McAnally, and Phillipson's earlier studies have already been mentioned, and Toenniessen and Brinkmann (1938) had reported similar findings during perfusion of rabbit's skeletal muscle with diluted blood. The summary of the new findings was that "Acetic acid, labeled with the mass isotope of carbon, C^{13}, in the carboxyl position, when administered as the sodium salt to the completely isolated, working mammalian heart, is readily converted to CO_2 as evidenced by the appearance of C^{13} in the respiratory CO_2." J. B.'s co-authors were in the Department of Physiology of the University of Minnesota

Medical School, and the collaboration of that Department in the experiments had been invited by the Agricultural Research Council in London. February 1946 also saw the publication of the first of J. B.'s Harben Lectures – the other two appeared in March – and in addition D. S. Torrens, of Trinity College, Dublin, was across during this month assisting J. B. in further work on sheep foetuses.

On 16 March Robbie and Betty Barcroft left Rangoon for England on S.S. *Ormonde*, and J. B. gave a lecture at the Royal Society of Medicine, presumably to the Section of Obstetrics, on intrauterine foetal movement. He projected a film made at the Isleworth, West Middlesex, Hospital in collaboration with Drs. Tidcombe and Dean. About two hundred persons attended, and after J. B. had finished some very complimentary remarks were made by the Chairman (Professor F. J. Browne), by Dame Louise McIlroy, and by others. It was in March, also, that J. B. finished his series of lectures to the Part II students at Cambridge, and after the last one Roughton said to him: "If in twenty-eight years' time I can stand up and give a lecture like that, I will be very proud." On 28 March the Barcrofts were saddened by the sudden death, while returning from London, of Sir John Clapham, who had been a schoolfellow of J. B. and later for many years, like J. B. himself, a Fellow of King's College; another Fellow, Lord Keynes, died on 21 April. Both J. B. and M. A. B. attended the Memorial Service for Sir John Clapham in King's College Chapel on 27 April, but M. A. B. alone was at the one on 4 May for Lord Keynes, for J. B., as we shall see, had to be in Ireland.

Offsetting this sorrow at the deaths of old friends was J. B. and M. A. B.'s delight at the arrival of Robbie and Betty in England on 11 April, and in Cambridge on 14 April. This biography has contained a number of references to Robbie, but inevitably Henry, with his career proceeding in the same scientific field as his father, has figured more definitely in the story. This may, therefore, be an appropriate point to recapitulate Robbie's story to date. He was born on 4 May 1909, and educated at Leighton Park – a Friends' school – and Christ's College, Cambridge. He was commissioned in August 1929, and after service with Skinner's Horse (Indian Cavalry) and the Indian Army Remount Department, was in Burmah for the last three and a half years of the campaign, and was mentioned in despatches. On 18 March 1939 he had (Chapter IX) married Betty Cartwright. If we may anticipate at this point the remainder of their joint story, the only child of the marriage, Anna Mary Hermione, was born on 9 September 1947, and all appeared to promise well. Tragedy, however, disrupted the happy family before another year was over, for on 1 August 1948 Betty Barcroft succumbed to illness at Nakenu, Kenya.

During April 1946, to revert after that digression, the last cooperative publication by J. B. and Barron (now at Yale) appeared in the *Anatomical Record.* It recounted "Observations upon the form and relations of the maternal and fetal vessels in the placenta of the sheep," such observations having been "made in a search for the structural basis of the precocious development of the cotyledons and for changes in the oxygen content of the fetal blood emerging from the placenta as gestation advances." The findings supported the following conclusions:-

"1. In the barren uterus the arteries extend toward the mucosal surface of the cotyledon and break up into capillaries which form a subepithelial plexus that is drained by capillaries and veins parallel to the arteries, though conducting in the opposite direction.

"2. Within the fetal villi, which extend from the mucosal surface of the cotyledon toward its depths, a central artery breaks up at the distal end into a superficial capillary net which drains into veins at the base of the villus.

"3. As a consequence of this arrangement the blood flows in opposite directions in parallel nets of maternal and fetal capillaries and the distance over which the flow is opposite but parallel increases as the length of the villi increases with advancing gestation.

"4. During the first three-fifths of the gestation period (total ca. 150 days) the fetal vascular bed and its supporting tissue – Wharton's Jelly – appear to reach their maximal development; the maternal vascular bed, destroyed in part by the invasion of the villi, expands very little.

"5. In the final two-fifths of gestation, the fetal vascular bed appears to remain unchanged; the Wharton's Jelly is reduced in volume and the maternal vascular bed increases steadily.

"The changes in the placenta of the sheep during gestation parallel changes in the degree to which the blood in the umbilical vein is saturated with oxygen. In the period during which the fetal vascular bed is expanding the saturation increases steadily to a maximum; thereafter it declines despite the apparent increase in the size of the maternal vascular net."

From 2 to 7 May J. B. was in Ireland, first in Dublin where on 3 May he delivered the John Mallet Purser Memorial Lecture at Trinity College, and then in Newry and Belfast. The Purser Lecture was on "Birth in relation to foetal development", and it integrated in interesting fashion observations on the rabbit, the sheep, and the human subject. At its end J. B. said:- "We have reviewed the development of mechanisms such as that of the eye, to which the fact of birth seemed to make little difference, mechanisms such as vagal tone which came increasingly into the picture as intra-uterine life proceeded and which in forms born in an immature state played no part in the economy of the foetus before birth, whilst in forms born in a mature state, they played so great a part that birth appeared to be almost a spring back. On the chemical side the richness of the blood in haemoglobin appeared to be in this category. We have reviewed yet other mechanisms which seemed to be developed but suppressed during intra-uterine life, only to spring into activity at birth, such as the respiratory mechanisms. We can give no general rule. Each phenomenon must be worked out on its merits, but the very impossibility of giving a general rule, to me, at all events, makes the study of birth more fascinating and the fact of birth more wonderful."

On 11 May J. B. and Torrens gave a communication to the Physiological Society, at its Cambridge meeting, on "The output of the heart of the foetal sheep." The detailed results cannot be reproduced here, but we can note that the output had been measured by a cardiometer luted with a special lute made of beeswax, paraffin and lanoline which, when warm, adhered to the tissues.

For some time before his visit to Ireland in connection with the Purser Lecture, J. B. had been troubled with pain in his right hip-joint, and it had become more acute a little while before he left for Dublin. Soon after his return he was examined by Dr. Nourse and the trouble was diagnosed as arthritis. It was to be an increasing source of disability in the future, but for one evening at least, soon after the diagnosis had been made, J. B. decided to forget his trouble, and on 16 May he and M. A. B. did what many of us would have liked to do; they went to London to see Tommy Handley and his company perform in the B.B.C. show, "It's that man again!" The arthritis – if we must return, as J. B. did, to that affliction – responded to some extent to massage and to deep X-ray therapy, but it did not, unfortunately, disappear.

On 15 June he and S. R. Elsden gave a communication to the Physiological Society at its meeting in King's College, London, on "The oxygen consumption of the sheep foetus." Carlyle (1945) had estimated the total consumption from determinations of the oxygen consumption of tissue slices, and the results from 112 days onwards had agreed very closely with those given by other observers for the intact and living foetus. J. B. and Elsden's new estimates, based upon the cardiac output measurements of J. B. and Torrens and upon the assumption that the flow through the placenta was half that through the heart, were, with one exception, substantially higher, expressed as O_2/kg./min., than those given by Carlyle's computation from tissue slices.

Late in June Robbie had to leave Cambridge and to sail in M. V. *Britannic* back to duty: Betty stayed on in No. 13 Grange Road. A week later, on 3 July, J. B. was in Oxford to take part in the Royal Empire Society's conference on nutrition, with special reference to problems of the Empire, but immediately after breakfast and before the conference began he slipped into the office of Blackwell Scientific Publications Limited to discuss points about his book, then in the press.

The following fortnight was an extremely busy, if successful, one for him, for as Chairman of the Nutrition Society (an office to which he had been appointed earlier in the year) he took the leading part in a European Conference arranged by the British Council in collaboration with that Society, and attended by thirty-two delegates from Belgium, Czechoslovakia, Denmark, Finland, France, the Netherlands, Norway, Poland, Switzerland, and the U.S.A. (Plate 59). As L. J. Harris (1947) wrote, "It was Barcroft who, with unflagging interest and zest, received the foreign delegates at the inaugural conversazione, who took the Chair at the first scientific session, who accompanied the visitors on their tour of the principal research centres of the British Isles, who was the guest of honour at the farewell banquet, and who took his full share in all the preliminary negotiations and planning – and this was all done with an unvarying grace, good humour, and evident relish and enjoyment. Many men of half his age would have found much that the Chairman was able to accomplish, and in his stride, almost beyond their physical endurance, and sometimes beyond their forbearance."

The Conference began at 5.30 p.m. on Thursday, 4 July, with a reception, given at 74 Brook Street, London, by the British Council in honour of the visiting delegates. On the following morning, under J. B.'s chairmanship, a closed meeting was held at the London School of Hygiene and Tropical Medicine, and the visitors were given a survey of British work on nutrition. In the afternoon there were reports on "human" nutrition in Denmark, Finland, Norway, and Sweden. On the following day there were corresponding reports concerning its state in Czechoslovakia, Greece, Poland, Yugoslavia, the U.S.A., Belgium, France, the Netherlands, and Switzerland.

On the Sunday afternoon there was a visit to Kew Gardens; on Monday, 8 July, there were reports on "animal" nutrition in the various countries. The next day some of the Conference members visited the National Institute for Research in Dairying at Shinfield, near Reading, while others went to see the Cereals Research Station at St. Albans. On the Wednesday there was a division into "clinical" and "scientific" programmes; the former was carried out at the M. R. C. Human Nutrition Unit, National Hospital, Queen's Square, at the London Hospital, and at the Medical Unit of University College Hospital, while the latter involved visits to the laboratories of the National Institute for Medical Research at Mount Vernon and Mill Hill, and to the Lister Institute. Thursday and Friday were spent in Cambridge and delegates saw what was being done in the Dunn Nutritional Laboratory, the Low Temperature Research Station, the Department of Experimental Medicine, the Animal Research Station, and J. B.'s own Unit of Animal Physiology. Oxford was visited on the Saturday, and on Sunday, 14 July, the venue changed to Edinburgh. On the following day there was a choice between "human" nutrition at the Royal Infirmary and "animal" nutrition at the Royal Dick Veterinary College, the University Department of Zoology, and the Moredun Institute, Liberton.

On Tuesday the party went on to Aberdeen, and that afternoon visited the Torry Research Station and the Macaulay Institute for Soil Research. Dinner was at Strathcona House, the Rowett Institute, and the guests included the Lord Provost and the Vice-Chancellor of the University; Principal Sir William Fyfe gave an address of welcome. The next morning members went back to the Rowett Institute to learn about the more scientific aspects of nutrition, and thereafter visited the Duthie Experimental Farm. In the evening they went on to Glasgow, where on 18 July they saw work in progress at the Royal Hospital for Sick Children, and whence they were taken out to the Hannah Dairy Research Institute, Ayr. Friday was scheduled for an excursion to Loch Lomond, Loch Long, and the Gareloch, and J. B. apparently went instead to the meeting of the Biochemical Society in Edinburgh, returning overnight to Cambridge.

With a rest obviously indicated, he left two days later, accompanied by M. A. B., for Belfast, crossing in the luxurious *Ulster Prince.* On 26 July he celebrated his seventy-fourth birthday and a few days later, after visiting The Glen, he and M. A. B. went on to Cushendun. There are no relevant details about this holiday except for a note, dated 9 August, in M. A. B.'s diary, which said that J. B. was then very busy correcting the proofs of his book, and that he was troubled with arthritis which her massaging efforts had been ineffective in relieving. On 23 August they were back at home in Cambridge.

Not long after their return M. A. B. said to him, "I wonder what period in our married life you think the happiest", and he, after reflection, replied, "The two years we spent together during the war when you were my Secretary." On 18 September he went to Oxford to be radiographed by Dr. A. E. Barclay and to be examined by Professor Ryle. The radiographs showed signs of arthritis in *both* hips and also in the right knee, which had been painful earlier but at the moment was quiescent. Letters came from Barclay and Ryle a few days later saying that there was not much that could be done to ameliorate the trouble. In spite of it, he carried on with amazing determination, and on 21 September he presided over a scientific conference of the Nutrition Society at the London School of Hygiene and Tropical Medicine. The object of the meeting was to give members of the Society an opportunity of hearing an account of the work and aims of the Food and Agriculture Organization. Sir John Orr, its Director-General, opened the explanations, Mr. D. Lubbock spoke on "Nutritional aspects of the world food picture", Dr. P. Lamartine Yates on "The development of food supplies",

Dr. W. R. Aykroyd on "The nutritional programme of F.A.O.", and Miss E. Fautz on "World needs for processed milk." In the afternoon there was a general business meeting of members of the Nutrition Society to discuss proposals for its new constitution, and we may perhaps anticipate and say that, but for his death in 1947, J. B. would have been nominated by the Council as President for 1947–8 under that new constitution. A pleasant feature of the business meeting was the reading of a very appreciative letter from the foreign delegates who had attended the European Conference in July. Five days after the Nutrition Society's meeting J. B. left for Copenhagen, where he was to stay with Professor Krogh and to talk to the Natural Sciences Society about the microflora of the alimentary canal; he returned by air on 1 October, and four days later went off overnight to Aberdeen.

During October-November, despite some relief afforded by X-ray therapy, he was much troubled with his arthritis, but courageously adhered to his commitments in respect of outside engagements, in particular of three special University of London lectures to be given at University College at 5 p.m. on 31 October and 14 and 28 November. The advertised subjects were respectively, "Movements of the human foetus", "Recent work on placental transmission", and "The flora of the alimentary canal", and Professor C. A. Lovatt Evans, F. R. S., Jodrell Professor of Physiology, was to take the chair at the first lecture. On the actual day the theatre was crowded and the audience most enthusiastic as J. B. gave his talk and projected his cine-film in illustration of it. "Afterwards", M. A. B. wrote, "his poor leg seemed to give out in a sad way and he had to get help from kind folk during the journey home, ending with a policeman taking his arm." Of the second lecture we have a description from Professor G. P. Crowden, who wrote in 1947 as follows. "In November last I heard him lecture to a packed and enthralled audience of the rising generation of students at University College, many of them sitting on the floor around him as every seat was filled. The whole atmosphere of that lecture theatre was permeated by his inspiring personality, which seemed to generate friendly cooperation in the pursuit of knowledge." From another source we learn that the impression J. B. made was such that *the applause continued after he had left the theatre*. About the third one in the series the present writer has been unable to get further details.

From mention of those public engagements we pass to some account of J. B.'s last book, *Researches on Pre-Natal Life,* Volume *1,* which appeared in mid-December, and was dedicated to D. H. Barron, "to whom the work, of which this book treats, owes so much." The Preface may conveniently be reproduced here in full, in as much as it explained the genesis of the work, the scope of that first Volume, and also the prospective scope of Volume *2,* which did not in the event materialize.

"This work" J. B. wrote "partakes very much of the nature of a will – I hope not my last. In the days of bombs it seemed to me only the due of the many who had given me encouragement and support, not least the Rockefeller Foundation, that I should set down in some connected from such information as I had accumulated concerning pre-natal life; then, if the bomb came my way, the information, for what it was worth, would remain. I say 'in some connected form' because not the least interesting part of the work has been the fitting together of individual items, dealt with in individual papers, into a picture from which a likeness of the organism is commencing to emerge.

"A will necessarily deals with the property of the testator at the moment at which that will is made. Some of his projects have come to fruition with assets safely secured, some may look promising, others may be doubtful, yet all must be dealt with. So, in this book, in so far as it is the bequest of such knowledge as I possess, or think I possess, I have put down all that is supported by experiment. There are cases, however, about which the last word has not been said, nor the last experiment completed. These I have indicated for the benefit of such as may wish to undertake future research.

"As regards the scope of the book, it purports to deal primarily with researches in which I have had a hand myself, and with observations by others germane to such, but it goes a little further and includes work by colleagues which I have been privileged to see, and even work carried out under the auspices of committees on which I have served. It does not purport to treat on any extensive scale of work with which I have had no personal contact; to take a single instance, the beautiful work carried out at Johns Hopkins University on the initiation of the heart beat – would that I could claim connection with that, but no! I must take up the pulse at the point at which I commenced to observe it.

"The general aim, then, of this book is to trace the development of function in the mammalian foetus, never losing sight of the fact that one day the call will come and the foetus will be born. Not only has the foetus to develop a fundamental life which will suffice for intra-uterine conditions, but at the same time it has to develop an economy which will withstand the shock of birth, and will suffice, nay more than suffice, for its new environment.

"The work is divided into two volumes. In the first the following topics are discussed.

1. Certain points concerning the function of the placenta necessary to the better understanding of foetal development (Chapters I and II).
2. Data with regard to the growth of the foetus, leading up to a discussion (if the word is not too flattering) of the extent to which the growth of the foetus can be influenced by diet (Chapters III–V).
3. The volume and distribution of blood in the foetal circulation, and the transfer of blood from the placenta to the foetus at birth (Chapters VI and VII).
4. Considerations affecting the amount of oxygen used by the foetus and the rate at which it is transported (Chapters VIII–X).
5. Blood pressure, pulse rate, and vascular reflexes (Chapters XI and XII).
6. The relations of the blood to oxygen and carbon dioxide (Chapters XIII–XVII).
7. The circulation in the chest (Chapters XVIII–XX).
8. Pre-natal and neo-natal respiration (Chapters XXI and XXII).

"The second volume will, I hope, deal largely with the nervous system and metabolic problems.

"The number of those who have helped me is so great as to make it impossible for me here to express my thanks to them in detail; their names will, for the most part, be found at the head of the papers to which reference is made, but four I must mention – Boyd, Barclay, Franklin, and Barron. Also, I should like to thank Dr. Clement A. Smith and Mr. L. R. Wallace, whose contributions to this book have cost them much personal effort.

"As regards corporate bodies, those primarily concerned are the Rockefeller Foundation, the Agricultural Research Council, and the Cambridge University Department of Agriculture where Mr. W. S. Mansfield, his farm managers and his shepherd have made the work possible by undertaking the buying, stocking, and keeping of the ewes which I have used.

"In conclusion, I should like to thank Mrs. D. Thacker, Miss M. M. Sutherland, and Mr. R. S. Comline for invaluable help in the preparation of the book."

Early in January 1947, one presumes, J. B. must have resigned from the Nutrition Committee of the Royal College of Obstetricians and Gynaecologists. At all events Eardley Holland wrote to him on 10 January, saying, "It was a pleasure indeed and a privilege to serve under you. You are a wonderful and an inspiring Chairman."

An even more heart-warming letter came a week or so later, in quite another connection, from Roughton. It read: "Dear J. B. Ever so many thanks for your blessing and flattering expectations about my new job. You know only too well of my hesitation during the period of decision, but now that the die is cast I must forget all that and do the best I can. I am certain that I can continue to look to you for the help that you know so well how to give, and my only regret, when I can think of it, is that I cannot count on such help for the whole of the rest of my days on this earth. Yours just as affectionately, Jack Roughton."

A third letter which one may quote was from Miss Sutherland, J. B.'s Secretary, and was written to him on her retirement. "When I scanned your note hurriedly in the Laboratory", it read, "I did not fully appreciate the kindness and generosity of your appraisal of my work. I shall cherish it more as a memento of an association that was at once a privilege and a pride, than as something of material use should the occasion arise. In the latter event, in all fairness I should be tempted to add that only a good master makes a good servant."

On 7 February J. B. received a letter from Barron thanking him for the inscribed copy of *Researches on Pre-Natal Life* which he had sent.

In mid-February came a note from Henry, saying, "Very many thanks for the view of the Fison Lectures and those to the Birmingham Medical School", and we know from Roughton (1949, *b*) that at this time J. B.'s "diary was packed with lectures and other engagements for many weeks ahead and in many different places. Even so he had felt obliged to decline some pressing invitations, which he would have liked to accept, for . . . he felt that he had so much yet to accomplish, especially in the rounding off of his research in foetal physiology, that his activities must necessarily be rationed firmly."

We pass on to the morning of Friday, 21 March, the first day of spring, and find J. B. awaiting Roughton at 10.15 a.m. on the stone stairs at the entrance to the Physiology Laboratory. He told Roughton that he wanted to talk to him about three things, (a) the allocation between their respective laboratories of apparatus bought jointly with personal grants before 1931, (b) the recent elections to the Royal Society, and (c) the experiments Roughton had been doing with blood which J. B. had lately been giving him from his pregnant ewes. After some friendly haggling in the dark room upstairs the fate of the apparatus was settled, and then they went on to discuss the physiologists who had just been elected F.R.S., and also those who had not succeeded – J. B. had just finished a term of office as Chairman of the Selection Committee in Physiology and Medical Sciences, and showed great interest in the claims to distinction of colleagues very much younger than himself.

Then he got on to the ewe blood, asked what Roughton had been doing with it, and why he had had no word. Roughton said that J. B. had claimed to be over-busy, so a progress report had been withheld until there was some definite news, as now there was. Roughton and his colleagues then showed and discussed with J. B. curves of the rate of carbon monoxide uptake by red blood corpuscles of one of the pregnant ewes, and of a ram. From these data, Roughton explained, it was possible, by a combination of mathematics and physical chemistry, to calculate the permeability of the red cell membrane to carbon monoxide and, from data obtained in similar experiments, to oxygen. When the explanation was over, J. B. gave a chuckle and said: "You know, this reminds me of an electric alarm-clock which Hartridge invented many years ago when he was a young man, and which not only woke him up but pulled him out of bed, made his tea, and did all sorts of other things. One evening Hartridge came into dinner at King's, sat down next Milner-White, the theological Dean of the College, and proceeded to explain to him how this clock worked. Milner-White listened

60—Joseph Barcroft's room in the Physiology Laboratory, Cambridge

61—The garden of No. 13 Grange Road, Cambridge, viewed from the house

with a polite expression on his face, but how much he understood of it I do not know. I think, however, that I have understood at least as much of what you have just told me as Milner-White did of Hartridge's electric clock." He then proceeded to make some of his usual shrewd points, and finally concluded: "Well, I'll take care of that particular ewe and, when she is non-pregnant, we will see whether her blood gives the same curve as the ram, which I suppose we may assume – with a fair degree of confidence – not to have been pregnant." Perhaps that was the very last scientific matter to occupy his attention.

By now it was nearly noon, and J. B. brought their time together to an end, as he so often did on such occasions, with a trivial, non-scientific matter. As he finished on the words, "Well, let's hear more news later", he backed towards the door with his characteristic gait, and a broad smile on his face, and a moment later he was gone.

Gone, unfortunately, as it turned out, for ever! For in his haste to catch a bus which would take him homeward to luncheon with M. A. B., he imposed too much strain on his incompletely fit heart, and collapsed and died as he travelled towards Grange Road. While an ambulance was being brought, a fellow-passenger (whose husband had died in similar fashion) took word to M. A. B., and led her to and fro until the ambulance eventually arrived and J. B.'s remains were laid in the little guest-room at No. 13. Though M. A. B. must have known since the Porton time that J. B. might sooner or later have a fatal heart attack, the impact of the actual blow on 21 March can be imagined, and she was unfortunately denied that measure of privacy that at such a time one needs. First the police came and interrogated her most closely about J. B.'s previous health, though fortunately in the end they were satisfied that there was no need for an inquest. Arrangements for the funeral had to be decided and a notice 'phoned to *The Times* for the next morning's number. Then it was difficult, owing to the storms, to get word to Henry in Belfast, though eventually M. A. B. got through by 'phone to Biddy, who said that Henry would cross at once. Plans finally took a more definite form when the Provost and the Chaplain of King's called, and it was arranged that there should be a Service in King's College Chapel on the afternoon of Tuesday, 25 March, and thereafter a private cremation. In these so sad hours, apart from the help of friends, M. A. B.'s only solace was the thought that

J. B. had been taken before he had become too crippled with his ever-spreading and worsening arthritis.

At the laboratory the news stunned J. B.'s colleagues on their return from luncheon, but they felt that no end could have been happier for him than to die suddenly, as he had done, while still in full activity. Later in the day a colleague said to Roughton, "I envy that man, Joseph Barcroft, going on doing first-class work right up to the last moment of his long life."

Henry arrived on the Saturday and relieved his mother of the bulk of the extra duties that befall a household at such a time. Offers of help of every kind came flowing in, and were followed by a stream of letters of sympathy that did much to mitigate the sorrow felt by M. A. B. and by Henry. On 24 March J. B.'s remains were removed to the Memorial Chapel in King's College, and the next morning the sun was shining as the final preparations were made. About noon Willy and Kathleen and Gwen Ball arrived, and at 2.15 p.m. the party from Grange Road left for King's College Chapel, where they were joined by various other relatives and friends, and with M. A. B. and Henry leading, passed to their seats in the stalls.

In that wonderful Chapel which J. B. and M. A. B. had so long and happily frequented, the beautiful words of the funeral service went solemnly forward to their conclusion in the words of King Henry VI's Prayer, the Grace, and the final hymn, "Abide with me; fast falls the eventide." Only a short time before his death, M. A. B. had asked J. B. if he would like that at his funeral and he had said that he would. It was exquisitely sung and touched everyone. Then came the slow procession out through the west end to the waiting cars, and the rest of the congregation stood in silent respect as the family mourners set off after the hearse to the Crematorium. There the service was conducted by the Reverend A. R. Graham Campbell, Chaplain to the College, who included in it the following Friends' Prayer:- "O God who holdest all souls in life and callest them unto Thee as seemeth Thee best, we give them back to Thee, dear God, Who gavest them to us. But as Thou didst not lose them in giving, so we have not lost them by their return. For not as the world giveth, givest Thou, O Lord of souls. That which Thou givest Thou takest not away. For life is eternal and love is immortal; and death is only the horizon, and the horizon is nothing save the limit of our sight. Lift us up, strong Son of God, that we may see further; cleanse our eyes that we may see more clearly; draw us closer to Thyself that so we may know ourselves nearer to our beloved who are with Thee. And as Thou dost prepare a place for us, prepare us for that happy place, that where Thou art and they are we too may be, Who livest and reignest with the Father and the Holy Spirit, one God world without end."

One has no wish to intrude upon private grief, but J. B. was so personal an influence in so many lives, and we have in this biography been taken so much into his family circle that it seems fitting, with M. A. B.'s consent, to reproduce some passages from her diary, kept up during even those sad days.

On the evening of 25 March she wrote:- "Looking back there seem to have been many little talks lately that indicated that 'The Great Plan' and 'Change over' was not far off, and now I can but feel that much severe suffering was before him had he lived, and so I lift up my heart in thankfulness that he was spared the misery of many weeks or perhaps months of sadness, and instead he has gone to the God he has always loved and served so faithfully."

Two days later she added:- "How much has been fitted into these past days! Letters flowing in at every post and now numbering nearly two hundred and fifty, but what a wealth of kindness and love they contained! Rarely one that did not include a tribute of genuine affection, and how touched we have been."

Twelve days later again, on 9 April, the entry read:- "Still more and more letters – they number now over three hundred and the one most recurring sentence is 'I loved him'. What comfort they have brought, helping us to glimpse at the life he led in the bigger world outside his home. How many have alluded to his smile saying that it had made them feel happier all day if they had met it. Others have stated how they could bring their troubles to him and have them chased away. I copy just a few words out of these many letters which help to keep his memory fresh in our thoughts . . . 'How gentle' – 'How modest' – 'What integrity' – 'What a friend' – 'So wise and witty' – 'Tolerant and sympathetic' – 'Brave as he was brilliant' – 'Was there ever a more delightful man?' – 'Such ability' – 'Such goodness' – 'Such cordiality' – 'His enthusiasm which never flagged' – 'His courage' – 'His courtesy made him to us the ideal of what a scientist could be.' Mrs. A. V. Hill writes 'When

I have thought of married happiness my thoughts have always turned to you and Joe who represented perfect companionship.' So we write no 'Finis' to his beautiful life – for goodness is eternal."

A week after J. B.'s death a fourth child, Roger Henry, had been born to Biddy and Henry Barcroft; not long thereafter, Sarah Barcroft, J. B.'s eldest sister, had died. Early in April the Bishop of Lichfield, as already mentioned in the Preface to this biography, came to M. A. B. and said she ought to ask someone to write J. B.'s life; towards the end of the month Mrs. Faichnie called – she was the lady who had broken the news to M. A. B. on 21 March.

We pass thence to 5 May, when M. A. B. saw the first appreciation, in *The Cambridge Review*, of J. B.'s new book, *Researches on Pre-Natal Life*, Volume *1*. On 2 July J. B.'s American colleague, Dr. D. H. Barron, to whom the book had been dedicated, called, and showed by all that he said how much he had loved J. B. Dr. F. H. A. Marshall spoke in the same way when he called later in the month, and there were tears in his eyes as he spoke about the help J. B. had extended to him in his younger days. On the first evening of August Henry and Biddy came to dinner; after the meal Don Barron dropped in, and the four of them sat round the open French doors of the drawing-room looking out into the garden, and recalled – particularly Don Barron – various facets of J. B.'s character. It was, as M. A. B. wrote, "an evening to be remembered with tenderness", and appropriately it was the subject of the last note in the long series of her diaries which have furnished material for this biography.

One does not normally, perhaps, publish extracts from letters of condolence, but any reader of those sent to Lady Barcroft would say that an exception must be made in this instance, for the letters reveal how widespread and great was his influence, and how deep the affection which he inspired, i.e., they amplify the picture given in the preceding part of this biography. We must, even at that, be content with samples only, for the total bulk is huge. Here, then, are the names of the writers and the words which they wrote:-

David Hill: "We shall miss him very much in the lab. It was only yesterday morning [21 March] that he came in to see me, and he seemed quite himself. We talked about various matters connected with respiration, and I thought at the time how nice it was of him to look in. But then, he was always so kind."

Thomas S. Frankland: "I know that I am speaking for all the other students in the Physiology labs when I say that he was universally loved."

Mrs. Nora Edkins: "The kindliest man that I have ever met."

Eric Barnard, Department of Scientific and Industrial Research: "It was my good fortune, as Director of Food Investigation, to have Sir Joseph as my Chairman for a number of years. No man ever had an abler, more interested, helpful and encouraging chairman and I not only admired him as a great scientist, but loved him as a man."

A. T. Narborough: "I always regarded him as one of my favourite patients, he was always so cheerful and amusing and never made any fuss about either his ailment or his treatment – his gentleness of manner was always so charming and the world will sadly miss the passing of these very courteous people."

Davenport Hooker: "One of the truly great minds of his time."

John Raison: "To him I was just a medical student but, when I met him only a few days ago, . . . he talked to me in that friendly and well-informed way for which he was so renowned in the University."

Geoffrey Barber: "He was everything a man should be: clever and modest, kind and humorous, and I never met him without catching some of his infectious goodness and happiness."

C. W. A. Searle: "It is probably presumptuous of me to say that you have lost the most perfect person and the country one of its greatest man."

H. Blaschko: "And now we shall have to be content with our memories of him as we have known him, an indefatigable worker, full of the explorer's tenacity and vision, a leader, a man full of humour but also of seriousness, of understanding and respect for others."

Sidney Elsden: "Sir Joseph has always been more of a father to me than a chief."

Donald H. Barron: "I loved Sir Joseph above all men. I loved him for his passionate devotion to the truth; for his charity towards his fellow man in all walks of life; for his devotion to young men and a host of other intangible qualities. To emulate him was and will remain my life's purpose; I can conceive no higher purpose.

"I have written only of my personal indebtedness to Sir Joseph. My countrymen owe to him the same coin. No one has contributed more generously to the physiological thought of this country than he. The host of students who went through his laboratory, learned his methods and acquired new vistas are spread throughout this country, and they recall with advantage the days and weeks they enjoyed as members of his School. And there are those yet unborn who will catch the spark of his wisdom through the thoughts he put to pen. Few have given so much; fewer there are who had so much to give."

Ian Cox: "His personal charm and individual kindness . . . the strongest of my memories of Cambridge."

C. G. Douglas: "Those who taught me what I know and inspired me more than anyone else – John Haldane, Yandell Henderson and now J. B. – have gone, but the affectionate memory will always remain."

Gilbert Adair: "I have never been able to express adequately the admiration and affection in which I have held Sir Joseph . . . I cannot yet imagine life at Cambridge without his guidance and encouragement."

Earl McCarthy: "My association with him was a most significant and enriching event in my life . . . I want you to know that among his many pupils there is an Irishman who will always remember him with honour and affection."

Sylva Harrison: "I shall never forget how, twenty-three years ago, the kindly twinkle in his eye made one lonely little American student feel suddenly happier in England."

Secker: "May I humbly and respectfully offer my sincerest and deepest sympathy to you in this great bereavement. I well remember the many happy days I served under him . . . I feel more than I can say in words and shall always look back on those days as being some of the happiest I have spent in my life."

A. V. Hill: "Sir Henry Tizard, who is a pretty good judge of men, said to me yesterday that Jo was one of the really great men in the world – to which I added, with his assent, one of the really good men. You can think with pride and happiness of so many good years with one of the really great and good people, of having shared his work and his friends, of having made the centre of his life from which so much of kindness, laughter and wisdom radiated to other people . . . We are all much poorer, the world is much poorer, 'now Greatheart is gone', but his memory will be always a joy and inspiration to all who knew and loved him."

Harold Hartley: "His fresh original mind that kept its youth right to the end – of how few can that be said. He set us all a tremendously high standard by his sincerity and thoroughness and by the quality of his brain. You always got a fearless objective judgment from him either about people or things. But quite apart from the quality of his intellect there was the charm of his character – simple, modest, and affectionate. It was a great joy to feel that you were a friend of his, and it meant a lot in one's life."

Mrs. W. B. Cannon: "My Walter had a great admiration and affection for him and as a family we all loved his gentle humor and his friendliness. To my children he was always the ideal Englishman tho an Irishman at that!"

Kenneth Pickthorn: "I know only one or two other men whom it is an encouragement and a comfort just to meet; even when we only waved at each other in Sidgwick Avenue or Grange Road, I always felt the better for it for the rest of the day."

A. C. Chibnall: "He had such a flair for the right word of advice at the right time, and there is nobody to take his place – just nobody!"

W. R. Wooldridge: "We in the veterinary profession, and particularly on the Loveday Committee and the Veterinary Educational Trust [now The Animal Health Trust], learned to value his sincere advice and understanding; indeed, he had become one of our most trusted councillors. We shall miss him very much but we shall always remember his kindly humour and approachability as well as his great scientific leadership."

F. H. A. Marshall: "I have known him for forty-seven years and during the whole of this time he was continually doing me kindnesses."

W. Feldberg: "The great friendliness he bestowed on us from the first days in 1925, when I came to Cambridge to work under him, until the last days of his life."

Helen Stephen: "His great learning I leave for others, only how easily it sat on his handsome shoulders, and how gratifying it was to listen to him talking on abstruse subjects, and to understand as one never thought one would – and never did, when any other Lecturer attempted to inform the uninitiated. In every aspect of your dear man's life how fine it was. And his smile that can never be forgotten, his very own, benevolence in every line of it."

A. N. Drury: "As a friend, I owe much happiness to him, and Peters and I still talk of the time when we sailed with him in Ireland.

A. Creech Jones: "As one of the original members of our Colonial Agricultural Research Committee he rendered the Colonial Office most valuable assistance and he gave us very useful advice on our Colonial agricultural problems."

D. P. O'Brien: "I know of no one whose memory will be cherished so fondly by so many people throughout the world, his friends and associates and the large number of his pupils."

Christabel Phillips: "His unvarying kindness, his wonderful gift of radiating happiness, and his simple modesty and complete negation of self, will ever be remembered as an inspiration and guidance."

J. H. Doggart: "I shall never forget his kindness to me – a kindness that steadily persisted even though I was one of his idlest students. When he came to lecture to us at the Children's Hospital, Great Ormond Street, last year, he had the same merry twinkle, the same boyish enthusiasm."

George Rylands: "No-one could spend ten minutes with Sir Joseph without being intensely aware of his rare sweetness and goodness. I admired and honoured and loved him and I think I shall always remember the tones of his voice and the gaiety of his smile."

J. D. Boyd: "He was a very great scientist – concerned always with first principles and taking the details in his stride. I shall always remember how he could put one back on the tracks again by pointing out how one's apparently bright thought transgressed one or other of the primary laws.

"Personally, nevertheless, I shall always remember him with gratitude, with respect and with real affection for his character and his characteristics. I have known other considerable scientists and, doubtless, I shall come to know yet others. But I wonder if I shall ever meet one who was so honest, so without guile, so concerned with the truth in the very best sense of this abstraction. And to this one must add friendliness, concern for the welfare of colleagues and friends, and a deep sense of justice. It always rather embarrassed me that he should be so grateful, so honestly and unaffectedly grateful, for the very small services that on several occasions I was able to perform for him. He was kind because that was his nature, not for ulterior motive or design.

"And now we shall no longer sense this kindly response, this ready friendliness. And, I can write it honestly and with conviction, something very cherished has gone from my life. I shall remember him with respect, affection and thanks."

From the individual condolences we may pass to one collective one. At a Congregation holden in the Combination Room of King's College on Saturday, 24 May, with the Provost, the Vice-Provost, and thirty-two others present, the following proposal by the Provost, seconded by Professor Adcock, was carried unanimously, the Provost and Fellows upstanding:-

"The Provost and Fellows desire to place on record their sorrow at the loss sustained by the Society through the death of Emeritus Professor Sir Joseph Barcroft, their grateful memory of his friendship and his gracious personality, his eminent services to science and unswerving devotion to the College, and their deep sympathy with Lady Barcroft and the other members of his family in their bereavement."

We may also look at a few of the more public notices. *The Cambridge Review* of 10 May, above the signatures of J. Gray and W. F. Reddaway, said that "Throughout the scientific world, Barcroft's name will live as one of the outstanding physiologists of his time, but with this will always be coupled the respect and affection of innumerable friends, remembering 'Joe' as the alert and captivating Irishman . . . In his younger days Barcroft was a keen yachtsman and a vigorous – but not scratch – golfer. He was also a keen gardener and once a year the Physiological Society foregathered in his beautiful garden in Grange Road. As a public speaker or as a dinner companion he was – as indeed he always was – a jovial, kindly Ulsterman. When not in College or in his laboratory he was usually to be found at home, where no man's life was fraught with greater happiness. Barcroft came into residence at King's in 1893, and no College had a more devoted son. For many years he served as an assistant tutor and in other ways. During the recent war he came back into College life – giving freely of his time to the agricultural problems connected with the College estates. His speeches at College meetings were terse and to the point, but it is, above all, for his human qualities that Kingsmen will remember him – for the merry twinkle in his eye and his unswerving faith in human nature."

The Friend of 4 April said: "He had an instinct for getting at essential facts and arranging them intelligently: as in the Sherlock Holmes stories, the explanation seemed obvious enough when revealed, but only a man with an imaginative 'genius for simplicity' could reveal it. . . . Professor A. V. Hill, who describes him as one of the world's really great men, speaks of 'The harmony of his adjustments,' his humility and wisdom, and the affection he inspired. He set a personal and scientific standard which few can equal, and will be gratefully remembered both by all who knew him and by many who did not."

The Times said, inter alia, that "His teaching, like his research, made hardly any parade of learning. He seemed to deal always in very simple ideas and yet to choose ideas which gave a new outlook on the subject."

Another statement read as follows:- "Physiology is not so much a subject as a point of view; and Sir Joseph, if he did not explicitly preach this text, lived it. The genius of simplicity brought him to the heart of the most complex problem, and the use of this gift earned him a place among the great physiologists. Whatever he touched fell into perspective and was illuminated – illuminated so clearly and with such a delightful play of wit and simile as to reawaken the fascination of discovery in the most disillusioned. He was not a specialist, but brought his zest for scientific adventure to the exploration of many fields – the physiology of the blood, the spleen, the kidney, the foetus, and the processes of ruminant digestion. He was not a hacker of the jungle, but made rather for the peaks; he seemed to delight in showing others the view, and to be on the lookout for those who could see it as he did. He did not pretend to know what was in each valley, but his recruits were there and rarely failed to find something worth while. His *Architecture of Physiological Function* was an attempt to find for physiology as a whole that coordinating central idea which he had revealed in so many of its parts. His interest latterly in the physiology of the foetus represented, perhaps, a final effort to come to closer grips with the fundamental mystery. With his passing, a spiritual link with the great period of English physiology has dissolved."

A further note, for which again no reference has been available, dealt with J. B.'s connection with veterinary science. "Sir Joseph's interest in the profession", it said, "was by no means purely academic, as was evidenced by his presence as a revered guest at social functions of the National Veterinary Medical Association. In all company he revealed the charm which was characteristic of his lecturing and writing . . . Sir Joseph's active interest in the profession was great stimulated by his membership of the Loveday Committee. He set himself diligently to understand the problems confronting the profession and contributed in large measure to the views expressed in the first and second reports of the Loveday Committee; he was, in fact, one of the most ardent supporters of the profession. Sir Joseph was one of the original members of the Council of the Veterinary Educational Trust and had been Chairman of the Trust's Educational Grants Committee. He had agreed to deliver this year's Fison Lectures which were to be given some time in May and which unfortunately now will have to be forgone. For several years, until quite recently, he was a Governor of the Royal Veterinary College, representing the Royal Society, and indeed, in his earlier days he carried out some physiological research at the College."

In May 1947 a posthumous publication by J. B. appeared in *Science News*. It was entitled, "The microflora of the alimentary canal", and was based on his lectures to the Royal Society of Edinburgh in 1944 and to the Natural Sciences Society in Copenhagen in the following year.

On Friday, 28 November 1947, but for his untimely death, he would have taken the chair at the third annual meeting of Cambridge researchers on haemoglobin. On his return after the first world war he had resumed his own studies of this blood pigment, and such had been his enthusiasm, energy, and inspiration that by the end of the second war work was being carried on in six Cambridge laboratories. In 1945 and 1946 the various participants had had a conference under his chairmanship, and the November 1947 one would have made the third in the series. Soon after his death, however, some of his colleagues met and decided that the next meeting should be on a much wider basis, and should be devoted to his special memory and honour. Leading workers on haemoglobin in many parts of the world received invitations to attend, and a three-day conference was held in Cambridge from 15 to 17 June 1948. The proceedings opened with a morning session, graced by the presence of Lady Barcroft, at which tributes were paid to her husband's memory by Professor Adrian, Sir Henry Dale, Professors Krogh, Douglas, Hill, and Peters, Dr. Adair, and Professor Roughton. If the present writer's recollection is correct, the silent film of J. B., made on the occasion of his retirement from the Cambridge chair, was thereafter projected, and this may be an appropriate moment to note that, though one's attention is inevitably drawn to J. B.'s face during the projection, the fineness of his hands and his manual dexterity are also impressive features in the film.

The tributes and the scientific proceedings of the Conference were published under the title *Haemoglobin* in 1949, and the Editors (F. J. W. Roughton and J. C. Kendrew) in their Preface expressed their belief "that the astonishing range of subjects comprised in this volume would have given the utmost delight to the late Sir Joseph Barcroft, who was indeed the fountain-head of so much of all this varied work. If so, there can be no more fitting memorial to him." A large proportion of the information contained in the personal tributes has been incorporated in the previous parts of this biography, but one or two stories have been left to be inserted here. Peters said that J. B.'s "capacity for knowing just when to help a research worker and when to leave him alone was extraordinary. He was there when you wanted him but when you wanted to be by yourself, he knew how to leave you. This rare quality is an important one. I can also recall coming back to the Physiological Laboratory in Cambridge after World War I; there was someone trying to do an operation which I could do, taught by Barcroft, and I was getting irritated because I felt that I could do it better. He beckoned me out of the room and closed the door saying: 'No, Peters; you must leave him because, you see, he has got to learn it for himself'."

A. V. Hill, in his tribute, recalled, inter alia, an accident that happened to an apparatus which J. B. had laboriously constructed. "Carelessness by another brought it all crashing to the floor. Instead of using sailor's language J. B. looked at it quietly and said: 'Oh well, we'll just put it up again.' That was characteristic of the patience of his work. I witnessed in those days that unique capacity of his, to which others have referred, for getting other people on to a useful job of work – a capacity which remained with him all his life in whatever he undertook."

Later on Hill said: "His loyalty to his friends and his loyalty to the institutions of any kind with which he was connected were among the most charming characteristics of his nature. I remember him – and the Provost of King's may remember also – proposing the toast 'Floreat Etona' at Founder's Feast one year; the theme of that speech was that each of us has his own Eton, his own loyalties and affections, that the toast of 'Floreat Etona' really meant a toast to all those individual loyalties."

Thence the speaker went on to other points. "J. B.," he said, "was quick, extraordinarily quick, in generous and effective repartee, never sarcastic or unkind. I corrected the proofs of the first edition of his book [*The Respiratory Function of the Blood*] for him, and conceived my duty to J. B. to outweigh my obligation to the public, who might otherwise have been highly delighted had I left in some of the gems which occurred in the original: such phrases as 'The muscle is not a steam engine in which combustion takes place in the boiler' and 'The chief error in Peters' experiments was the accurate measurement of 2 cc of blood'. When I pointed these out as being more suitable to conversation than to a learned treatise, he at once remarked that the chief virtue of the Irish bull was that it was always pregnant; but he accepted my corrections. The humorous and tactful phrase is illustrated in a sentence that occurs in the paper in the *Philosophical Transactions* on the Peru expedition, referring to the mental effects of high altitudes. He remarks: 'Meakins has a feeling akin to what he thought would be produced in him by excess of alcohol.' You can see it all revolving in J. B.'s mind. What Meakins had really said (in J. B.'s words) was that it made him feel squiffy; but J. B. did not like to infer that Meakins had any personal experience of that condition."

The tribute ended: "In a personal record of J. B. those who knew and loved him would not wish to recall him – indeed they could not – without also recalling Lady Barcroft. As I wrote in the *Lancet* fifteen months ago, the laughter which like a nosegay decorated their joint lives made them the most perfect partners and the most perfect hosts. They realized that the most serious things can often be better said and done gaily and they said and did them so. Lady Barcroft is joint creditor with J. B. in our bankruptcy. I think he would like us, and I know she would like us, in all seriousness, to remember him not only with love but with gaiety."

Just a few more completions and our story is finished. At J. B.'s bedside, at the time of his death, were found the rough notes for his address to the Student Christian Movement at Newnham College on 5 December 1944. They were a collection written on old envelopes and the like, but were thought worthy of publication and appeared, as mentioned in the previous Chapter, in the *Lancet* of 22 December 1951 under the title, "Christianity and Medicine". Obviously it was to some extent by chance that J. B.'s final printed paper on any subject was this particular one, but it was perhaps significant that these notes of two and a half years earlier had been at his bedside when he died, and we are reminded by that fact that his religion was the keynote to his whole life. We have not stressed that point very much, because there has not been much opportunity for so doing. But we remember his attitude in the first war, and the reasons underlying it. We know also from Verzár (1947) that, when the latter said goodbye to J. B. at the end of their researches together, the latter presented him with a copy of the New Testament in which he had marked and annotated two passages. The first of these, around the sentence, "For the body is not one member, but many", had the annotation, "The theory of hormones. That feeling which should exist in a laboratory." The second passage was "Dearly beloved, avenge not yourselves, but rather give place unto wrath: for it is written, Vengeance is mine, I will repay, saith the Lord." J. B.'s addition was, "This is why we avoid polemics." We could adduce further evidence, but J. B. did not parade his religion and it will suffice if we quietly remember the central place which it occupied in his whole life.

Towards the beginning of the *Lancet* article, to pass to another point, is a reminder that in J. B.'s earlier years the old-style general practitioner of medicine, whom some of us can recall, was not yet being replaced by one with a more scientific upbringing. "Medicine was empirical. The doctor came into the sickroom; he made a diagnosis; he said to himself 'Old Greenfield (or someone else at whose feet he had sat as a student) found that such and such a prescription was useful in such cases.' He wrote down the prescription; the bottle came; if the patient improved all was well, if not he tried something else." We who have followed J. B.'s life in these pages recall how he had begun a medical course in the early part of his career, but had had to give it up. While his immediate reason for wishing to qualify in medicine had been to improve his prospects of promotion in physiology and he had never intended to practise, his obvious attraction from time to time thereafter to things medical, and to patients, suggest to us what a fine, scientific, discerning and sympathetic consultant he could have become, and there is little doubt that, of the many honours which he received, the honorary Doctorates of Medicine and the honorary Fellowship of the Royal College of Obstetricians and Gynaecologists were among those which brought him the keenest pleasure. For they linked him with a profession which he himself had once been fain to follow and with which he had always a strong practical and spiritual affinity.

Late in the following year, 1952, the present writer received the following letter from Dr. J. P. Baumberger, Professor of Physiology in Stanford University, Stanford, California: "Dr. Edwin J. Baldes of the Mayo Clinic asked me if I would send you the following information which you might find of interest in connection with the biography of Joseph Barcroft, which you are now in the process of writing. The University of California has located a high altitude laboratory on a mountain very close to Mt. Whitney, and having a height almost as great. At the request of the physiologists who are primarily concerned in establishing the laboratory, Dr. Nello Pace and Dr. S. F. Cook, the University of California took up the matter with the National Board of Geographic Names and had the name Joseph Barcroft assigned to the Mountain. The latest issue of *Science* indicates that the laboratory is receiving substantial support and may become one of the most important high altitude laboratories in the United States."

The news was passed on to Lady Barcroft and Professor Henry Barcroft, also to Professor Sir Bryan Matthews of the Physiology Laboratory, Cambridge, and to the Physiological Society. All who received it were delighted with the typically generous American gesture, and with the very permanent association of J. B.'s name with research in one of the spheres of physiology in which he had been so notable a pioneer. It would be appropriate if an annual Lectureship could be founded to commemorate equally his other work on haemoglobin, on the blood distribution within the body, and on foetal and comparative physiology, though for some years at least to come there is likely to be no serious forgetting of his major contributions within each of these fields.

"Science", according to Winston Churchill, "is organized curiosity", and this biography will have served one of its purposes if it recalls to his friends, and portrays faithfully for those who will carry on the succession, how one particular scientist successfully organized, for the general benefit of humanity, his own individual curiosity. Two other quotations have been in the writer's mind, for the story has been not only of a great scientist but of a great man, and of that man not only as a person but as an important member of the dramatis personae of the times in which he lived. The quotations in question are, "We are the sum of all the moments of our lives", and "At the close of a man's life, to estimate his work it is wise to see him in relation to his life's surroundings, to know not only the part he played as an individual, but also as a component part of the great events to which he contributed in the betterment of mankind."

Words written about his great-uncle, William James Barcroft, are equally applicable to J. B. "He was highly esteemed by those amongst whom he dwelt for his sincerity and uprightness of character. His judgment was clear, and he was always ready to exert himself to serve those who stood in need of his advice or assistance."

That passage, however, does not convey the driving force which characterized J. B. right up to the end, and Tennyson's *Ulysses* (particularly as its hero was, like J. B., devoted to the sea) seems to add some of the essentials:-

> " . . . . all times I have enjoy'd
> Greatly, have suffer'd greatly, both with those
> That loved me, and alone. . . . .
>
> . . . .
>
> Much have I seen and known; cities of men
> And manners, climates, councils, governments,
>
> . . . .
>
> I am a part of all that I have met;
> Yet all experience is an arch wherethro'
> Gleams that untravell'd world, whose margin fades
> For ever and for ever when I move.

How dull it is to pause, to make an end,
To rust unburnish'd, not to shine in use!
As tho' to breathe were life. Life piled on life
Were all too little, and of one to me
Little remains: but every hour is saved
From that eternal silence, something more,
A bringer of new things . . . . ''

Those and other lines from the same poem seem very appropriate, especially when one thinks of J. B.'s still vigorous last years. The really significant thing, however, is that his driving force continues, after his death, to influence the lives and activities of others. For that reason this last Chapter of his biography did not finish with the tragic event of 21 March 1947, but inevitably went on to the witness, provided by so many others, that his beneficent and stimulating example and his spiritual presence remain. They should long continue so to do, and this story of his life will, one hopes, aid in prolonging their influence both among those who had the good fortune to be friends and colleagues of so fine a man and scientist, and also among those who, without having known him, will carry on the scientific succession which he did so much, during his lifetime, to foster and improve. So *frater ave*, but surely not *vale*!

CHRONOLOGICAL LIST OF JOSEPH BARCROFT'S PUBLICATIONS*

BARCROFT, J. (1895). "The properties of the surface of liquids." *Rep. Belfast nat. Hist. Soc.*, 24–26.

BARCROFT, J. (1898). "An apparatus for estimating the gases of successive small quantities of blood." *J. Physiol.*, **23**, Suppl., 64. The Supplement, dated 1899, is "An account of the Proceedings of the Fourth International Physiological Congress held at Cambridge, England, August 23–26, 1898."

BARCROFT, J. (1900). "The gaseous metabolism of the submaxillary gland. Part. I. On methods, with a description of an apparatus for gas analysis." *J. Physiol.*, **25**, 265–282.

BARCROFT, J. (1900). "Apparatus for the analysis of gases in small quantities of blood." *Proc. Camb. phil. Soc.*, **11**, 1–10.

BARCROFT, J. (1900). "The present needs of the Dukhobors." *The Friend, n.s.*, **40**, 709–710.

BARCROFT, J. (1900). "The gaseous metabolism of the submaxillary gland. Part II. On the absorption of water from the blood during its passage through the active gland." *J. Physiol.*, **25**, 479–486.

BARCROFT, J. (1901). "The Doukhobors." *Friends' Quarterly Examiner*, January, 91–121.

BARCROFT, J. (1901). "The gaseous metabolism of the submaxillary gland. Part III. The effect of chorda activity on the respiration of the gland." *J. Physiol.*, **27**, 31–47.

BARCROFT, J. (1902). "Respiration." *Rep. Belfast nat. Hist. Soc.*, 26–31.

BARCROFT, J., and HALDANE, J. S. (1902). "A method of estimating the oxygen and carbonic acid in small quantities of blood." *J. Physiol.*, **28**, 232–240.

BARCROFT, J. (1902). "The estimation of urea in physiological fluids." (Paper read, but only title given.) *Rep. Brit. Ass.*, **72**, 784.

BARCROFT, J. (1903). "The estimation of urea in blood." *J. Physiol.*, **29**, 181–187.

BARCROFT, J. (1903). "The origin of water in saliva". (Communicated in title only). *Rep. Brit. Ass.*, **73**, 700.

GOTCH, F., BARCROFT, J., FOSTER, M., and STARLING, E. H. (1904). "Metabolism of the Tissues. – Report of the Committee, consisting of Professor Gotch (Chairman), Mr. J. Barcroft (Secretary), Sir Michael Foster, and Professor Starling." *Rep. Brit. Ass.*, **74**, 343—344.

BARCROFT, J., and BRODIE, T. G. (1904). "The gaseous metabolism of the kidney." *Arch. int. Physiol.*, **2**, 42–43.

BARCROFT, J., and STARLING, E. H. (1904). "The oxygen exchange of the pancreas." *J. Physiol.*, **31**, 491–496.

BARCROFT, J., and BRODIE, T. G. (1904). "The gaseous metabolism of the kidney." *J. Physiol.*, **32**, 18–27.

BARCROFT, J., and BRODIE, T. G. (1905). "The gaseous metabolism of the kidney". *Zbl. Physiol.*, **18**, 835.

BARCROFT, J. (1905). "Modification of Bohr's blood-gas receiver." *J. Physiol.*, **32**, 50–51 *P.*

GOTCH, F., BARCROFT, J., FOSTER, M., and STARLING, E. H. (1905). "Metabolism of the Tissues. – Report of the Committee, consisting of Professor Gotch (Chairman),

* *Proceedings* and *Reports* of scientific meetings are in general listed as though published at the times of those meetings, but in the case of the 1935 International Congress of Physiologists the delay before subsequent appearance in the relevant journal was three years, and the pertinent references are therefore given in that one instance as 1389.

Mr. J. Barcroft (Secretary), Sir Michael Foster, and Professor Starling." *Rep. Brit. Ass.*, **75**, 223–226.

Barcroft, J., and Brodie, T. G. (1905). "The gaseous metabolism of the kidney." *J. Physiol.*, **33**, 52–68.

Barcroft, J. (1906). "The oxygen tension in the submaxillary glands and certain other tissues." *Biochem J.*, **1**, 1–10.

Schäfer, E. A., Vincent, S., Macallum, A.B., Shore, L. E., and Barcroft, J. (1906). "The Ductless Glands. – Second Interim Report of the Committee, consisting of Professor Schäfer (Chairman), Professor Swale Vincent (Secretary), Professor A. B. Macallum, Dr. L. E. Shore, and Mr. J. Barcroft. (Drawn up by the Secretary). The Nature of the 'Islets of Langerhans' in the Pancreas." *Rep. Brit. Ass.*, **76**, 423.

Brunton, T. L., Barcroft, J., *et al.* (1906). "The Effect of Climate upon Health and Disease. – Report of the Committee, consisting of Sir R. Lauder Brunton (Chairman), Mr. J. Barcroft (Secretary), Colonel D. Bruce, Dr. A. Buchan, Dr. F. Campbell, Sir Kendal Franks, Professor J. G. McKendrick, Sir A. Mitchell, Dr. W. C. F. Murray, Dr. Porter, Dr. A. J. Wright, and the Heads of the Tropical Schools of Liverpool and London." *Rep. Brit. Ass.*, **76**, 424–426.

Gotch, F., Barcroft, J., Foster, M., and Starling, E. H. (1906). "The 'Metabolic Balance Sheet' of the Individual Tissues. – Report of the Committee, consisting of Professor F. Gotch (Chairman), Mr. J. Barcroft (Secretary), Sir Michael Foster, and Professor E. H. Starling. (Drawn up by Dr. F. G. Hopkins and the Secretary.)" *Rep. Brit. Ass.*, **76**, 426–428.

Barcroft, J., and Hamill, P. (1906). "The estimation of the oxygen dissolved in salt solutions." *J. Physiol.*, **34**, 306–314.

Barcroft, J. (1906). "Physiology at the British Association". *Nature, Lond.*, **74**, 479–481.

Barcroft, J. (1907). "The velocity and nature of the blood emerging from the submaxillary gland of the cat during stimulation of the cervical sympathetic nerve." (*Preliminary Communication.*) *J. Physiol.*, **35**, 29–30 *P.*

Barcroft, J., and Dixon, W. E. (1907). "The gaseous metabolism of the mammalian heart. Part I." *J. Physiol.*, **35**, 182–204.

Gotch, F., Barcroft, J., and Starling, E. H. (1907). "The 'Metabolic Balance Sheet' of the Individual Tissues. – Report of the Committee, consisting of Professor F. Gotch (Chairman), Mr. J. Barcroft (Secretary), and Professor E. H. Starling. (Drawn up by the Secretary.) *Rep. Brit. Ass.*, **77**, 401–403.

Brunton, T. L., Simpson, R. J. S., Barcroft, J., *et al.* (1907). "The Effect of Climate upon Health and Disease. – Second Report of the Committee, consisting of Sir T. Lauder Brunton (Chairman), Lieut.-Col. Simpson and Mr. J. Barcroft (Secretaries), Colonel D. Bruce, Dr. A. Buchan, Dr. S. G. Campbell, Sir Kendal Franks, Professor J. G. McKendrick, Sir A. Mitchell, Dr. C. F. K. Murray, Dr. C. Porter, Professor G. Sims Woodhead, Sir A. E. Wright, and the Heads of the Tropical Schools of Liverpool, London and Edinburgh." *Rep. Brit. Ass.*, **77**, 403–407.

Barcroft, J. (1907). "Der Gaswechsel des Säugetierherzens." *Dtsch. med. Wschr.* **33**, 1566.

Barcroft, J. (1907). "Der Gaswechsel der Amphibienniere". *Dtsch. med. Wschr.*, **33**, 1566.

Barcroft, J. (1907). "Gaswechsel in der Speicheldrüse der Katze". *Dtsch. med. Wschr.*, **33**, 1566.

Barcroft, J. (1907). "Échanges gazeux de la glande sous-maxillaire du chat pendant l'excitation du sympathique cervical". *Arch. int. Physiol.*, **5**, 89.

Barcroft, J., and Mines, G. R. (1907). "The effect of hirudin upon the gases in arterial blood." *J. Physiol.*, **36**, 275–282.

BARCROFT, J. (1908.) "Differential method of blood gas analysis." *J. Physiol.*, **36**, 52 *P.*

BARCROFT, J. (1908). "The mechanism of vasodilation in the cat's submaxillary gland." (*Preliminary Communication.*) *J. Physiol.*, **36**, 53 *P.*

BARCROFT, J., and MORAWITZ, P. (1908). "Estimation of gases in human blood by the chemical method." *J. Physiol.*, **36**, 56 *P.*

BARCROFT, J. (1908). "Differential method of blood-gas analysis." *J. Physiol.*, **37**, 12–24.

BARCROFT, J., and MORAWITZ, P. (1908). "Über die Ferricyanidmethode zur Blutgasbestimmung für klinische Zwecke." *Dtsch. Arch. klin. Med.*, **93**, 223–231.

BARCROFT, J. (1908). "Simplification of Bohr's method of raising mercury in the Töpler pump." *J. Physiol.*, **37**, 55 *P.*

GOTCH, F., BARCROFT, J., STARLING, E. H., and BRODIE, T. G. (1908). "The 'Metabolic Balance Sheet' of the Individual Tissues. – Final Report of the Committee, consisting of Professor Gotch (Chairman), Mr. J. Barcroft (Secretary). Professor E. H. Starling, and Professor T. G. Brodie." *Rep. Brit. Ass.*, **78**, 436–440.

BRUNTON, T. L., BARCROFT, J., *et al.* (1908). "The Effect of Climate upon Health and Disease. – Third Report of the Committee, consisting of Sir Lauder Brunton (Chairman), Mr. J. Barcroft and Lieut.-Col. R. J. S. Simpson (Secretaries), Colonel Sir D. Bruce, Dr. S. G. Campbell, Sir Kendal Franks, Professor J. G. McKendrick, Sir A. Mitchell, Dr. C. F. K. Murray, Dr. C. Porter, Professor G. Sims Woodhead, and the Heads of the Schools of Tropical Medicine of Liverpool, London, and Edinburgh." *Rep. Brit. Ass.*, **78**, 442–457.

BARCROFT, J. (1908). "Zur Lehre vom Blutgaswechsel in den verschiedenen Organen". *Ergebn. Physiol.*, **7**, 699–794.

BARCROFT, J., and CAMIS, M. (1909). "The dissociation curve of blood." *J. Physiol.*, **39**, 118–142.

BARCROFT, J., and ROBERTS, FF. (1909). "The dissociation curve of haemoglobin." *J. Physiol.*, **39**, 143–148.

BRUNTON, T. L., BARCROFT, J., *et al.* (1909). "The Effect of Climate upon Health and Disease. – Fourth Report of the Committee, consisting of Sir Lauder Brunton (Chairman), Mr. J. Barcroft and Lieut.-Colonel R. J. S. Simpson (Secretaries), Colonel Sir D. Bruce, Dr. S. G. Campbell, Sir Kendal Franks, Professor J. G. McKendrick, Sir A. Mitchell, Dr. C. K. F. Murray, Dr. C. Porter, Dr. J. L. Todd, Professor G. Sims Woodhead, Sir A. E. Wright, and the Heads of the Schools of Tropical Medicine of Liverpool, London, and Edinburgh." *Rep. Brit. Ass.*, **79**, 319–320.

BARCROFT, J., and HILL, A. V. (1909). "The heat of combination of oxygen with haemoglobin and its relation to the molecular weight of haemoglobin." *Proc. Physiol. Soc.*, 11 December (not in *J. Physiol.*, **39**).

BARCROFT, J., and KING, W. O. R. (1909). "The effect of temperature on the dissociation curve of blood." *J. Physiol.*, **39**, 374–384.

BARCROFT, J., and HILL, A. V. (1910). "The nature of oxyhaemoglobin, with a note on its molecular weight." *J. Physiol.*, **39**, 411–428.

BARCROFT, J., and ROBERTS, FF. (1910). "Improvements in the technique of blood-gas analysis." *J. Physiol.*, **39**, 429–437.

STARLING, E. H., BARCROFT, J., and HARDY, W. B. (1910). "The Dissociation of Oxy-Haemoglobin at High Altitudes. – Report of the Committee, consisting of Professor E. H. Starling (Chairman), Mr. J. Barcroft (Secretary), and Dr. W. B. Hardy." *Rep. Brit. Ass.*, **80**, 280–281.

BRUNTON, T. L., BARCROFT, J., *et al.* (1910). "The Effect of Climate upon Health and Disease. – Fourth Report of the Committee, consisting of Sir Lauder Brunton (Chairman), Mr. J. Barcroft and Lieut.-Colonel R. J. S. Simpson (Secretaries), Colonel Sir D. Bruce, Dr. S. G. Campbell, Sir Kendal Franks, Professor J. G.

McKendrick, Sir A. Mitchell, Dr. C. F. K. Murray, Dr. C. Porter, Dr. J. L. Todd, Professor G. Sims Woodhead, and the Heads of the Schools of Tropical Medicine of Liverpool, London, and Edinburgh." *Rep. Brit. Ass.*, **80**, 290–292.

Barcroft, J., and Straub, H. (1910). "The secretion of urine." *J. Physiol.*, **41**, 145–167.

Barcroft, J., and Orbeli, L. (1910). "The influence of lactic acid upon the dissociation curve of blood." *J. Physiol.*, **41**, 355–367.

Barcroft, J., and Straub, H. (1910). Quoted. "The secretion of urine." *Arch. Fisiol.*, **9**, 227.

Barcroft, J. (1910). Quoted. "Differential method of blood-gas analysis." *Trav. Ass. Inst. Marey*, **2**, 126–132.

Barcroft, J. (1911). "The effect of altitude on the dissociation curve of blood." *J. Physiol.*, **42**, 44–63.

Barcroft, J., and Higgins, H. L. (1911). "The determination of the constants of the differential blood-gas apparatus." *J. Physiol.*, **42**, 512–518.

Starling, E. H., Barcroft, J., and Hardy, W. B. (1911). "The Dissociation of Oxy-Haemoglobin at High Altitudes. – Report of the Committee, consisting of Professor E. H. Starling (Chairman), J. Barcroft (Secretary), and W. B. Hardy." *Rep. Brit. Ass.*, **81**, 153–154.

Barcroft, J., and Müller, F. (1911). "The formation and estimation of methaemoglobin." (*Preliminary Note.*) *J. Physiol.*, **43**, 20 *P.*

Barcroft, J., and Müller, F. (1912). "The relation of blood-flow to metabolism in the submaxillary gland." *J. Physiol.*, **44**, 259–264.

Barcroft, J., and Piper, H. (1912). "The gaseous metabolism of the submaxillary gland with reference especially to the effect of adrenalin and the time relation of the stimulus to the oxidation process." *J. Physiol.* **44**, 359–373.

Brunton, T. L., Barcroft, J., *et al.* (1912). "The Effect of Climate upon Health and Disease. – Report of the Committee, consisting of Sir Lauder Brunton (Chairman), Mr. J. Barcroft and Lieut.-Colonel Simpson (Secretaries), Colonel Sir D. Bruce, Dr. G. S. Campbell, Sir Kendal Franks, Professor J. G. McKendrick, Sir A. Mitchell, Dr. Porter, Dr. J. L. Todd, Professor Sims Woodhead, and the Heads of the Tropical Schools of Liverpool, London, and Edinburgh." *Rep. Brit. Ass.*, **82**, 290.

Starling, E. H., Barcroft, J., and Hardy, W. B. (1912). "The Dissociation of Oxy-haemoglobin at High Altitudes. – Report of the Committee, consisting of Professor E. H. Starling (Chairman), Mr. J. Barcroft (Secretary), and Mr. W. B. Hardy." *Rep. Brit. Ass.*, **82**, 290–291.

Barcroft, J., and Shore, L. E. (1912). "The gaseous metabolism of the liver. Part I. In fasting and late digestion." *J. Physiol.*, **45**, 296–306.

Barcroft, J., Peters, R. A., Roberts, Ff., and Ryffel, J. H. (1913). "The effect of exercise on the dissociation curve of blood." (*Preliminary communication.*) *J. Physiol.*, **45**, 45 *P.*

Barcroft, J., Camis, M., Mathison, G. C., Roberts, Ff., and Ryffel, J. H. (1913). "The effect of altitude on the dissociation curve of blood." (*Preliminary communication.*) *J. Physiol.*, **45**, 46 *P.*

Barcroft, J., Graham, G., and Higgins, H. L. (1913). "The effect of carbohydrate-free diet on the dissociation curve of blood." (*Preliminary communication.*) *J. Physiol.*, **45**, 47 *P.*

Barcroft, J., Camis, M., Mathison, G. C., Roberts, Ff., and Ryffel, J. H. (1913). "The effect of moist heat on the dissociation curve of blood." (*Preliminary communication.*) *J. Physiol.*, **45**, 47–48 *P.*

Barcroft, J., and Burn, J. H. (1913). "Determination of the constant of the differential blood gas apparatus, with a note on the specific oxygen capacity of blood." *J. Physiol.*, **45**, 493–497.

Barcroft, J., and Poulton, E. P. (1913). "The effect of carbonic acid on the dissociation curve of blood." *J. Physiol.*, **46**, 4–5 *P.*

Barcroft, J. (1913). "The effect of altitude on mesectic curves of individuals." *J. Physiol.*, **46**, 30–31 *P.*

Lewis, T., Ryffel, J. H., Wolf, C. G. L., Cotton, T., Evans, G. L., and Barcroft, J. (1913). "Observations on respiration and metabolism in cardio-renal patients, with special reference to acid intoxication." *J. Physiol.*, **46**, 53–54 *P.*

Starling, E. H., Barcroft, J., and Hardy, W. B. (1913). "The Dissociation of Oxy-Haemoglobin at High Altitudes. – Report of the Committee, consisting of Professor E. H. Starling (Chairman), Mr. J. Barcroft (Secretary), and Mr. W. B. Hardy." *Rep. Brit. Ass.*, **83**, 260–261.

Lewis, T., Ryffel, J. H., Wolf, C. G. L., Cotton, T., and Barcroft, J. (1913). "Observations relating to dyspnoea in cardiac and renal patients." *Heart*, **5**, 45–92.

Barcroft, J. (1913). "The combinations of haemoglobin with oxygen and with carbon monoxide. II." *Biochem. J.*, **7**, 481–491.

Barcroft, J., and Means, J. H. (1913). "The effect of CO_2 on the dissociation curve of haemoglobin." *J. Physiol.*, **47**, 27 *P.*

Cooke, A., and Barcroft, J. (1913). "Direct determination of the percentage saturation of arterial blood with oxygen in a normal person." *J. Physiol.*, **47**, 35 *P.*

Barcroft, J. (1914). "The respiratory function of the blood." Cambridge: At the University Press.

Barcroft, J., Camis, M., Mathison, C. G., Roberts, Ff., and Ryffel, J. H. (1914). "Report of the Monte Rosa Expedition of 1911." *Phil. Trans., B*, **206**, 49–102.

Wolf, C. G. L., and Barcroft, J. (1914). "The metabolism of the salivary gland. I. The nitrogen metabolism of the resting gland." *J. Physiol.*, **49**, 95–112.

Lewis, T., and Barcroft, J. (1915). "Notes of further observations upon dyspnoea and its relation to blood reaction." *Quart. J. Med.*, **8**, 97–113.

Barcroft, J., and Piper, H. (1915). "The secretion of urine in decerebrate animals". *J. Physiol.*, **49**, 13–14 *P.*

Barcroft, J. (1915). "The effect of sodium sulphate in the submaxillary gland." *J. Physiol.*, **49**, 14–15 *P.*

Barcroft, J. (1915). "A comparison between some physiological and pathological conditions." The Oliver-Sharpey Lectures, delivered before the Royal College of Physicians of London. *Brit. med. J.*, i, 713–715, 760–762.

Barcroft, J., and Kato, T. (1915). "The effect of functional activity upon the metabolism, blood-flow, and exudation in organs." *Proc. roy. Soc., B*, **88**, 541–543.

Barcroft, J. (1915). Thomas H. Huxley's "Lessons in elementary physiology." Enlarged and revised edition by J. Barcroft. New York: The Macmillan Company. Reprinted September 1915.

Barcroft, J., and Kato, T. (1915). "Effects of functional activity in striated muscle and the submaxillary gland." *Phil. Trans., B*, **207**, 149—182.

Tribe, E. M., and Barcroft, J. (1916). "The vascular and metabolic conditions of the normal kidney in rabbits". (*Preliminary Communication.*) *J. Physiol.*, **50**, 10–11 *P.*

Tribe, E. M., Hopkins, F. G., and Barcroft, J. (1916). "Vascular and metabolic conditions in kidneys of rabbits injected with uranium acetate." *J. Physiol.*, **50**, 11–12 *P.*

Tribe, E. M., Harvey, W. H., and Barcroft, J. (1916). "Vascular and metabolic conditions in kidneys of rabbits injected with diphtheria toxin". (*Preliminary Communication.*) *J. Physiol.*, **50**, 12–13 *P.*

Lewis, T., Cotton, Barcroft, J., Milroy, T. R., Dufton, D., and Parsons, T. R. (1916). "Breathlessness in soldiers suffering from irritable heart." *Brit. med. J.*, ii, 517–519.

LEWIS, T., COTTON, J., BARCROFT, J., MILROY, T. R., DUFTON, D., and PARSONS, T. R. (1918). "Cause of breathlessness on exertion." (Abstract.) *Spec. Rep. Ser. med. Res. Comm.*, **8**, 19–21.

BARCROFT, J., HUNT, G. H., and DUFTON, D. (1918). "The treatment of chronic cases of gas poisoning by continuous oxygen administration in chambers." *Rep. chem. Warf. med. Comm., Lond.*, **4**, 13–64.

BARCROFT, J. (1918). "Report on the condition of the blood in cases of gas poisoning." *Rep. chem. Warf. med. Comm., Lond.*, **6**, 4–6.

BARCROFT, J., and WOLF, C. G. L. (1918). "Report on the change in fixed alkalinity of the blood produced by the administration of saline and other substances." *Rep. chem. Warf. med. Comm., Lond.*, **6**, 6–9.

BARCROFT, J., HUNT, G. H., and DUFTON, D. (1918). "Treatment of patients suffering from 'effort syndrome' by continuous inhalation of oxygen." *Rep. chem. Warf. med. Comm., Lond.*, **12**.

BARCROFT, J. (1918). "The delayed effects of phosgene in rabbits, with special reference to the influence of muscular contraction." *Rep. chem. Warf. med. Comm., Lond.*, **14**.

BARCROFT, J. (1918). Quoted. Thomas H. Huxley's "Lessons in elementary physiology". Enlarged and revised edition by J. Barcroft. New York: The Macmillan Company.

BARCROFT, J., BOYCOTT, A. E., PETERS, R. A., and DUNN, J. S. (1919). "Measurement of the blood-flow through the chest in the goat." (*Preliminary communication.*) *J. Physiol.*, **53**, 2 *P.*

BARCROFT, J., and DUNN, J. S. (1919). "The measurement of the work performed by the heart." *J. Physiol.*, **53**, 4–5 *P.*

BARCROFT, J. (1919). "On the nature of the respiratory centre". *J. Physiol.*, **53**, 48–50 *P.*

BARCROFT, J., BOYCOTT, A. E., DUNN, J. S., and PETERS, R. A. (1919). "Observations on respiration and circulation in the goat." *Quart. J. Med.*, **13**, 35–45.

BARCROFT, J., HUNT, G. H., and DUFTON, D. (1920). "The treatment of chronic cases of gas poisoning by continuous oxygen administration in chambers." *Quart. J. Med.*, **13**, 179–200.

BARCROFT, J. (1920). "Some problems of the circulation during gas poisoning." *J. R. Army med. Cps.*, **34**, 155–173.

PARSONS, T. R., PARSONS, W., and BARCROFT, J. (1920). "Reaction changes in the blood during muscular work." *J. Physiol.*, **53**, 110–111 *P.*

BARCROFT, J., COOKE, A., HARTRIDGE, H., PARSONS, T. R., and PARSONS, W. (1920). "The flow of oxygen through the pulmonary epithelium." *J. Physiol.*, **53**, 450–472.

BARCROFT J. (1920). In "Discussion on the therapeutic uses of oxygen." *Proc. R. Soc. Med.*, **13**, Section of Therapeutics and Pharmacology, 59–68.

BARCROFT, J. (1920). "Anoxaemia". *Lancet*, ii, 485–489.

BARCROFT, J. (1920). "Physiological effects of insufficient oxygen supply." *Nature, Lond.*, **106**, 125–129.

BARCROFT, J. R. (1920). "The supply of oxygen to the tissues." *Sci. Mon., N. Y.*, **11**, 440–445.

BARCROFT, J. (1920). Address to the Physiological Section. *Rep. Brit. Ass.*, **88**, 152–168.

BARCROFT, J. (1921). "Anoxaemia as a factor in acute gas poisoning." *J. R. Army med. Cps.*, **36**, 1–18.

BARCROFT, J. (1921). "Alpinism." *Lancet*, i, 1277–1279.

BARCROFT, J. (1921). "Haemoglobin". *Lancet*, ii, 46.

ADAIR, G. S., BARCROFT, J., and BOCK, A. V. (1921). "The identity of haemoglobin in human beings." *J. Physiol.*, **55**, 332–338.

BARCROFT, J., and NAGAHASHI, M. (1921). "The direct measurement of the partial pressure of oxygen in human blood." *J. Physiol.*, **55**, 339–345.

BARCROFT, J., ROUGHTON, F. J. W., and SHOJI, R. (1921). "The measurement of the oxygen content of the mixed venous blood, and of the volume of blood circulating per minute." *J. Physiol.*, **55**, 371–380.

BARCROFT, J., BOCK, A. V., and ROUGHTON, F. J. (1921). "Observations on the circulation and respiration in a case of paroxysmal tachycardia." *Heart*, **9**, 7–13.

BARCROFT, J., BOCK, A. V., HILL, A. V., PARSONS, T. R., PARSONS, W., and SHOJI, R. (1922). "On the hydrogen-ion concentration and some related properties of normal human blood." *J. Physiol.*, **56**, 157–178.

BARCROFT, J. (1922). "The physiology of life in the Andes." *Nature, Lond.*, **110**, 152–156.

BARCROFT, J. (1922). "The raison d'être of the red corpuscle", pp. 146–163 in "The Harvey Lectures", 1921–1922, ser. **17**. Philadelphia and London: J. B. Lippincott Company.

BARCROFT, J. (1922). Physiology of Respiration. *Nature, Lond.*, **110**, 803–804.

BARCROFT, J., BINGER, C. A., BOCK, A. V., DOGGART, J. H., FORBES, H. S., HARROP, G., MEAKINS, J. C., and REDFIELD, A. C. (1923). "Observations upon the effect of high altitude on the physiological processes of the human body, carried out in the Peruvian Andes, chiefly at Cerro de Pasco." Report to the Peru High-Altitude Committee. *Phil. Trans., B.*, **211**, 351–480.

BARCROFT, J., and UYENO, K. (1923). "The effect of concentration of the red blood corpuscles on the dissociation curve of blood." *J. Physiol.*, **57**, 200–202.

BARCROFT, J. (1923). Adsorption and haemoglobin. *Nature, Lond.*, **111**, 844.

BARCROFT, J. (1923). "The circulation in the spleen." *Abstr. Comm. Int. Physiol. Congress, Edinburgh.*

BARCROFT, J., and BARCROFT, H. (1923). "Observations on the taking up of carbon monoxide by the haemoglobin in the spleen." *J. Physiol.*, **58**, 138–144.

BARCROFT, J., and MARSHALL, E. K., JR. (1923). "Note on the effect of external temperature on the circulation in man." *J. Physiol.*, **58**, 145–156.

BARCROFT, J. (1923). "The circulation in the spleen." *Quart. J. exp. Physiol.*, suppl. vol., 49.

SCOTT, J. M. D., and BARCROFT, J. (1924). "The blood volume and the total amount of haemoglobin in anaemic rats." *Biochem. J.*, **18**, 1–8.

BARCROFT, J., and BARCROFT, H. (1924). "The blood pigment of Arenicola." *Proc. roy. Soc., B*, **96**, 28–42.

ANSON, M. L., BARCROFT, J., BARCROFT, H., MIRSKY, A. E., OINUMA, S., and STOCKMAN, C. F. (1924). "The relation between the spectrum of, and the affinity for certain gases for, vertebrate haemoglobin." *J. Physiol.*, **58**, 29 *P*.

BARCROFT, J. (1924). "The significance of hemoglobin." *Physiol. Rev.*, **4**, 329–351.

BARCROFT, J. (1924). "Sir William Bayliss, F.R.S." *Nature, Lond.*, **114**, 474–476.

ANSON, M. L., BARCROFT, J., MIRSKY, A. E., and OINUMA, S. (1924). "On the correlation between the spectra of various haemoglobins and their relative affinities for oxygen and carbon monoxide." *Proc. roy. Soc., B*, **97**, 61–83.

BARCROFT, J., MURRAY, C. D., and SANDS, J. (1924). "The effect of splenectomy on carbon monoxide poisoning." *J. Physiol.*, **59**, 37–38 *P*.

BARCROFT, J. (1925). "Recent knowledge of the spleen." A Lecture delivered to the Manchester Medical Students' Club on Jan. 15th, 1925. *Lancet*, i, 319–322.

BARCROFT, J. (1925). "Neue Milzforschungen," transl. from *Lancet*, 1925, i, 319–322 by Prof. Dr. Viktor Schilling, Berlin. *Naturwissenschaften*, **13**, 325–330.

BARCROFT, J. (1925). "The pigmentation of animals." *Nature, Lond.*, **115**, 679–681.

BARCROFT, J., MURRAY, C. D., ORAHOVATS, D., SANDS, J., and WEISS, R. (1925). "The influence of the spleen in carbon monoxide poisoning." *J. Physiol.*, **60**, 79–84.

BARCROFT, J. (1925). "The significance of hemoglobin in submammalian forms of life." *Physiol. Rev.*, **5**, 596–617.

BARCROFT, J., HARRIS, H. A., ORAHOVATS, D., and WEISS, R. (1925). "A contribution to the physiology of the spleen." *J. Physiol.*, **60**, 443–456.

BARCROFT, J. (1925). "The respiratory function of the blood Part I Lessons from high altitudes." Cambridge: At the University Press.
BARCROFT, J. (1926). "Haemoglobin." A Lecture delivered before the Chemical Society on February 11th, 1926. *J. chem. Soc.*, **129**, 1146–1170.
BARCROFT, J. (1926). "Some recent work on the functions of the spleen." *Lancet*, i, 544–547.
BARCROFT, J., DRYERRE, H., MEAKINS, J. C., PARSONS, T. R., and PARSONS, W. (1926). "On the hydrogen-ion concentration and some other properties of the blood from two cases of autotoxic enterogenous cyanosis." *Quart. J. Med.*, **19**, 257–27?.
BARCROFT, J. (1926). "Sir William Maddock Bayliss — 1866–1924." *Proc. roy.Soc., B*, **99**, xxvii–xxxii.
BARCROFT, J. (1926). "Weitere Forschungen über die Milzfunktion", transl. from *Lancet*, 1926, i, 544–547 by Prof. Dr. Victor Schilling, Berlin. *Naturwissenschaften*, **14**, 797–801.
BARCROFT, J. (1926). "Die Stellung der Milz im Kreislaufsystem". *Ergebn. Physiol.*, **25**, 818–861.
BARCROFT, J. (1926). "The respiratory function of the blood Part I Lessons from high altitudes." New York: Macmillan & Co.
BARCROFT, J. (1927). "Physiology of Life in the High Andes." The Wilde Memorial Lecture. *Mem. Manchr. lit. phil. Soc.*, **71**, xvii–xviii.
BARCROFT, J. (1927). "Étude des rapports entre la rate et la masse sanguine." *Sang*, **1**, 97–113.
BARCROFT, J. (1927). "Die Atmungsfunktion des Blutes", ins Deutsche übertragen von Dr. Wilhelm Feldberg. "Erster Teil. Erfahrungen in grossen Höhen." Berlin: Verlag von Julius Springer.
BARCROFT, J., and STEPHENS, J. G. (1927). "Observations upon the size of the spleen." *J. Physiol.*, **64**, 1–22.
BARCROFT, J., and POOLE, L. T. (1927). "The blood in the spleen pulp." *J. Physiol.*, **64**, 23–29.
BARCROFT, J. (1928). "Le groupement protéique dans l'hémoglobine." *Bull. Soc. Chim. biol., Paris*, **10**, 279–282.
BARCROFT, J. (1928). "The respiratory function of the blood Part II Haemoglobin." Cambridge: At the University Press.
BARCROFT, J. (1928). "L'hémoglobine et son rôle biologique." *C.R. Soc. Biol., Paris*, **99**, Réunion plénière, 3–28.
BARCROFT, J. and STEPHENS, J. G. (1928). "Alterations in the size of the spleen during pregnancy in dogs." *Arch. Sci. biol., Napoli*, **12**, 94–101.
BARCROFT, J., and STEVENS, J. G. (1928). "The effect of pregnancy and menstruation on the size of the spleen." *J. Physiol.*, **66**, 32–36.
BARCROFT, J., and FLOREY, H. W. (1928). "Some factors involved in the concentration of blood by the spleen." *J. Physiol.*, **66**, 231–234.
ABELOOS, M., BARCROFT, J., CORDERO, N., HARRISON, T. R., and SENDROY, J. (1928). "The measurement of the oxygen capacity of haemoglobin." *J. Physiol.*, **66**, 262–266.
BARCROFT, J., and ROBINSON, C. S. (1929). "A study of some factors influencing intestinal movements." *J. Physiol.*, **67**, 211–220.
BARCROFT, J. (1929). "Das Hämoglobin und seine biologische Bedeutung," transl. by G. Lemmel. *Naturwissenschaften*, **17**, 261–269.
BARCROFT, J. (1929). "Hemoglobin". Abstract of Mayo Foundation Lecture. *Proc. Mayo Clin.*, **4**, 290–292.
BARCROFT, J. (1929). "The spleen and the circulation." Abstract of Mayo Foundation Lecture. *Proc. Mayo Clin.*, **4**, 302–404.
BARCROFT, J., and FLOREY, H. (1929). "The effects of exercise on the vascular conditions in the spleen and the colon." *J. Physiol.*, **68**, 181–189.

Barcroft, J. (1929). Articles "Anoxaemia", "Blood", "Excretion", "Physiology", "Pigments of skin and hair", and "Respiration", in *Encyclopaedia Britannica*, 14th Edn., **2**, 7–10, **3**, 740–743, **8**, 957–960, **17**, 887–891, 922–923, **19**, 215–223.
Barcroft, J. (1929). "Die Atmungsfunktion des Blutes," ins Deutsche übertragen von Dr. Wilhelm Feldberg. "Zweiter Teil. Hämoglobin." Berlin: Verlag von Julius Springer.
Barcroft, J. (1930). "Alterations in the volume of the normal spleen and their significance." Being the Twenty-first Mary Scott Newbold Lecture of the College of Physicians of Philadelphia. *Amer. J. med. Sci.*, **179**, 1–10.
Barcroft, J. (1930). "Some effects of emotion on the volume of the spleen." *J. Physiol.*, **68**, 375–382.
Barcroft, J., and Rothschild, P. (1930). "The effect of certain anaesthetics on the volume of the exteriorised spleen". *Arch. int. Pharmacodyn.*, **38**, 569–576.
Barcroft, J. (1931). "The toxicity of atmospheres containing hydrocyanic acid gas." *J. Hyg., Camb.*, **31**, 1–34.
Barcroft, J., and Izquierdo, J. J. (1931). "The relation of temperature to the pulse rate of the frog." *J. Physiol.*, **71**, 145–155.
Barcroft, J. and Izquierdo, J. J. (1931). "The effect of temperature on the frequency of heart and respiration in the guinea-pig and cat." *J. Physiol.*, **71**, 364–372.
Barcroft, J., and Verzár, F. (1931). "The effect of exposure to cold on the pulse rate and respiration of man." *J. Physiol.*, **71**, 373–380.
Barcroft, J., and Margaria, R. (1931). "Some effects of carbonic acid on the character of human respiration." *J. Physiol.*, **72**, 175–185.
Barcroft, J. (1931). "The limits placed by altitude to physical exercise." *Rep. Brit. Ass.*, **99**, 459–460.
Lemberg, R., Barcroft, J., and Keilin, D. (1931). "Uteroverdin." *Nature, Lond.*, **128**, 967–968.
Barcroft, J., Benatt, A., Greeson, C. E., and Nisimaru, Y. (1931). "The rate of blood flow through cyanosed skin." *J. Physiol.*, **73**, 344–348.
Barcroft, J., Douglas, C. G., Kendal, L. P., and Margaria, R. (1931). "Muscular exercise at low barometric pressures." *Arch. Sci. biol., Napoli*, **16**.
Barcroft, J. Nisimaru, Y., and Ray, G. B. (1932). "Observations on the time taken for corpuscles to traverse the liver." *J. Physiol.*, **74**, 44–48.
Barcroft, J. (1932). "La fixité du milieu intérieur est la condition de la vie libre." (Claude Bernard) *Biol. Rev.*, **7**, 24–87.
Barcroft, J., and Margaria, R. (1932). "Some effects of carbonic acid in high concentration on respiration." *J. Physiol.*, **74**, 156–162.
Barcroft, J., Khanna, L. C., and Nisimaru, Y. (1932). "Rhythmical contraction of the spleen." *J. Physiol.*, **74**, 294–298.
Barcroft, J., and Nisimaru, Y. (1932). "Cause of rhythmical contraction of the spleen." *J. Physiol.*, **74**, 299–310.
Barcroft, J., and Nisimaru, Y. (1932). "Undulatory changes of blood-pressure." *J. Physiol.*, **74**, 311–320.
Barcroft, J., Nisimaru, Y., and Puri, S. R. (1932). "The action of the splanchnic nerves on the spleen." *J. Physiol.*, **74**, 321–326.
Barcroft, J., Nisimaru, Y., and Steggerda, F. R. (1932). "The effects of intestinal rhythm on general blood-pressure." *J. Physiol.*, **74**, 490–498.
Lemberg, R., and Barcroft, J. (1932). "Uteroverdin the green pigment of the dog's placenta". *Proc. roy. Soc., B*, **110**, 362–372.
Barcroft, J. (1932). "The effect of some accidental lesions on the size of the spleen." *J. Physiol.*, **76**, 436–442.
Barcroft, J. (1932). "Alterations in the size of the denervated spleen related to pregnancy." *J. Physiol.*, **76**, 443–446.

BARCROFT, J., and ROTHSCHILD, P. (1932). "The volume of blood in the uterus during pregnancy." *J. Physiol.*, **76**, 447–459.

BARCROFT, J., and STEGGERDA, F. R. (1932). "Observations on the proximal portion of the exteriorized colon." *J. Physiol.*, **76**, 460–471.

BARCROFT, J. (1932). "Stores of blood." *Vet. J.*, **87**, 466–483.

BARCROFT, J., HERKEL, W., and HILL, S. (1933). "The rate of blood flow and gaseous metabolism of the uterus during pregnancy." *J. Physiol.*, **77**, 194–206.

BARCROFT, J. (1933). "The conditions of foetal respiration". The substance of an address given at the meeting of the American Association of Science in Chicago, on June 20th, 1933. *Lancet*, ii, 1021–1024.

BARCROFT, J. (1934). "Some forms of apparatus for the equilibration of blood." *J. Physiol.*, **80**, 388–393.

BARCROFT, J. (1934). "Features in the architecture of physiological function." Cambridge: At the University Press.

BARCROFT, J. (1934). "Experiments on man." *Fight ag. Dis.*, **22**, 22–33; *Lancet*, i, 1211–1216.

BARCROFT, J. (1934). "Respiratory function of bood in the foetus." *Rep. Brit. Ass.*, **102**, 362.

BARCROFT, J., ELLIOTT, R. H. E., FRASER, F. R., HERKEL, W., MATTHEWS, B. H. C., and TALAAT, M. (1934). "A case of deficient acclimatization to low oxygen pressure". *J. Physiol.*, **82**, 369–376.

BARCROFT, J. (1934). "Conditions of foetal respiration." *Rev. Soc. argent. Biol.*, suppl. to **10**, 164–177.

BARCROFT, J., FLEXNER, L. B., and MCCLURKIN, T. (1934). "The output of the foetal heart in the goat." *J. Physiol.*, **82**, 498–508.

BARCROFT, J., ELLIOTT, R. H. E., FLEXNER, L. B., HALL, F. G., HERKEL, W., MCCARTHY, E. F., MCCLURKIN, T., and TALAAT, M. (1934). "Conditions of foetal respiration in the goat." *J. Physiol.*, **83**, 192–214.

BARCROFT, J., FLEXNER, L. B., HERKEL, W., MCCARTHY, E. F., and MCCLURKIN, T. (1934). "The utilization of oxygen by the uterus in the rabbit." *J. Physiol.*, **83**, 215–221.

BARCROFT, J. (1935). in "Discussion on haemoglobinuria." *Proc. R. Soc. Med.*, **28**, 671–672.

BARCROFT, J. (1935). "The mammal before and after birth." Being the John Mallet Purser Lecture delivered at the School of Physic, University of Dublin, June 25th, 1935. *Irish J. med. Sci.*, 7 *S.*, 289–301.

BARCROFT, J. (1935). "Chemical conditions of mental development." Being the second John Mallet Purser Lecture delivered at Trinity College, Dublin . . . on June 26th, 1935. *Irish J. med. Sci.*, 7*s.*, 302–313.

BARCROFT, J. (1935). "Foetal respiration." The Croonian Lecture. *Proc. roy. Soc.*, *B.*, **118**, 242–263.

BARCROFT, J. (1935). "Respiratory and vascular changes in the mammal before and after birth." The John Mallet Purser Memorial Lecture, given at Trinity College, Dublin, on June 25th, 1935. *Lancet*, ii, 647–652.

BARCROFT, J. (1935). "Methoden zur Untersuchung von Veränderungen in der Grösse der Milz", pp. 363–376 in "Handbuch der biologischen Arbeitsmethoden", ed. by E. Abderhalden, Abt. V, Teil 8. Transl. by Frau Dr. Hilde Nellman. Berlin: Urban & Schwarzenberg.

BARCROFT, J. (1935). "Certain changes in circulation and respiration occurring at birth." *Sechenov J. Physiol.* **19**, 29–41.

BARCROFT, J. (1936). "Fetal circulation and respiration." *Physiol. Rev.*, **16**, 103–128.

BARCROFT, J., BARRON, D. H., and MATTHEWS, B. H. C. (1936). "The genesis of respiratory movements in the sheep." *J. Physiol.*, **86**, 29 P.

BARCROFT, J. (1936). "Prof. I. P. Pavlov, For. Mem. R.S." *Nature, Lond.*, **137**, 483–485.

ADAIR, G. S., BARCROFT, J., BARRON, D. H., GOODMAN, E. N., HALL, E. H., HAYASI, K., O'BRIEN, A., PACE, J. F., and PHILLIPS, A. E. (1936). "The oxygen content of blood in the carotid and umbilical arteries of the foetal sheep." *J. Physiol.*, **87**, 37 *P*.

BARCROFT, J., BARRON, D. H., and WINDLE, W. F. (1936). "Some observations on genesis of somatic movements in sheep embryos." *J. Physiol.*, **87**, 73–78.

BARCROFT, J., and ELLIOTT, R. H. E. (1936). "Some observations on the denervated spleen." *J. Physiol.*, **87**, 189–197.

[BARCROFT, J.] (1936). "The Harvard Tercentenary Celebrations." *Nature, Lond.*, **138**, 667–670.

BARCROFT, J., and BARRON, D. H. (1936). "The genesis of respiratory movements in the foetus of the sheep." *J. Physiol.*, **88**, 56–61.

ROUGHTON, F. J. W., with ADAIR, G. S., BARCROFT, J., GOLDSCHMIDT, G., HERKEL, W., HILL, R. M., KEYS, A. B., and RAY, G. B. (1936). "The thermochemistry of the oxygen-haemoglobin reaction. II. Comparison of the heat as measured directly on purified haemoglobin with that calculated indirectly by the Van 't Hoff isochore". *Biochem. J.*, **30**, 2117–2133.

BARCROFT, J., and BARRON, D. H. (1936). "The development of the 'righting' movements in the foetal sheep." *J. Physiol.*, **89**, 19–20 *P*.

BARCROFT, J., and BARRON, D. H. (1937). "The establishment of certain reflex arcs in foetal sheep." *Proc. Soc. exp. Biol., N.Y.*, **36**, 86–87.

BARCROFT, J., and BARRON, D. H. (1937). "Experimental 'chronic' lesions in the central nervous system of the sheep's foetus." *J. Physiol.*, **89**, 55–56 *P*.

BARCROFT, J., and GOTSEV, T. (1937). "Acquisition of blood by the foetus from the placenta at birth." *J. Physiol.*, **90**, 27 *P*.

BARCROFT, J., KRAMER, K., and MILLIKAN, G. A. (1937). "The attainment of saturation by the arterial blood at birth." *J. Physiol.*, **90**, 28 *P*.

BARCROFT, J., BARRON, D. H., KRAMER, K., and MILLIKAN, G. A. (1937). "The effect of urethane on the onset of respiration at birth." *J. Physiol.*, **90**, 29 *P*.

QUIGLEY, J. P., BARCROFT, J., ADAIR, G. S., and GOODMAN, E. N. (1937). "The difference in potential across gastric membranes and certain factors modifying the potential." *Amer. J. Physiol.*, **119**, 763–767.

BARCROFT, J. (1937). "Physical unfitness in relation to density of population." *Lancet*, ii, 891–893.

BARCROFT, J., and BARRON, D. H. (1937). "Movements in midfoetal life in the sheep embryo." *J. Physiol.*, **91**, 329–351.

BARCROFT, J., and BARRON, D. H. (1937). "The fundamental nature of the respiratory rhythm." *Sechenov J. Physiol.*, **22**, 273–283.

BARCROFT, J. (1938). "The velocities of some physiological processes." *Sechenov J. Physiol.*, **21**, 333–340.

BARCROFT, J., and BARRON, D. H. (1938). "The initiation of respiration at birth." *Sechenov J. Physiol.*, **21**, 527.

BARCROFT, J. (1938). "Features in the architecture of physiological function." Second printing. Cambridge: At the University Press.

BARCROFT, J. (1938). "The brain and its environment." New Haven: Yale University Press. London: Humphrey Milford, Oxford University Press.

BARCROFT, J., KENNEDY, J. A., and MASON, M. F. (1938). "The relation of the vagus nerve to the ductus arteriosus in the guinea-pig." *J. Physiol.*, **92**, 1–2 *P*.

BARCROFT, J. (1938). "Signification physiologique de la rate." *Brux. méd.*, **18**, 441–449.

BARCROFT, J. (1938). "The development of respiration in the mammal." *Scientia, Bologna*, **63**, 76–83.

Windle, W. F., and Barcroft, J. (1938). "Some factors governing the initiation of respiration in the chick." *Amer. J. Physiol.*, **121**, 684–691.

Mason, M. F., Kennedy, J. A., and Barcroft, J. (1938). "Direct determination of foetal oxygen consumption." *J. Physiol.*, **93**, 21–22 *P.*

Barcroft, J., and Mason, M. F. (1938). "The atmosphere in which the foetus lives." *J. Physiol.*, **93**, 22–23 *P.*

Barron, D. H., and Barcroft, J. (1938). "A case of amputation of leg, 90 days before birth." *J. Physiol.*, **93**, 29–30 *P.*

Barclay, A. E., Barcroft, J., Barron, D. H., and Franklin, K. J. (1938). "Closing of ductus arteriosus." *J. Physiol.*, **93**, 36 *P.*

Barcroft, J. (1938). "Problems of foetal respiration." *Kongressber. I des XVI. Internat. Physiologenkongresses*, 33–35.

Barclay, A. E., Barcroft, J., Barron, D. H., and Franklin, K. J. (1938). "The time and manner of closing of the ductus arteriosus." *Kongressber. II des XVI. Internat. Physiologenkongresses*, 35–36.

Barclay, A. E., Barcroft, J., Barron, D. H., and Franklin, K. J. (1938). "X-ray studies of the closing of the ductus arteriosus." *Brit. J. Radiol. N.S.*, **11**, 570–585.

Barcroft, J., Barron, D. H., Kramer, K., and Millikan, G. A. (1938). "Factors which influence the oxygen supply of the brain at birth." *Sechenov J. Physiol.*, **24**, 43–55.

Barcroft, J., Kramer, K., and Millikan, G. A. (1939). "The oxygen in the carotid blood at birth." *J. Physiol.*, **94**, 571–578.

Barcroft, J., Kennedy, J. A., and Mason, M. F. (1939). "The blood volume and kindred properties in pregnant sheep." *J. Physiol.*, **95**, 159–172.

Barcroft, J., and Kennedy, J. A. (1939). "The distribution of blood between the foetus and the placenta in sheep." *J. Physiol.*, **95**, 173–186.

Barcroft, J., Kennedy, J. A., and Mason, M. F. (1939). "The direct determination of the oxygen consumption of the foetal sheep." *J. Physiol.*, **95**, 269–275.

Barcroft, J., Barron, D. H., Cowie, A. T., Forsham, P. H., and MacDonald, A. (1939). "The effect of asphyxia on inhibition of respiratory movement in the sheep's foetus." *J. Physiol.*, **96**, 12–13 *P.*

Barcroft, J., and Barron, D. H. (1939). "The development of behavior in foetal sheep." *J. comp. Neurol.*, **70**, 477–502.

Barcroft, J., and Barron, D. H. (1939). "Further observations on the development of respiratory movement in the foetal sheep." Pp. 43–48 in "Livro de Homenagem" aos Professores Alvaro e Miguel Ozorio de Almeida. Rio de Janeiro:

Barcroft, J., and Barron, D. H. (1939). "Movement in the mammalian foetus." *Ergebn. Physiol.*, **42**, 107–152.

Barcroft, J. (1939). "Food conservation in relation to national food supply." *Brit. med. J.*, ii, 324–327.

Barclay, A. E., Barcroft, J., Barron, D. H., and Franklin, K. J. (1939). "A radiographic demonstration of the circulation through the heart in the adult and in the foetus, and the identification of the ductus arteriosus." *Brit. J. Radiol. N.S.*, **12**, 505–517.

Barcroft, J. (1939). "The intra-uterine development of respiratory effort." *Brit. med. J.*, ii, 986–987.

Barcroft, J., Barron, D. H., Cowie, A. T., and Forsham, P. H. (1940). "The oxygen supply of the foetal brain of the sheep and the effect of asphyxia on foetal respiratory movement." *J. Physiol.*, **97**, 338–346.

Barcroft, J., Kennedy, J. A., and Mason, M. F. (1940). "Oxygen in the blood of the umbilical vessels of the sheep." *J. Physiol.*, **97**, 347–356.

Barcroft, J. (1941). "The oxygen capacity of foetal and neo-natal blood." *Schweiz. med. Wschr.* **71**, 246–247.

Barcroft, J. (1941). "The development of function in the mammalian organism." *Not. Proc. roy. Instn.*, **31**, 485–497.
Barcroft, J. (1941). "Evolution of function in the mammalian organism". *Nature, Lond.* **147**, 762–765.
Barcroft, J. (1941). "Four phases of birth." Abstract of the Sharpey-Schafer lecture given at the University of Edinburgh on Feb. 28. *Lancet*, ii, 91–95.
Barcroft, J. (1941). The evaluation of nutritional status. Summing Up. *Proc. Nutr. Soc.*, **1**, 18.
Barclay, A. E., Barcroft, J., Barron, D. H., Franklin, K. J., and Prichard, M. M. L. (1941). "Studies of the foetal circulation and of certain changes that take place after birth." *Amer. J. Anat.*, **69**, 383–406.
Barcroft, J., and Barron, D. H. (1942). "Circulation in the placenta of the sheep." *J. Physiol.*, **100**, 20–21 *P.*
Barcroft, J. (1942). Food production and distribution in relation to nutritional needs. Summing up. *Proc. Nutr. Soc.*, **1**, 41.
Barcroft, J. (1942). "Gas attacks: what to do and when to do it." *Ulster med. J.*, **11**, 51–61.
Barclay, A. E., Barcroft, J., Barron, D. H., and Franklin, K. J. (1942). "A radiographic demonstration of the circulation through the heart in the adult and in the foetus, and the identification of the ductus arteriosus." *Amer. J. Roentgenol.*, **47**, 678–690. (Reprinting of *Brit. J. Radiol. N.S.*, 1939 paper).
Barcroft, J. (1942). Problems of collective feeding in war time. Summing Up. *Proc. Nutr. Soc.*, **1**, 112.
Barcroft, J. (1942). "The utilization of desiccated foods." *Proc. Nutr. Soc.*, **1**, 137–140.
Barcroft, J. (1942). "The onset of respiration at birth.". *Lancet*, ii, 117–120.
Barcroft, J., Barron, D. H., and Forsham, P. (1942). "The blood pressure in the umbilical vein of the foetal sheep." *Science*, **96**, 179–180.
Barcroft, J., and Barron, D. H. (1942). "Observations on the functional development of the foetal brain." *J. comp. Neurol.*, **77**, 431–452.
Barcroft, J. (1942). Trace elements in relation to health. Discussion. *Proc. Nutr. Soc.*, **1**, 192–193, 219.
Barclay, A. E., Barcroft, J., Barron, D. H., Franklin, K. J., and Prichard, M. M. L. (1942). "Pulmonary circulation times before and after functional closure of the ductus arteriosus." *J. Physiol.*, **101**, 375–377.
Barcroft, J. (1942). "Respiratory patterns at birth." *Camb. Univ. med. Soc. Mag.*, **20**, 6–9.
Barcroft, J. (1943). "Phases in foetal life." *Glasg. med. J.*, **139**, *N.S.*, **21**, 1–13.
Barcroft, J. (1943). Nutrition in pregnancy. Discussion. *Proc. Nutr. Soc.*, **2**, 13, 20.
Barcroft, J. (1943). "Nutritional functions of the placenta." *Proc. Nutr. Soc.*, **2**, 14–18.
Barcroft, J., McAnally, R., and Phillipson, A. (1943). Physiological action of acetic acid in living tissues. *Nature, Lond.*, **151**, 304.
Barcroft, J. (1943). Nutrition in infancy. Discussion. *Proc. Nutr. Soc.*, **2**, 78.
Barcroft, J. (1943). "The preservation of food." *Nutr. Abstr. Rev.*, **13**, 1–8.
Barcroft, J. (1943). "The preservation of foods by drying." *Not. Proc. roy. Instn.*, **33**, 4–13.
Barcroft, J., and Young, I. M. (1943). "Oxygen in the blood emerging from the brains of post-mature foetal rabbits." *J. Physiol.*, **102**, 25–26 *P.*
Barcroft, J., McAnally, R. A., and Phillipson, A. T. (1944). "The production of acetic, propionic and butyric acids in the alimentary canal." *Biochem. J.*, **38**, ii.
Barcroft, J., McAnally, R. A., and Phillipson, A. T. (1944). "Absorption of acetic, propionic and butyric acids from the alimentary canal." *Biochem. J.*, **38**, iii.
Barcroft, J., McAnally, R. A., and Phillipson, A. T. (1944). "The destruction of acetic acid by the beating heart." *Biochem. J.*, **38**, iv.

BARCROFT, J. (1944). The late Professor Topley. *Lancet*, i, 233.

BARCROFT, J., MCANALLY, R., and PHILLIPSON, A. T. (1944). "Absorption of volatile acids from the alimentary tract of the sheep and other animals." *J. exp. Biol.*, **20**, 120–129.

BARCROFT, J., MCANALLY, R., and PHILLIPSON, A. T. (1944). "The absorption of sodium ortho-iodo-hippurate from the rumen of lambs." *J. exp. Biol.*, **20**, 132–133.

BARCROFT, J. (1944). Budgetary and dietary surveys of families and individuals. Part 2. Discussion. *Proc. Nutr. Soc.*, **3**, 152.

BARCROFT, J., and POPJÁK, G. (1944). "Lipids in maternal and foetal blood-plasma of sheep." *J. Physiol.*, **103**, 32–33 *P*.

BARCROFT, J., DANIELLI, J. F., HARPER, W. F., and MITCHELL, P. D. (1944). "Wharton's jelly considered as a conducting path." *Nature, Lond.* **154**, 667.

BARCROFT, J. (1944). "The utilization of volatile acids." *Proc. Nutr. Soc.*, **3**, 247–251.

BARCROFT, J., and YOUNG, I. M. (1945). "Internal oxygen environment of the brains of post-mature rabbit embryos". *J. exp. Biol.*, **21**, 70–76.

BARCROFT, J. (1945). Factors affecting the nutritive value of bread as human food. Discussion. *Proc. Nutr. Soc.*, **4**, 27.

BARCROFT, J. (1945). "The microflora of the alimentary canal." *Proc. roy. Soc. Edinb.*, *B*, **62**, 105–113.

BARCROFT, J. (1945). "The preparation and biological effects of iodinated proteins. I. Introduction." *J. Endocrin.*, **4**, 219–220.

BARCROFT, J., (1945). "The range of weights of foetal sheep at various ages." *J. Physiol.*, **104**, 32–33 *P*.

BARCROFT, J., and BARRON, D. H. (1945). "Blood pressure and pulse rate in the foetal sheep". *J. exp. Biol.*, **22**, 63–74.

BARCROFT, J. (1946). "The storage of food by refrigeration." *Scot. J. Agric.*, **25**, 183–188.

LORBER, V., LIFSON, N., WOOD, H. G., and BARCROFT, J. (1946). "The metabolism of acetate by the completely isolated mammalian heart investigated with carboxyl-labeled acetate." *Amer. J. Physiol.*, **145**, 557–560.

BARCROFT, J. (1946). "The respiratory function of the blood. Lecture I. – The usefulness of haemoglobin. Lecture II – Man under conditions of stress. Lecture III. – The transition from placental to pulmonary respiration." *J. roy. Instn. pub. Health Hyg.*, **9**, 44–58, 74–85, 86–95.

BARCROFT, J., and BARRON, D. H. (1946). "Observations upon the form and relations of the maternal and fetal vessels in the placenta of the sheep." *Anat. Rec.*, **94**, 569–596.

BARCROFT, J., and TORRENS, D. S. (1946). "The output of the heart of the foetal sheep." *J. Physiol.*, **105**, 22 *P*.

BARCROFT, J., and ELSDEN, S. R. (1946). "The oxygen consumption of the sheep foetus." *J. Physiol.*, **105**, 25 *P*.

BARCROFT, J. (1946). "Birth in relation to foetal development". Being the John Mallet Purser Memorial Lecture, delivered at Trinity College, Dublin, May 3rd, 1946. *Irish J. med. Sci.*, 603–614.

BARCROFT, J. (1946). "Researches on pre-natal life." Vol. **1**. Oxford: Blackwell Scientific Publications, Ltd.

BARCROFT, J. (1947). "The Microflora of the Alimentary Canal." *Sci. News*, No. 3, 159–186.

BARCROFT, J., and KARVONEN, M. J. (1948). "The action of carbon dioxide and cyanide on foetal respiratory movements; the development of chemoreflex function in sheep." *J. Physiol.*, **107**, 153–161.

BARCROFT, J. (1948). Quoted. "Recientes observaciones sobre la naturaleza de la placenta." *Revista Euclides*, **7**.

BARCROFT, J. (1951). "Christianity and Medicine." *Lancet*, ii, 1176–1178.

OTHER REFERENCES

Adair, G. S. (1925). "A critical study of the direct method of measuring the osmotic pressure of haemoglobin." *Proc. roy. Soc., A*, **108**, 627–637.

Adair, G. S. (1949). Pp. 23–26 in Roughton, F. J. W., and Kendrew, G. J. (1949).

Adolph, E. F., and Ferry, R. M. (1921). "The oxygen dissociation of haemoglobin, and the effect of electrolytes upon it." *J. biol. Chem.*, **47**, 547–555.

Adrian, E. D. (1949). Pp. 3–4 in Roughton, F. J. W., and Kendrew, J. C. (1949).

Anon. (1730). "A Brief Narrative of the Life, Convincement, Conversion, and Labours of Love in the Gospel – Ministry of that *Worthy* Servant of Jesus Christ, John Barcroft. Who departed this Life, at his House at *Arkill*, in the Kingdom of *Ireland*, the 24th of the Eleventh Month, 1723". Dublin: Printed by and for Sam. Fuller, at the *Globe* and *Scales* in *Meath-Street*.

Anon. (1886). "An Electric Tramway." *Ayrshire post*, April.

Anon. (1906). "Barcroft Hall." *Preston Guardian*, Spring.

Anon. (1915). Reports of Societies. The Royal Society. Thursday, February 25th, 1915. *Brit. med. J.*, i, 420.

Anon. (1915). Reports of Societies. Royal Academy of Medicine in Ireland. Section of Anatomy and Physiology. *Brit. med. J.*, i, 892–894.

Anon. (1920). Reports of Societies. Oxygen therapy. *Brit. med. J.*, i, 150–152.

Anon. (1922). The physiology of life on the Andes. *Brit. med. J.*, i, 648.

Anon. (1922). Physiological effects at high altitudes. *Brit. med. J.*, i, 966.

Anon. (1922). High altitudes and want of oxygen. *Lancet*, ii, 574–575.

Anon. (1922). Recent expedition to the Andes for the study of the physiology of high altitudes. *Lancet*, ii, 685–686.

Anon. (1934). Physiology and pathology of blood. *Nature, Lond.*, **134**, 705–706.

Anon. (1935). "International Physiological Congress in Leningrad and Moscow." *Lancet*, ii, 447–448.

Anon. (1936). "Ulster Quakers 200th Anniversary Bi-Centenary Celebrations at Moyallon." *The Lurgan Mail*. 3 October.

Anon. (1937). Medical Society of London. *Lancet*, ii, 1140–1142.

Anon. (N. D.). "Bessbrook A record of industry in a Northern Ireland village community and of a social experiment, 1845–1945." Belfast: *Issued by* The Bessbrook Spinning Co., Ltd. and J. N. Richardson, Sons & Owden, Ltd.

Anon. (1947). "Sir Joseph Barcroft, C.B.E., F.R.S." *Brit. med. J.*, i, 470–471.

Anon. (1947). "Joseph Barcroft, Kt., C.B.E., M.A. Camb., D. Sc., Hon. M. D., Hon. F.R.C.O.G., F.R.S." *Lancet*, i, 430–431.

Anson, M. L., and Mirsky, A. E. (1925). "On haemochromogen and the relation of protein to the properties of the haemoglobin molecule." *J. Physiol.*, **60**, 50–68.

Anson, M. L., and Mirsky, A. E. (1925). "On helicorubin and its relation to haemoglobin." *J. Physiol.*, **60**, 221–228.

Ball, W. V. (1915). "Reminiscences and Letters of Sir Robert Ball," Edited by his son W. Valentine Ball. London, New York, Toronto and Melbourne: Cassell and Company, Ltd.

Ball, W. V. (1947). In King's College, Cambridge (1947).

Barcroft, H. (1929). "A mechanical Stromuhr." *J. Physiol.*, **67**, 402–408.

Barcroft, M. (1938). "Derrymore House." *Ulster Journal of Archaeology*, 3 s., **1**, 153–154.

Barcroft, M. (1942). "Coin found at Newry." *Ulster Journal of Archaeology*, 3 s., **5**, 66.

Barron, D. H. (1947). "Obituary – Sir Joseph Barcroft 1872–1947". *Science*, **106**, 160–161.

BOER, S. DE, and CARROLL, D. C. (1924). "The mechanism of the splenic reaction to general CO poisoning." *J. Physiol.*, **59**, 312–332.

BOER, S. DE, and CARROLL, D. C. (1924). "The significance of the action of pituitrin on the splenic volume." *J. Physiol.*, **59**, 381–386.

BOHR, C. (1904). "Die Sauerstoffaufnahme des genuinen Blutfarbstoffes und des aus dem Blute dargestellten Hämoglobins." *Cbl. Physiol.*, **17**, 689–691.

BOOTHBY, W. and LOVELACE, R., II. (1938). "Oxygen in aviation. The necessity for the use of oxygen and a practical apparatus for its administration to both pilots and passengers." *J. Aviat. Med.*, **9**, 172–198.

BROWN, W. E. L., and HILL, A. V. (1923). "The oxygen-dissociation curve of blood, and its thermodynamical basis." *Proc. roy. Soc.*, *B*, **94**, 297–334.

BURY, A. (1938). "Who's Who in British portrait painting." *The Studio*, **116**, 71–83.

CARLYLE, A. (1945). "The weights of certain tissues of the sheep foetus during gestation, relative to the total body weight." *J. Physiol.*, **104**, 34 *P*.

CHURCHILL, W. S. (1948). "The Second World War", Volume **1**, "The Gathering Storm". London, Toronto, Melbourne, Syndey, Wellington: Cassell & Co. Ltd.

COHNSTEIN, J., and ZUNTZ, N. (1884). "Untersuchungen über das Blut, den Kreislauf und die Athmung beim Säugethier-Fötus. *Pflüg. Arch. ges. Physiol.*, **34**, 173–233.

COOTE, Sir CHARLES, BART. (1804). "Statistical survey of the County of Armagh, with observations on the means of improvement; drawn up in the years 1802, and 1803, for the consideration, and under the direction of The Dublin Society." Dublin: Printed by Graisberry and Campbell.

CRUTTWELL. C. R. M. F. (1934). "A history of the Great War 1914–1918." Oxford: At the Clarendon Press.

CUSHING, H. (1940). "The Life of Sir William Osler." London, New York, Toronto: Oxford University Press.

DALE, H. H. (1943). Medal Awards for 1943 of the Royal Society. Copley Medal. *Nature, Lond.*, **152**, 665. Remarks made by Henry Dale in presenting the award to Sir Joseph Barcroft on 30 September 1943.

DALE, H. H. (1947). "Sir Joseph Barcroft." *The Leys Fortnightly*, **71**, 145–147.

DALE, H. H. (1949). Pp. 4–10 in Roughton, F. J. W., and Kendrew, J. C. (1949).

DOBELL, C. (1949). "D'Arcy Wentworth Thompson 1860–1948." *Obit. Not. roy. Soc.*, **6**, 599–617.

DOUGLAS, C. G. (1949). Pp. 12–16 in Roughton, F. J. W., and Kendrew, J. C. (1949).

DOUGLAS, C. G., HALDANE, J. S., and HALDANE, J. B. S. (1912). "The laws of combination of haemoglobin with carbon monoxide and oxygen." *J. Physiol.*, **44**, 275–304.

DOUGLAS, C. G., and PRIESTLEY, J. G. (1937). "Human Physiology A practical course." 2nd Edn. Oxford: At the Clarendon Press.

FAY, C. R. (1907). "King's College Cambridge." London: J. M. Dent & Co. New York: E. P. Dutton & Co.

FAYLE, H. (1946). "The narrow gauge railways of Ireland." London: Greenlake Publications Limited.

FEGLER, J., and BANISTER, J. (1946). "A study of some conditions influencing the rate of exchange of oxygen in vitro." *Quart. J. exp. Physiol.*, **33**, 163–182.

FITZMAURICE, *Lord* EDMUND (1895). "The Life of Sir William Petty 1623–1687." London: John Murray.

FLETCHER, W. M. (1900). In "Text-book of physiology", ed. by E. A. Schäfer, **1**, 911. Edinburgh & London: Young J. Pentland.

FRANKLIN, K. J. (1938). "A short history of the International Congresses of Physiologists." *Ann. Sci.*, **3**, 241–335.

FRANKLIN, K. J. (1949). "A short history of physiology", 2nd Edn. London: Staples Press Limited. New York: Staples Press Incorporated.

FRY, A. RUTH (1933). "Quaker ways. An attempt to explain Quaker beliefs and practices and to illustrate them by the lives and activities of Friends of former days." London, Toronto, Melbourne and Sydney: Cassell and Company, Limited.

FULTON, J. F. (1946). "Harvey Cushing A biography." Springfield, Ill.: Charles C Thomas. Toronto: The Ryerson Press. Oxford: Blackwell Scientific Publications, Ltd.

FULTON, J. F. (1948). "Aviation medicine in its preventive aspects. An historical survey." London, New York, Toronto: Geoffrey Cumberlege Oxford University Press.

FULTON, J. F. (1952). "Sir Charles Scott Sherrington, O. M. (1857–1952)." *J. Neurophysiol.*, **15**, 167–190.

GRAB, W., JANSSEN, S., and REIN, H. (1929). "Die Leber als Blutdepot." *Klin. Wschr.*, **8**, 1539.

GRUBB, ISABEL (1927). "Quakers in Ireland 1654–1900." London: The Swarthmore Press Ltd.

HAGEDORN, H. C. (1949). "August Krogh 15/11 1874–13/9 1949." *Medd. Akad. tekn. Vidansk.*, 33–50.

HALDANE, J. (1898). "Some improved methods of gas analysis." *J. Physuol.*, **22**, 465–480.

HALDANE, J., and SMITH, J. L. (1900). "The mass and oxygen capacity of the blood in man." *J. Physiol.*, **25**, 331–343.

HANAK, A., and HARKAVY, J. (1924). "Observations on the taking up of carbon monoxide by the haemoglobin of the spleen." *J. Physiol.*, **59**, 121–128. Note by J. Barcroft on p. 128.

HARRIS, FANNY (1909). "Jane M. Richardson, of Moyallon, County Down." *The Friend*, 22 January.

HARRIS, L. J. (1947). "Obituary Sir Joseph Barcroft, C.B.E., M.A., D.Sc., Hon. M.D., Hon. F.R.C.O.G., F.R.S." *J. Nutr. Soc.*, **1**, 1–3.

HARTRIDGE, H., and ROUGHTON, F. J. W. (1925). "The kinetics of haemoglobin. – II. The velocity with which oxygen dissociates from its combination with haemoglobin." *Proc. roy. Soc., A*, **104**, 395–430.

HARTRIDGE, H., and ROUGHTON, F. J. W. (1925). "The kinetics of haemoglobin. III. – The velocity with which oxygen combines with reduced haemoglobin." *Proc. roy. Soc., A*, **107**, 654–683.

HASTINGS, A. B., SLYKE, D. D. VAN, NEILL, J. M., HEIDELBERGER, M., and HARINGTON, C. R. (1924). "Studies of gas and electrolyte equilibria in blood. VI. The acid properties of reduced and oxygenated haemoglobin." *J. biol. Chem.*, **60**, 89–153.

HENDERSON, Y. (1917). "Effects of altitude on aviators." *Aviation, N.Y.*, **2**, 145–147.

HILL, A. V. (1910). "The possible effects of the aggregation of the molecules of haemoglobin on its dissociation curves." *J. Physiol.*, **40**, 4–7 *P*.

HILL, A. V. (1913). "The combinations of haemoglobin with oxygen and with carbon monoxide." *Biochem. J.*, **7**, 471–480.

HILL, A. V. (1922). "The combinations of haemoglobin with oxygen and carbon monoxide, and the effects of acid and carbon dioxide." *Biochem., J.*, **15**, 577–586.

HILL, A. V. (1949). Pp. 16–19 in Roughton, F. J. W., and Kendrew, J. C. (1949).

HILL, L. (1894). "A simple form of gas pump." *J. Physiol.*, **17**, 353–355.

HILL, L. (1920). "The capillary blood-pressure." *J. Physiol.*, **54**, 24–25 *P*.

HILL, L., and NABARRO, D. N. (1895). "On the exchange of blood-gases in brain and muscle during states of rest and activity." *J. Physiol.*, **18**, 218–229.

HILL, R. (1925). "Haemoglobin in relation to other metallo-haemotoporphyrins." *Biochem. J.*, **19**, 341–349.

HOLLAND, C. T. (1937). "X-rays in 1896." *Liverpool med.-chir. J.*, **45**, 61–77.

HUGGETT, A. ST. G. (1927). "Foetal blood-gas tensions and gas transfusion through the placenta of the goat." *J. Physiol.*, **62**, 373–384.

HUSSEY, C. (1926). "King's College Chapel, Cambridge and the College Buildings." London: Country Life, Ltd.

IZQUIERDO, J. J. (1947). "Elogios academicos a proposito del fallecimiento de Sir Joseph Barcroft (1872–1947), Socio honorario de la Academia." *Gac. méd. Méx.*, **77**, 261–265.

JACOBJ (1902). Quoted from Barcroft, J., and Mines, G. R. (1907), as not traced. *Dtsch. med. Wschr.*, 1902, No. 32.

KATO, T. (1915). "The effect of alkalis on the rates of oxidation and reduction of blood." *Biochem. J.*, **9**, 393–411.

KEILIN, D. (1925). "On cytochrome, a respiratory pigment, common to animals, yeast, and higher plants." *Proc. roy. Soc., B*, **98**, 312–339.

KELLOGG, H. B. (1930). "Studies on the fetal circulation of mammals." *Amer. J. Physiol.*, **91**, 637–648.

KING'S COLLEGE, Cambridge (1947). Annual Report of the Council under Statute D. III. 10 on the general and educational condition of the College. *November*, 1947, 2–5.

KROGH, A. S. (1949). Pp. 10–12 in Roughton, F. J. W., and Kendrew, J. C. (1949).

LANGDON-BROWN, W. (1946). "Some Chapters in Cambridge Medical History." Cambridge: At the University Press.

LEIGH, A. A. (1899). "King's College." London: F. E. Robinson and Co.

LIDDELL, E. G. T. (1952). "Charles Scott Sherrington 1857–1952". *Obit. Not. roy. Soc.*, **8**, 241–270.

LILJESTRAND, G. (1950). "Obituary Notice. August Krogh. 1874-1949." *Acta physiol. scand.*, **20**, 109–116.

LILJESTRAND, G. (1950). "The Prize in Physiology and Medicine", pp. 135–316 in "Nobel, The Man and his Prizes", ed. by the Nobel Foundation. Stockholm: Published by the Nobel Foundation.

M. R. (1938). "Arthur Edwin Boycott. Born 6th April 1877. Died 12th May 1938." *J. Path. Bact.*, **47**, 161–194.

MCDOUGALL, (Miss) E., and HARRIS, (Miss) MURIEL G. E. (1942). "Anne Wakefield Richardson". *The Friend*, 27 February.

MACMUNN, C. A. (1886). "Further observations en enterochlorophyll, and allied pigments." *Phil. Trans.*, **177**, 235–266.

MAYO, C. H., and MAYO, W. J. (1951). "Aphorisms of Dr. Charles Horace Mayo 1865–1939 and Dr. William James Mayo 1861–1939", collected by F. A. Willius. Springfield, Ill.: Charles C Thomas. Oxford: Blackwell Scientific Publications, Ltd. Toronto: The Ryerson Press.

MOMOSE, G. (1915). "The effect of ingestion of urea, sodium lactate and sodium bicarbonate on the reaction of the blood and the composition of the alveolar air in man." *Biochem. J.*, **9**, 485–491.

MONGE, C. (1948). "Acclimatization in the Andes Historical confirmations of 'climatic aggression' in the development of Andean man." Transl. by Donald F. Brown, with a foreword by Isaiah Bowman. Baltimore: The Johns Hopkins Press.

MOORE-ANDERSON, A. P. (1947). "Sir Robert Anderson K. C. B., Ll.D. and Lady Agnes Anderson." London, Edinburgh: Marshall, Morgan & Scott, Ltd.

PETERS, R. A. (1912). "Chemical nature of specific oxygen capacity of haemoglobin." *J. Physiol.*, **44**, 131–149.

PETERS R. A. (1929). "Cell surfaces". *J. State Med.*, **37**, 683–709.

PETERS, R. A. (1949). Pp. 20–23 in Roughton, F. J. W., and Kendrew, J. C. (1949).

R[EDDAWAY], W. F. (1947). "A Leysian Memory." *The Leys Fortnightly*, **71**, 148.

R[ICHARDSON], J. M. (1893). "Six Generations of Friends in Ireland (1655 to 1890)." London: Edwards Hicks, Jun.

ROLLESTON, H. D. (1925). "Right Hon. Sir Clifford Allbutt, K. C. B., F.R.S." *Nature, Lond.*, **115**, 387–389.

ROLLESTON, H. D. (1932). "The Cambridge Medical School A Biographical History." Cambridge: At the University Press.

ROUGHTON, F. J. W. (1949, *a*). Pp. 26–31 in Roughton, F. J. W., and Kendrew, J. C. (1949).

ROUGHTON, F. J. W. (1949, *b*). "Joseph Barcroft 1872–1947." *Obit. Not. roy. Soc.*, **6**, 315–345.

ROUGHTON, F. J. W., and KENDREW, J. C. (1949). "Haemoglobin A symposium based on a Conference held at Cambridge in June 1948 in memory of Sir Joseph Barcroft", ed. by J. F. W. Roughton and J. C. Kendrew. London: Butterworth Scientific Publications.

SCOTT, J. M. D. (1923). "Studies in anaemia. I. The influence of diet on the occurrence of secondary anaemia following repeated haemorrhages in rats." *Biochem. J.*, **17**, 157–165.

SCOTT, J. M. D. (1923). "Studies in anaemia. II." *Biochem. J.*, **17**, 166–169.

SHARPEY-SCHAFER, E. (1927). "History of the Physiological Society during its First Fifty Years 1876–1926." Suppl. to *J. Physiol.*, December, 1927. London: Cambridge University Press.

SHERRINGTON, C. S. (1935). "Nineteenth Fin-de-Siècle." An unpublished lecture, given at Oxford in February.

SMITH, CHARLOTTE FELL (1925). "James Nicholson Richardson of Bessbrook." London: Longmans, Green and Co.

SPÄRCK, R. (1949). "August Krogh. 15. november 1874–13. september 1949." *Vidensk. Medd. dansk. naturh. Foren. Kbh.*, **3**, v–xxx.

STEPHEN, CAROLINE EMELIA (1911). "The Vision of Faith and other Essays." With Memoirs by her niece Katharine Stephen (Principal of Newnham College) and Dr. T. Hodgkin. Cambridge: W. Heffer & Sons Ltd. London: Headley Bros.; Simpkin, Marshall, Hamilton, Kent & Co. Ltd.

STIRLING, W. (1895–6). "In memoriam – Carl Ludwig." *Med. Chron., n.s.*, **3**, 178–191.

UNDERWOOD, E. A. (1945). "Wilhelm Conrad Röntgen (1845–1923) and the early development of radiology." *Proc. R. Soc. Med.*, **38**, 697–706.

UYENO, K. (1923). "Studies on the respiration and circulation in the cat. III. The effect of rise of body temperature." *J. Physiol.*, **57**, 203–209.

VERZÁR, F. (1943). "Theorie der Muskelkontraktion." Basel: Verlag Benno Schwabe & Co.

VERZÁR, F. (1947). "Sir Joseph Barcroft (26. Juli 1872 bis 21. März 1947)." *Experientia*, **3**, 298–300.

WHITAKER, T. D. (1872, 1876). "An History of the original Parish of Whalley, and Honor of Clitheroe. To which is subjoined an Account of the Parish of Cartmell." 4th Edn., revised and enlarged, Vol. **1**, 1872, by J. G. Nichols and P. A. Lyons, Vol. **2**, 1876, by the late J. G. Nichols and P. A. Lyons, continued and completed by the latter. Vol. **1**, London: George Routledge and Sons. Manchester: L. C. Gent. Vol. **2**, London: George Routledge and Sons, and Lynch Conway Gent.

WILKINSON, T., and TATTERSALL, J. F. (1889). "Memories of Hurstwood, Burnley, Lancashire. With tales and traditions of the neighbourhood." Burnley: J. & A. Lupton. London: J. S. Virtue & Co., Ltd.

WILSON, R. M. (1918). "The Hearts of Man." London: Henry Frowde, Oxford University Press; Hodder and Stoughton.

WOLLHEIM, E. (1927). "Zur Funktion der subpapillären Gefässplexus in der Haut." *Klin. Wschr.*, **6**, 2134–2137.

YEO, G. F. (1885). "An attempt to estimate the gaseous interchange of the frog's heart by means of the spectroscope." *J. Physiol.*, **6**, 93–121.

YOUNGHUSBAND, F. (1926). "The epic of Mount Everest." London: Edward Arnold & Co.

INDEX OF PERSONAL NAMES